Earth's Geography
and Environment

Earth's Geography
and Environment

Charles L. Mitsakos

 McDougal, Littell & Company

Evanston, Illinois

New York   Dallas   Sacramento   Columbia, SC

Charles L. Mitsakos is Superintendent of Schools in Winchester, Massachusetts. A former elementary school teacher and social studies supervisor, he is also a lecturer in curriculum and instruction. Dr. Mitsakos is the author of a variety of social studies materials and has served as a consultant to schools throughout the United States.

Acknowledgements: Grateful acknowledgement is made to the following publishers, authors, and agents for permission to use and adapt copyrighted material:

Miriam Berkley for the excerpt from the article "Volcano" on page 65 from *Popular Photography* (Nov. 1983). Copyright © 1983 by Miriam Berkley. Reprinted by permission from the author.

Jacques-Yves Cousteau for the quotation on page 472 from "The Ocean: A Perspective" from *National Geographic Magazine* 160, no. 6 (December 1981). Copyright © 1981 by Jacques-Yves Cousteau. Reprinted by permission of *National Geographic Magazine.*

McGill-Queen's University Press for the excerpt on page 315 from *To the Arctic by Canoe 1819–21; The Journal and Painting of Robert Hood, Midshipman with Franklin.* Edited by C. Stuart Houston. Copyright © 1974 by McGill-Queen's University Press. Reprinted by permission of the publisher.

William Morrow and Company for the excerpt on page 41 from *A Walk Across America* by Peter Jenkins. Copyright © 1979 by William Morrow and Company. Reprinted by permission of the publisher.

Princeton University Press and Routledge and Kegan Paul for the excerpt on page 201 from *The Great Mother: An Analysis of the Archetype,* trans. by Ralph Manheim, Bollingen Series 47. Copyright © 1955 renewed 1983 by Princeton University Press. Reprinted by permission of Princeton University Press and Routledge and Kegan Paul.

Routledge and Kegan Paul for the excerpt on page 315 from *Ibn Battuta Travels in Asia and Africa 1325–54* translated and selected by H.A.R. Gibb. Copyright © 1929 by Robert McBride and Company. Reprinted by permission of the publisher.

Viking Penguin Inc. and William Heinemann Ltd., for the excerpt on page 18 from *Travels with Charley: In Search of America* by John Steinbeck. Copyright © 1961, 1962 by the Curtis Publishing Co., Inc. Copyright © 1962 by John Steinbeck. Reprinted by permission of Viking Penguin Inc. and William Heinemann Ltd.

McDougal, Littell & Company would like to thank the following sources for granting permission to use selected features of their maps in preparation of those for this program. American Heritage Publishing Co., Inc.; Cambridge University Press; Carnegie Institute of Washington; Edward Arnold (Publishers) Ltd.; Encyclopaedia Britannica, Inc.; W. H. Freeman and Company, Publishers; Florida State University; Irwin Publishing, Inc.; National Geographic Society; Oxford University Press; Rand McNally & Company; St. Martin's Press, Incorporated; University of Minnesota; and John Wiley & Sons, Inc. Details of specific map sources are included in the Teacher's Edition for this grade.

Credits appear on page 512.

TABLE OF CONTENTS

Unit 3 The Living Earth 156

Unit 4   *People on Earth*   **198**

Unit 5 Different Ways of Living

Unit 6   The Modern Industrial World

Unit 7   A Changing World   434

Maps

Charts, Graphs, and Diagrams

What to Look for in Your Book

A book's plan is like a key that helps to open up its meaning. Here is the plan of *Earth's Geography and Environment*.

The Unit Opener

The Unit Opener lists the unit's chapters, major concepts, and geographic themes. It also poses the **Big Question** for the unit.

The Chapter Opener

The Chapter Opener lists the titles of the lessons, the key words for the chapter, and includes a chapter introduction.

Special People/Special Feature

Each unit has at least one **Special People** and one **Special Feature**. **Special People** is about men and women whose lives have made a difference to us all. **Special Feature** deals with one of four themes: Technology, Environment, Celebrations, or Citizenship.

Can You Imagine?
Past and Present

Features called **Can You Imagine?** help you to picture life in other places. Features called **Past and Present** compare ways of the past with ways of today.

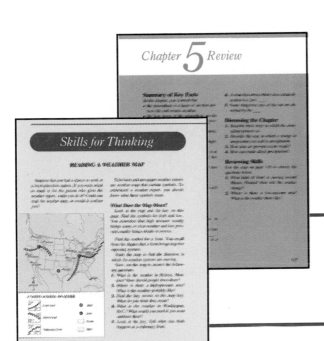

Chapter Review

Each chapter ends with a summary of key facts and lists discussion questions.

Skills for Thinking

These lessons will teach you how to use maps and charts, and how to build other important skills.

Unit Review and Test

Units end with reviews of key facts and special activities. A Test tries out your skills and vocabulary, reviews a geographic theme, and asks the **Big Question.**

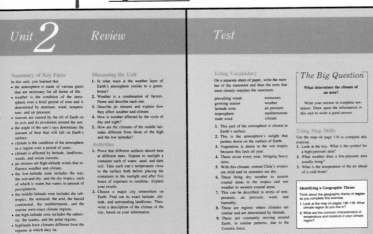

Other Parts of Your Book

At the front of the book the **table of contents** details the information in the book, and the **introduction** describes the five geographic themes.

At the back of the book the **dictionary of geography words** defines terms that refer to landforms and bodies of water; the **glossary** gives the meanings of all the vocabulary words; and the **index** lists persons, places, and topics mentioned in the book. The **atlas** includes maps. A chart contains many interesting statistics about the nations of the world.

Enjoy your book and use it well!

Introduction

Questions Geographers Ask

Geographers study Earth's features—including mountains, cities, lakes, and climates. They look at where these features are located. They also consider how these features are related to one another and to the way people live. As you begin to learn about geography, you will ask two main questions: (1) Why are features located in particular places? and (2) How do those places affect our lives?

By finding answers to these questions, you will more fully understand the world around you. You will have a clearer idea of how features got to be where they are. You also will better understand where features such as cities should be located in order to make our lives better.

The Five Geographic Themes

The study of geography focuses on five main building blocks, or themes. They are **location, place, human-environment interactions, movement,** and **region**. As you will see, some of these themes overlap. For example, the themes of both place and movement examine patterns of communication and transportation.

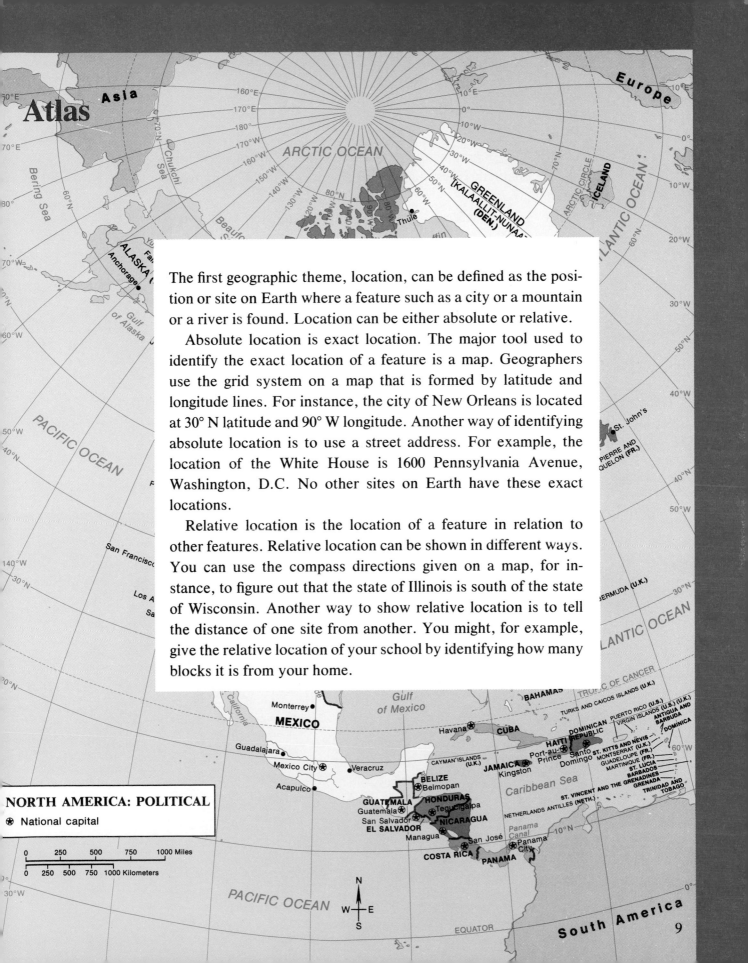

Atlas

The first geographic theme, location, can be defined as the position or site on Earth where a feature such as a city or a mountain or a river is found. Location can be either absolute or relative.

Absolute location is exact location. The major tool used to identify the exact location of a feature is a map. Geographers use the grid system on a map that is formed by latitude and longitude lines. For instance, the city of New Orleans is located at 30° N latitude and 90° W longitude. Another way of identifying absolute location is to use a street address. For example, the location of the White House is 1600 Pennsylvania Avenue, Washington, D.C. No other sites on Earth have these exact locations.

Relative location is the location of a feature in relation to other features. Relative location can be shown in different ways. You can use the compass directions given on a map, for instance, to figure out that the state of Illinois is south of the state of Wisconsin. Another way to show relative location is to tell the distance of one site from another. You might, for example, give the relative location of your school by identifying how many blocks it is from your home.

NORTH AMERICA: POLITICAL

⊛ National capital

0   250   500   750   1000 Miles

0 250 500 750 1000 Kilometers

Place

The second geographic theme, place, describes the physical and human characteristics that make one location different from another.

The physical characteristics of a place include landforms, elevation, climate, soil, vegetation, and bodies of water. For example, a geographer might describe the physical characteristics of Chicago as an area that lies on a flat lake plain near a large body of water, Lake Michigan. Because of its location, Chicago has a fairly humid climate with warm summers and cold winters. Geographers also study natural processes—how physical features got to be the way they are. They study how these processes are related to each other.

Little of Earth's original natural landscape has remained untouched by humans. For that reason, geographers also study the human characteristics of a place. These characteristics include the number of people who live in a place, how close together the people live, and how they make a living. Other areas related to

this category are language and religion, communication and transportation networks, architecture, and the use of the land. In addition, geographers study how the processes of human settlement fit into worldwide systems and patterns.

Human-Environment Interactions

The third geographic theme is human-environment interactions. No matter where people live, they interact with their environment. To some extent people adapt to the natural environment. However, they also try to change it to make life better. Geographers study the effects of these changes.

All places on Earth have advantages and disadvantages for human settlement. For example, many more people live in flat, well-watered river valleys than in very dry deserts. However, there are exceptions. People choose to live where they do for many reasons. Much depends on how much time and money people are able and willing to spend. Skills in technology and agriculture are also important.

Movement

Geographers also study how people interact with each other around the world. For instance, people in many places produce more than they need of some goods. They produce less than they need of others. As a result, people trade with each other.

They also travel. They share ideas and information. Movement—of goods, people, and ideas—is the fourth theme in geography.

Geographers study the patterns created by worldwide transportation and communication. These patterns result from our use of railways and roads, of airplanes and sea routes. These patterns explain how we use books and newspapers, the mail and telephone, radio and television. As you study movement, you will discover how dependent people are on each other.

Region

The world is so huge that it is impossible to study it all at once. So geographers divide Earth into smaller areas called regions. Region is the fifth theme in geography.

A region is any area on Earth that has common characteristics. These characteristics can be human or physical. A region can be large, such as the continent of Europe. It can be small, such as your school.

There are different kinds of regions. For example, California is an area with its own state government. It is a political region. Latin America is an area in which most of the people speak the Latin languages of Spanish or Portuguese. It is a cultural region. The valley drained by the Mississippi River and its branches is a region created by natural boundaries. The central business district of a city is an economic region.

The boundary of a region is not always easy to define. For instance, what is the extent of the region in the United States known as the Midwest? or the region of the world known as the Middle East? Regional boundaries can change, and regions can overlap. Region is a tool that we use to learn more about Earth.

You have now looked at the five basic themes of geography—location, place, human-environment interactions, movement, and region. These themes occur again and again in this book. Keep them in mind as you read to help you in your study of your home—Earth.

Questions

1. What are the two main questions asked in geography?

2. What are the two parts of the grid system that gives exact location on a map?

3. What do the physical characteristics of a place include?

4. Besides adapting, how do people interact with the natural environment?

5. Transportation and communication reflect which themes in geography?

6. What do geographers call an area with common characteristics?

Unit 1

Portrait of a Planet

Earth—this word refers to the ground on which we walk and the planet on which we live. Its high mountains, broad plateaus, and wide oceans provide the homes in which all its living things—including you—reside.

Earth is a diverse and a changing planet. Land wears down, and new land forms. Oceans rise, and oceans recede. Rivers flood, and rivers dry up.

Concepts

environment	tectonic plates
continent	hydrologic cycle

The Big Question

What are Earth's main landforms, what are the processes that have shaped them, and how do these processes unify Earth?

Focus on a Geographic Theme

In this unit you will study the geographic themes of **location** and **place**. Location identifies where on the Earth a feature such as a mountain is found. Maps help you to locate features. Place can be identified by its physical characteristics, such as climate and vegetation. Place is also identified by its human characteristics, including language and architecture.

14

Alaska's Glacier Bay suggests the many forms of land that are found on Earth.

Looking at Earth

Chapter 1

Introduction

Dawn breaks over the flat Florida coast. Two astronauts, strapped to their seats in the cockpit, await lift-off. Outside their spacecraft, pelicans fly up and down the beach. The astronauts wait.

The countdown goes on as engineers make sure that everything is ready. At last, the message comes from Mission Control: "10, 9, 8, 7, we have ignition, 6, 5, 4, 3, 2, 1, we have lift-off!"

As its rocket boosters boom, the spacecraft clears the launchpad and streaks skyward. Within 11 seconds, the craft is 29 miles (46.7 km) high and is racing eastward. Two minutes later, the astronauts get the word from Mission Control in Houston to cut off the main engine. The spacecraft rolls over smoothly, and the astronauts see the whole Earth from space for the first time.

"What a view! What a view!" they exclaim. "The colors are coming through beautifully. The oceans are a beautiful blue-green. We can see the landmasses in a brown to reddish brown...."

From their vantage point in space, astronauts have contributed greatly to our understanding of Earth. What is the study of Earth called? Who else contributes to our knowledge of Earth? What do we know about Earth? In this chapter, you will find some of the answers to these questions.

◀**As an astronaut on the moon watching an Earthrise, what facts and feelings would you include in a radio report?**

17

STUDYING EARTH

A number of years ago, the writer John Steinbeck set out on a trip by car across the United States with his dog, Charley. His view of Earth was made at closer range than that seen by orbiting astronauts. But he, too, was fascinated with what he saw. Partway through his journey, as he crossed the Missouri River in North Dakota, he wrote:

Someone must have told me about the Missouri River at Bismarck, North Dakota, or I must have read about it.

While exploring America with his dog, Charley, John Steinbeck wrote vivid descriptions of the country's geography.

In either case, I hadn't paid attention. I came on it in amazement. Here is where the map should fold. Here is the boundary between east and west. On the Bismarck side, it is eastern landscape, eastern grass, with the look and smell of eastern America. Across the Missouri, on the Mandan side, it is pure west, with brown grass and water scorings and small outcrops. The two sides of the river might well be a thousand miles apart.

In this passage, Steinbeck is describing the physical features of Earth that he observed. He is telling us what is located where and showing how one area differs from another. In doing so, he has given us a brief **geography**. Geography means "writing (*-graphy*) about Earth" (*geo-*). Throughout history, explorers, scientists, travelers, and others have added to our understanding of geography.

Geography is a broad subject, but it can be divided into small, manageable fields of study. Each field, or branch, of geography focuses on a special area.

Physical Geography

Steinbeck wrote about the land and the water that he found in North Dakota. Such physical features of Earth are important concerns of the branch of study known as physical geography. Physical geographers study the forms that land takes in different parts of Earth. They study the soil and the vegetation that cover the land and the animals that inhabit it. Earth's weather is another concern of physical geographers. So is Earth's place in the universe.

Human Geography

Human geography is the study of the ways in which people affect their **environments** and are affected by them. An environment includes everything that surrounds a person or a community. Human geographers study the way in which a given area of Earth has supported and continues to support human populations. They ask and try to find answers to such questions as: How do people live in their particular environment? How have they changed it and been affected by it?

Human geographers often focus on the study of specific forms of human activity. A cultural geographer, for example, studies the connections between human **culture** and physical environment. Culture, as you will learn in Chapter 11, is the way of life of a group of people—all the things they do.

Imagine that you are a cultural geographer. You are studying a group of people in a remote area. These people live by hunting forest animals. They believe that the animals that they hunt have spirits, just like human beings. You want to see how this belief affects the way in which the people hunt. You will spend some time observing the people as they hunt.

Political geography is another branch of human geography. Political geographers study how governments in different places are alike and not alike and how the world is divided into political units.

What name is used to describe a branch of human geography that studies how people have interacted with their environments in the past? If you answered historical geography, you are correct.

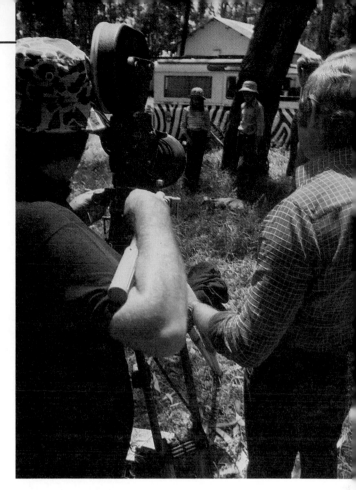

Human geographers often use film to record and to study different ways of life.

Why Study Geography?

Why study Earth and its peoples? For the same reason that you study anything—to learn how to solve problems and how to live fully and more effectively.

Geography reveals what Earth offers us to help us to live better. Where are the areas that produce food abundantly? Where are necessary minerals such as iron ore and coal found? Knowing both the opportunities and the limitations of Earth can help us to make wise decisions about how to use Earth.

In addition, geography helps to explain world events. For example, why is the United States so closely involved in the affairs of the Middle East, that area of the

19

You can learn a lot about a natural environment by exploring it for yourself.

world where Europe, Asia, and Africa meet? The answer relates partly to our need for oil, which is abundant there.

Also, geography helps us to understand people—those in other lands, those in our own land, and even ourselves. Knowing about the natural environments in which people live can help us to understand their problems and their reasons for doing things. Knowing about our own natural environments gives us insights into both our problems and how we might solve them. Geography helps to explain both the differences and the similarities among people throughout Earth.

Finally, there is our own curiosity. We want to know about our environment, how it came to be the way it is, and how it affects us. Knowing and understanding our surroundings, both near and far, can help us to live in harmony with nature.

In this book, you will study both physical and human geography. The first nine chapters deal mainly with the physical Earth. The remaining 14 chapters focus on how humans live on Earth.

Lesson 1 Review

Recalling Information
1. What is *geography*?
2. What are the two major branches of geography, and what is the major focus of each?

Interpreting Information
3. What areas of a geographer's study would be particularly useful to a farmer? Why?
4. Suppose that a group of people were moving to an area where they have never been before. What kinds of geographical knowledge would be helpful to them?

Applying Information
5. In what areas of your daily life have you found a knowledge of geography to be necessary or helpful?
6. Why do you think that a person might want to become a geographer?

EARTH—A BODY IN SPACE

From earliest times, people have looked at the night sky in wonder. How many stars are there? How far away is the farthest star? Is there any end at all to space? What is Earth, and what is its place in space?

Scientists are learning more every year, but their questions have not been answered easily or quickly. Not until the telescope was invented in the early 1600s did people have a chance to learn about the uneven, mountainous surface of the moon. Not until 1930 did anyone know for certain about the existence, beyond Neptune, of the planet Pluto.

You know more about the universe than the most learned scientists knew a few hundred years ago. You know that the planet Earth is a body in space. You know that space is vast and is only partly charted. Scientists still have to guess at the limits of space. For convenience, they say—and so can you—that it has no end.

The Milky Way

Earth is one part of a **galaxy** that is known as the Milky Way. A galaxy is a huge system that is composed of gases and

A spiral galaxy such as the Milky Way looks like a huge pinwheel. Our solar system is located on one arm of the spiral.

A TYPICAL SPIRAL GALAXY

Artist's conception

THE MILKY WAY

Sun

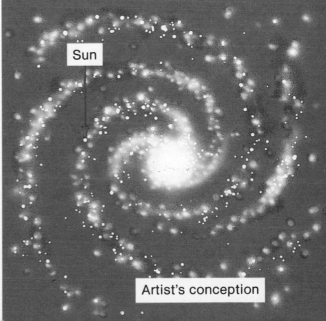

Sun

Artist's conception

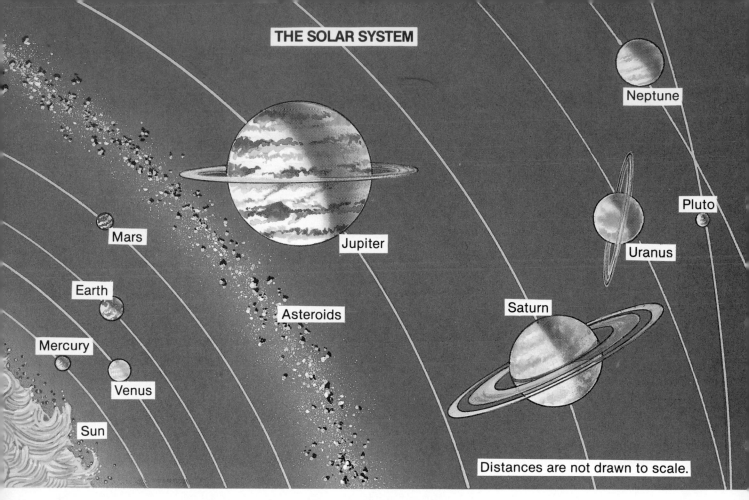

Neptune

Pluto

Uranus

Mars

Jupiter

Earth

Asteroids

Saturn

Mercury

Venus

Sun

Distances are not drawn to scale.

This diagram shows the planets of our solar system in order of their distance from the sun. It also shows their relative sizes.

dust and billions of stars. A star is a roundish mass of extremely hot gases. About one million galaxies are detectable through the largest telescopes. If you could view the Milky Way from another galaxy, it would look like a swirl of light. It would somewhat resemble the galaxy that is pictured on page 21.

The sun is a medium-sized star in the Milky Way. Yet, its diameter is 109 times greater than that of Earth. The gases of which the sun consists burn at so high a temperature that they throw off light that is visible at great distances. Our sun—as do all stars—acts as a giant heating and light-

ing factory. Its burning gases continuously give off energy. This energy shoots out from the sun, thus providing a powerful energy source for all of the stars and planets that surround the sun.

The Solar System

The sun is the center of the **solar system**. The solar system includes bodies of gases and frozen dust that are called comets. It also includes meteoroids, which are chunks of matter that hurtle through space. Sometimes, they can be seen in the night sky. In addition, there are asteroids, or small bodies that revolve around the sun. These are

THE PLANETS OF THE SOLAR SYSTEM

Planet	Average distance from the sun	Diameter	Number of satellites	Special features
MERCURY	36,000,000 miles (57,900,000 km)	3,031 miles (4,878 km)	0	Planet nearest to the sun. Hot, dry, with very thin atmosphere.
VENUS	67,250,000 miles (108,230,000 km)	7,520 miles (12,100 km)	0	Similar in size to Earth. Brightest planet as seen from Earth. Heavy atmosphere, mostly CO_2.
EARTH	92,950,000 miles (149,590,000 km)	7,926 miles (12,756 km)	1	Only planet with significant amount of oxygen in atmosphere.
MARS	141,500,000 miles (227,720,000 km)	4,200 miles (6,790 km)	2	The "red planet." Thin atmosphere, with minute traces of water.
JUPITER	483,500,000 miles (778,120,000 km)	88,700 miles (142,700 km)	16	The largest planet. Covered by dense clouds. Has faint rings .
SATURN	887,500,000 miles (1,428,300,000 km)	74,600 miles (120,000 km)	23	Large visible ring system . Covered by dense clouds.
URANUS	1,785,000,000 miles (2,872,700,000 km)	31,570 miles (50,800 km)	15	Has nine faint rings.
NEPTUNE	2,795,000,000 miles (4,498,100,000 km)	30,200 miles (48,600 km)	2	Little is known about the surface or the atmosphere of the distant planets.
PLUTO	3,675,000,000 miles (5,914,300,000 km)	1,900 miles (3,000 km)	1	Planet farthest from the Earth and the sun.

How many more satellites does Saturn have than does Neptune? About how far are Venus and Jupiter from Earth?

like tiny, oddly shaped planets. Finally, there are the largest objects—the sun itself, the nine **planets**, and the moons of the planets. Earth is the fifth-largest planet.

The word *planet* comes from the Greek word that means "wanderer." Ancient Greeks who studied the heavens noted that many of the objects that they saw were fixed in space. The fixed objects that they saw were the stars. Some objects, ancient scientists thought, wandered in space. Several of these were the planets.

The planets do move, but they do not wander. Their movements are orderly and predictable.

Each planet follows a certain path around the sun. This path is called an **orbit**. The picture on page 22 shows the orbits of the nine planets around the sun.

Mercury is the planet that passes closest to the sun. Venus is the next closest. Then comes Earth, which orbits the sun at an average distance of 93 million miles (150 million km). The chart above shows the distances at which the other planets circle the sun, as well as other information about the planets. It shows that Pluto's distance from the sun is the greatest—more than 3 1/2 billion miles (5 1/2 billion km), or 39 times farther than Earth is from the sun.

Light travels at 186,000 miles (299,329.8 km) per second. Even at that speed, it takes eight minutes for the sun's light to reach Earth. It takes more than five hours for the sun's light to reach Pluto.

Earth in the Solar System

Suppose that you could visit every other planet in the solar system. Even as a well-equipped space traveler, you would still be more than a little uncomfortable. On Venus, the second planet from the sun, you would have to put up with temperatures of about 800°F (426.7°C). On Mars, the fourth planet from the sun, you would find it distinctly cold—about -80°F (-62.2°C).

You would probably be lonely on your visits to other planets. You would find no other humans to talk to, no flowers to pick, no animals to befriend or to run away from. Of the nine planets in the solar system, only Earth is home to life.

Earth is unique partly because of its distance from the sun. It is just the right distance to receive the heat that is needed to support life. Earth also has water and oxygen, two other necessities for plant and animal life.

Look again at the diagram of the orbits of the planets on page 22. Earth takes 365 1/4 days to complete 1 orbit around the sun. In contrast, it takes Mercury only 88 Earth days to complete an orbit. Far-off Pluto, on the other hand, takes nearly 250 Earth *years* to complete each orbit.

Earth spins continuously as it travels around the sun. Picture a wheel on a bicycle. The wheel is attached to the bicycle on an axle. The wheel turns around, or *rotates*, on this axle. Earth rotates in a similar way on an imaginary axle, which is called an **axis**. This axis runs through the center of Earth from the North Pole to the South Pole at a 23 1/2° angle. Earth rotates on its axis, making a complete rotation every 24 hours—1 day.

Earth's rotation creates day and night. As Earth rotates, part of it is turned toward the sun, and the other part of it is turned away from the sun. On the sunlit side, it is day. On the dark side, it is night. In Chapter 6, you will learn more about how Earth's orbit, tilt, and rotation affect life on our planet.

Lesson 2 Review

Recalling Information
1. What is Earth's galaxy called?
2. How does a star differ from a planet?

Interpreting Information
3. How is Earth different from the other eight planets in the solar system?
4. How would life be different if Earth rotated once every 12 hours instead of once every 24 hours?

Applying Information
5. Why would life on Earth be impossible if there were no sun?
6. What features of planet Earth are essential to you as a human being?

If you were standing on this California beach, which ocean would you see? Which lands lie at this ocean's farthest edges?

Lesson 3

OCEANS AND CONTINENTS

Look back at the picture of Earth on page 16. The clouds swirling around Earth help to show that Earth is enclosed in an envelope of air. The broad, blue expanses indicate that much of Earth is covered by water. About seven-tenths of Earth's surface consists of water, though some of it is frozen all year.

Earth's Oceans

Most of Earth's water is one immense ocean. An ocean is a large body of salt water. This vast body of water is divided into four parts, each of which is also called an ocean.

The largest of the four oceans is the Pacific. It is almost as large as the other three combined. The Pacific is also the deepest ocean. In one part of the Pacific, called the Mariana Trench, the ocean is almost 36,000 feet (10,972.8 m) deep. That distance is greater than the height of Earth's tallest mountain, Mount Everest, which rises 29,028 feet (8,847.7 m).

The second-largest ocean on Earth is the Atlantic, followed closely in size by the Indian Ocean. Each of these oceans takes up

**This photograph shows portions of three of Earth's continents.
Name them and the bodies of water that almost surround them.**

about one-fifth of Earth's total ocean area. The fourth and the smallest ocean is the Arctic, which surrounds the great frozen area near the North Pole.

Suppose that you are looking down on Earth from a spacecraft far above the North Pole. You see about 60 percent water and 40 percent land. If you were to look down toward the South Pole, your view would be quite different. You would see about 80 percent water and a mere 20 percent land.

Earth's Landmasses

The large landmasses that you see from your spacecraft are called **continents**. There are seven continents—Asia, Europe, Africa, North America, South America, Australia, and Antarctica.

Continents are often described as large landmasses that are completely surrounded by oceans. That description is not quite accurate, however. Of the seven continents, many are bounded by oceans, but only Australia and Antarctica are completely surrounded by water.

At certain points, the other five continents are attached to other pieces of land, or would be attached if humans had not disconnected them. Asia and Europe form a huge landmass that is called Eurasia. Africa is attached to Asia by a narrow neck of land known as an isthmus. North America and South America are also joined by an isthmus.

26

This astronaut's eye view of Australia shows why it is called the island continent. It is completely surrounded by water.

For many centuries, people knew that if canals were built across these two isthmuses, they would provide shortcuts for interocean travel. Now, canals do cut through both isthmuses. The Suez Canal, which was completed in 1859, connects the Mediterranean Sea and the Red Sea and separates Africa from Asia. The Panama Canal, which opened in 1914, connects the Atlantic and the Pacific Oceans and separates North America from South America.

How do the continents rank in size? Asia is the largest. It includes the subcontinent of India plus several large peninsulas, among them Asia Minor and the Arabian Peninsula. Africa is the second-largest continent. Then come North America, South America,

Antarctica, and Europe. The smallest continent is Australia, and it is the only one that is composed of one country.

Earth's Islands

Australia is often called an island continent because it looks more like an **island** than do any of the other continents. An island is land that is completely surrounded by water. An island is much smaller than a continent. The largest island, Greenland, is only about 28 percent as large as Australia.

Islands make up about 7 percent of all the land on Earth. Among the largest islands, after Greenland, are New Guinea and Borneo in the Pacific Ocean, Madagascar in the Indian Ocean, Baffin Island in the Arctic

Ocean, and Sumatra in the Indian Ocean. Find these islands on the world map on pages 32 and 33.

Earth has countless islands, ranging from Greenland and Sumatra to tiny spots of land that are only a few yards wide. A group of islands is called an **archipelago.** The West Indies in the Caribbean Sea form an archipelago. Cuba, Jamaica, and Puerto Rico are among the islands in this archipelago.

Lesson 3 Review

Recalling Information
1. What is Earth's deepest ocean?
2. Which continents make up Earth's largest landmass? What is this landmass called?

Interpreting Information
3. Do you live on a continent or on an island? Would it be possible to live on an island within a continent? Explain.
4. Which two bodies of water near you might be connected by a canal? What purpose would the canal serve?

Applying Information
5. What kind of boat or ship would you use to cross the Pacific Ocean? Why?
6. What advantages and disadvantages would you find in living on an island?

Small islands such as these near Marblehead, Massachusetts, are common in coastal areas.

Chapter 1 Review

Summary of Key Facts

In this chapter, you learned that

- geography is the study of Earth and of the ways in which people live on Earth.
- Earth is one of nine planets that travel around the sun in our galaxy, the Milky Way.
- each galaxy has billions of stars.
- the sun is the center of the solar system.
- Earth takes one year to orbit the sun.
- Earth rotates on its axis once a day, causing day and night.
- about seven-tenths of Earth's surface consists of water.
- Earth's landmasses have been divided into seven continents; Asia is the largest and Australia is the smallest.

Using Vocabulary

On a separate sheet of paper, write the number of each term and then its meaning.

1. galaxy   very large body of salt water
2. solar system   line on which Earth rotates
3. planet   study of people and their environments
4. orbit   small land areas that are completely surrounded by water
5. ocean   the sun and what lies around it
6. axis   surroundings
7. continents   object that moves in an orbit around the sun
8. islands   system with billions of stars
9. environment   path of a planet
10. geography   Earth's largest landmasses

Discussing the Chapter

1. Describe some characteristics and the movement of the objects in our solar system.
2. How is Earth unique?
3. Define *geography*, and name three branches of human geography.
4. Why is the study of geography useful?

Map and Globe Handbook

You have probably heard the old saying that one picture is worth 1,000 words. This saying is true of a map, also. One map often can contain the same information that would require several written pages. Some important facts in this textbook are found on maps. With this handbook, you can review how to read and to understand maps.

Map Scales

Look at the maps on this page. The big map shows all of Australia. The small map shows Australia's largest city, Sydney. The map of Sydney is an inset map. An inset map shows one part of a larger map in greater detail. On the map that shows all of Australia, Sydney is just a dot. On the map

One map is a large-scale map. The other is a small-scale map. The small-scale map provides more detail. Why?

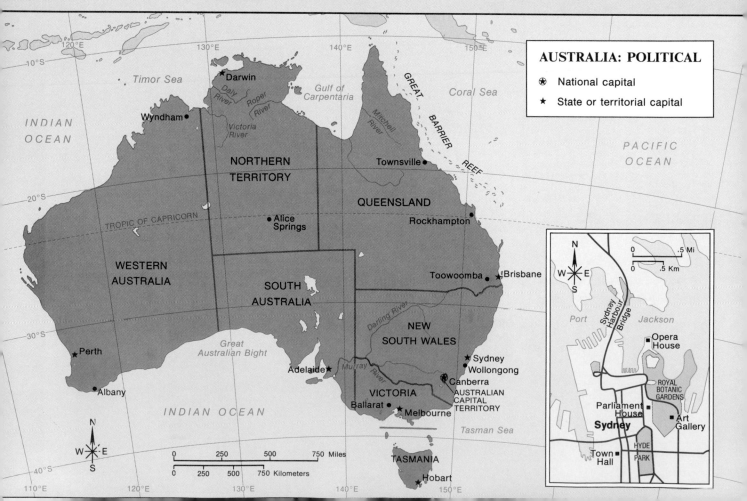

AUSTRALIA: POLITICAL

✳ National capital

★ State or territorial capital

of Sydney, you can see such details as streets and parks.

Compare the distance scales on both maps. Measure 1/2 inch (1.27 cm) on the distance scale for the map of Australia. How many miles does it represent? Now, measure a 1/2 inch (1.27 cm) on the distance scale for the map of Sydney. You can see that the same length represents a much shorter distance. A distance scale depends on how much of Earth is represented on the map. When a map shows a larger area of Earth, each unit on the distance scale must represent a greater number of miles.

Look at the larger map again. Is Sydney north or south of Canberra? To determine this, you must use the compass rose. A compass rose is a circle with either lines or arrows that point to the four cardinal, or main, directions. A compass rose also can indicate intermediate directions, northeast, southeast, northwest, and southwest. Which direction best describes where Sydney is in relation to Canberra?

Kinds of Maps

There are many different kinds of maps. The map on pages 32 and 33 is a political map. It shows how continents are divided politically into countries and states. Sometimes, capitals and other cities are also shown. A political map usually shows the major rivers, oceans, and other major bodies of water, including lakes, gulfs, and seas. Which are the largest countries in Africa? In Asia? In Europe? In North America and South America? In which continent is Egypt? Iran? Norway?

The map on this page is a distribution

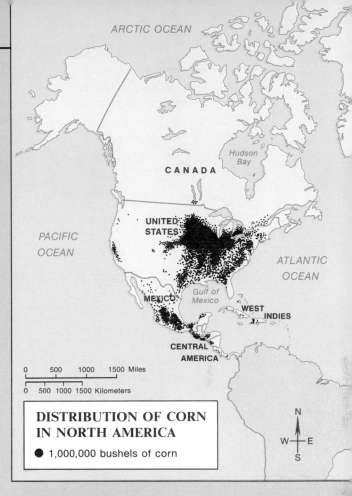

On this distribution map, how many bushels of corn are represented?

map. It shows the area in which corn is grown in North America. To understand this map, you need to use the map key. A map key explains the meaning of the symbols on a map. Symbols are things, such as pictures or colors, that represent something else. What symbol is used to represent corn-growing areas on this distribution map?

There are many different uses for symbols on a map. For instance, on other distribution maps, symbols may represent population, rainfall, or resources. On a political map, symbols may represent capital cities and other major cities, as well as cities' sizes. On a physical map, color is used to indicate the height of the land. Different

THE WORLD: POLITICAL

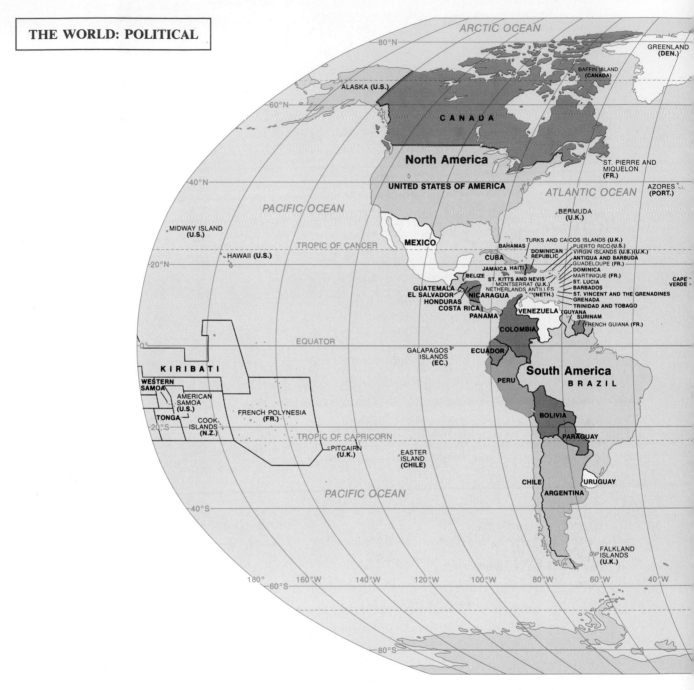

ARCTIC OCEAN

GREENLAND (DEN.)

80°N

BAFFIN ISLAND (CANADA)

ALASKA (U.S.)

60°N

C A N A D A

North America

ST. PIERRE AND MIQUELON (FR.)

AZORES (PORT.)

40°N

UNITED STATES OF AMERICA

ATLANTIC OCEAN

PACIFIC OCEAN

BERMUDA (U.K.)

MIDWAY ISLAND (U.S.)

TROPIC OF CANCER

MEXICO

TURKS AND CAICOS ISLANDS (U.K.)

BAHAMAS

PUERTO RICO (U.S.)

DOMINICAN REPUBLIC

VIRGIN ISLANDS (U.S.)(U.K.)

20°N

HAWAII (U.S.)

CUBA

ANTIGUA AND BARBUDA

GUADELOUPE (FR.)

JAMAICA HAITI

DOMINICA

BELIZE

MARTINIQUE (FR.)

ST. KITTS AND NEVIS

ST. LUCIA

CAPE VERDE

GUATEMALA

MONTSERRAT (U.K.)

BARBADOS

EL SALVADOR

NETHERLANDS ANTILLES (NETH.)

ST. VINCENT AND THE GRENADINES

HONDURAS

NICARAGUA

GRENADA

COSTA RICA

TRINIDAD AND TOBAGO

PANAMA

VENEZUELA

GUYANA

SURINAM

FRENCH GUIANA (FR.)

COLOMBIA

EQUATOR

GALAPAGOS ISLANDS (EC.)

ECUADOR

South America

K I R I B A T I

PERU

B R A Z I L

WESTERN SAMOA

AMERICAN SAMOA (U.S.)

BOLIVIA

TONGA

COOK ISLANDS (N.Z.)

FRENCH POLYNESIA (FR.)

PARAGUAY

20°S

TROPIC OF CAPRICORN

PITCAIRN (U.K.)

EASTER ISLAND (CHILE)

CHILE

URUGUAY

ARGENTINA

PACIFIC OCEAN

40°S

FALKLAND ISLANDS (U.K.)

180°   160°W   140°W   120°W   100°W   80°W   60°W   40°W

60°S

80°S

Abbreviations

AFG.	—AFGHANISTAN	E. GER.	—EAST GERMANY	NETH.	—NETHERLANDS	
ALB.	—ALBANIA	HUN.	—HUNGARY	P.D.R. OF YEMEN	—PEOPLE'S DEMOCRATIC REPUBLIC OF YEMEN	
AND.	—ANDORRA	ISR.	—ISRAEL			
AUST.	—AUSTRIA	LEB.	—LEBANON	SWITZ.	—SWITZERLAND	
BEL.	—BELGIUM	LIECH.	—LIECHTENSTEIN	U.A.E.	—UNITED ARAB EMIRATES	
CZECH.	—CZECHOSLOVAKIA	LUX.	—LUXEMBOURG	W. GER.	—WEST GERMANY	
				YUG.	—YUGOSLAVIA	

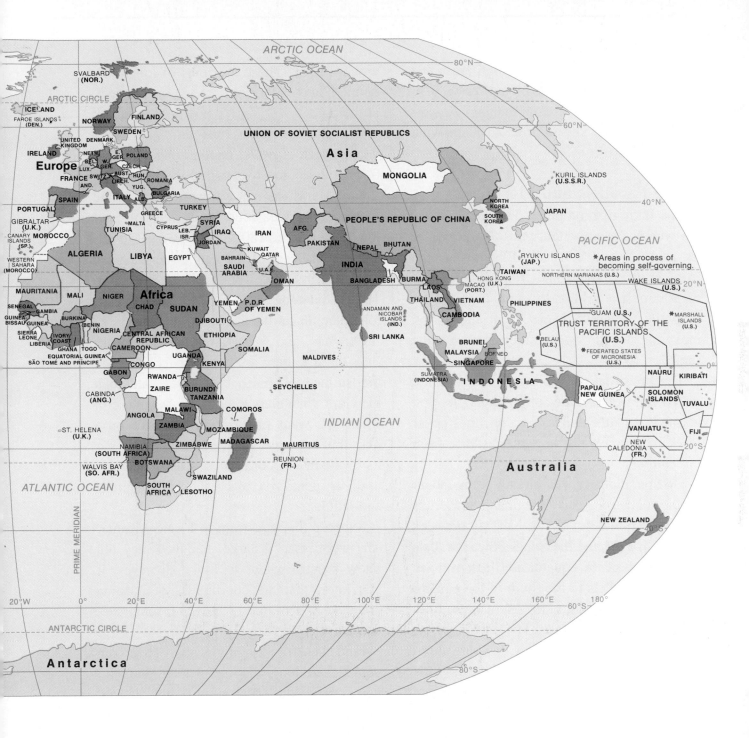

ARCTIC OCEAN

SVALBARD
(NOR.)

80°N

ARCTIC CIRCLE

ICELAND

FAROE ISLANDS
(DEN.)

NORWAY   FINLAND

60°N

SWEDEN

UNITED   DENMARK
KINGDOM

UNION OF SOVIET SOCIALIST REPUBLICS

Asia

KURIL ISLANDS
(U.S.S.R.)

IRELAND

NETH. E.
BEL. GER. POLAND
LUX. W.
GER. CZECH.
AUST. HUN.
ROMANIA

Europe

MONGOLIA

FRANCE SWITZ.
AND. LIECH.
YUG.
BULGARIA

NORTH
KOREA

JAPAN

40°N

SPAIN

ITALY ALB.

PEOPLE'S REPUBLIC OF CHINA

SOUTH
KOREA

PORTUGAL

GREECE   TURKEY

PACIFIC OCEAN

GIBRALTAR
(U.K.)

MALTA
CYPRUS LEB.
SYRIA IRAQ IRAN
ISR.
JORDAN

AFG.

RYUKYU ISLANDS
(JAP.)

*Areas in process of
becoming self-governing.

CANARY
ISLANDS
(SP.) MOROCCO

PAKISTAN

NEPAL BHUTAN

TAIWAN

NORTHERN MARIANAS (U.S.)

WAKE ISLANDS
(U.S.) 20°N

WESTERN
SAHARA
(MOROCCO)

TUNISIA

KUWAIT
BAHRAIN QATAR

HONG KONG

ALGERIA

LIBYA   EGYPT

SAUDI
ARABIA

U.A.E.

INDIA

BURMA

MACAO (U.K.)
(PORT.)

ALGERIA

LIBYA   EGYPT

OMAN

BANGLADESH

LAOS

MAURITANIA

MALI

NIGER

Africa

YEMEN P.D.R.
OF YEMEN

ANDAMAN AND
NICOBAR
ISLANDS
(IND.)

THAILAND VIETNAM

PHILIPPINES

GUAM (U.S.)

*MARSHALL
ISLANDS
(U.S.)

SENEGAL
GAMBIA

CHAD

SUDAN

DJIBOUTI

TRUST TERRITORY OF THE
PACIFIC ISLANDS
(U.S.)

GUINEA-
BISSAU GUINEA

BURKINA

BENIN

CENTRAL AFRICAN
REPUBLIC

ETHIOPIA

SRI LANKA

CAMBODIA

*BELAU
(U.S.)

*FEDERATED STATES
OF MICRONESIA
(U.S.)

SIERRA
LEONE
LIBERIA

IVORY
COAST
GHANA TOGO

NIGERIA

MALDIVES

BRUNEI
MALAYSIA BORNEO

NAURU

KIRIBATI

EQUATORIAL GUINEA
SÃO TOMÉ AND PRÍNCIPE

CAMEROON

UGANDA

SOMALIA

SINGAPORE

GABON

CONGO

KENYA

SUMATRA
(INDONESIA)

INDONESIA

PAPUA
NEW GUINEA

SOLOMON
ISLANDS

CABINDA
(ANG.)

RWANDA

ZAIRE BURUNDI
TANZANIA

SEYCHELLES

TUVALU

ANGOLA

MALAWI

COMOROS

INDIAN OCEAN

VANUATU

FIJI

ST. HELENA
(U.K.)

ZAMBIA

MOZAMBIQUE

MADAGASCAR

MAURITIUS

NEW
CALEDONIA
(FR.)

20°S

NAMIBIA
(SOUTH AFRICA)

ZIMBABWE

REUNION
(FR.)

Australia

WALVIS BAY
(SO. AFR.)

BOTSWANA

SWAZILAND

ATLANTIC OCEAN

SOUTH
AFRICA LESOTHO

NEW ZEALAND

PRIME MERIDIAN

20°W   0°   20°E   40°E   60°E   80°E   100°E   120°E   140°E   160°E   180°   60°S

ANTARCTIC CIRCLE

Antarctica

80°S

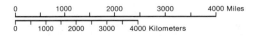

0   1000   2000   3000   4000 Miles

0   1000   2000   3000   4000 Kilometers

shades of color represent the high areas and the low area. Labels identify physical features such as rivers and mountains. Always look at the map key in order to learn what each symbol means.

Using Parallels and Meridians

The large map on pages 32 and 33 shows the world. An important part of this map is its grid. A grid consists of lines that run from north to south and from east to west on a map. The grid on this map is called the graticule. (GRAT*uh*kyool). It appears on most maps of the world, and it is always the same.

The lines that run from east and west are called lines of latitude, or parallels. As you learned in mathematics, parallel lines never meet and are always the same distance from one another.

One parallel that you already know about is the equator. This imaginary line runs along the middle of Earth, halfway between the North Pole and the South Pole. Parallels to the north of the equator are lines of north latitude. Parallels to the south of the equator are lines of south latitude. All of these lines are measured in degrees. The equator is 0°. The parallels that are north of it are numbered up to 90°N. The North Pole is 90°N latitude. Similarly, the parallels that are south of the equator are numbered up to 90°S. The South Pole is 90°S latitude. Now, look at the lines that run from north to south

The political map on pages 32 and 33 shows how the continents are divided into countries. Which continent has the greatest number of countries? Which has the least?

around Earth. These are lines of longitude, or meridians. Meridians meet, or intersect, at the poles.

The first meridian runs through Greenwich, which is near London, England. It is 0° longitude, and it is called the prime meridian. Meridians that are west of the prime meridian are measured in degrees of west longitude, up to 180°W longitude. Meridians that are east of the prime meridian are measured in degrees of east longitude, up to 180°E longitude. In all, there are 360° of longitude on Earth.

Parallels and meridians are imaginary lines because they are not actually found on the surface of Earth. However, although they are imaginary, they are very useful when you want to locate some place on a map. For example, each place on a map has its own pair of coordinates. Coordinates are used to identify a place's exact longitude and latitude.

Suppose that you want to locate Albania. The world map is large, and you may not know exactly where to look. However, if you know that the coordinates of Albania are about 40°N latitude and 20°E longitude, it is easy.

Find the 20°E longitude line. Then, run your finger along this line of longitude until you come to the 40°N latitude line. It is at this point that you will find the country of Albania on the map.

The Four Hemispheres

You know that Earth is like a round ball. One way to show this is on a globe. A globe is a model of Earth. It shows Earth's landmasses and oceans.

The drawings on this page each show a part of Earth that is called a hemisphere. The word *hemisphere* is easy to understand. *Hemi* means "half." *Sphere* refers to the ball-like shape of Earth. So, a hemisphere is a half of Earth.

The equator divides Earth into the Northern Hemisphere and the Southern Hemisphere. The other two hemispheres of Earth are the Eastern Hemisphere and the Western Hemisphere.

One way in which you can identify the hemispheres is by knowing the continents that they contain. Notice that most of Earth's landmasses are found in the Northern Hemisphere. In later chapters, you will read about how the distribution of land and water affects life on Earth. The Eastern Hemisphere contains Asia, Africa, Europe, and Australia. Which continents do you see in the Western Hemisphere? In which hemisphere do you live?

The center of the Northern Hemisphere consists of the North Pole and the Arctic Ocean. The center of the Southern Hemisphere is the South Pole and Antarctica. Which continents are partly or entirely in the Southern Hemisphere? Which continents are partly or entirely in the Northern Hemisphere? Which of them contains the most land? Which oceans lie partly or entirely in the Northern Hemisphere? The United States is located in two hemispheres. Can you name them?

Boundaries between the Eastern and the Western Hemispheres are usually drawn along the meridians of 20°W and 160°E. What divides the Northern Hemisphere from the Southern Hemisphere?

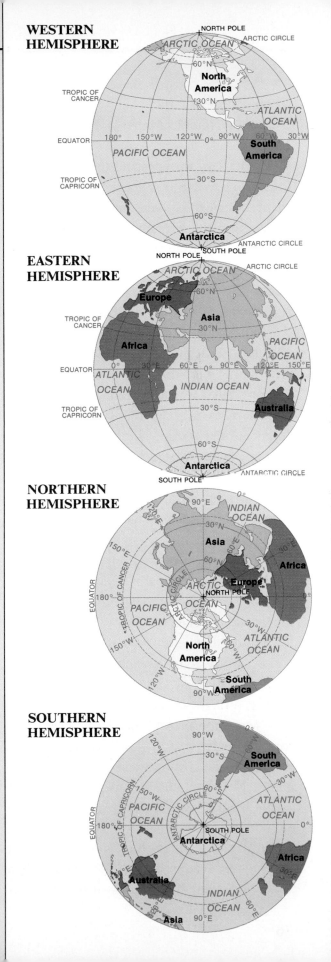

Map Projections

Earth is round. Maps of Earth are flat. This causes a problem for mapmakers. When they try to represent the ball shape of Earth on a piece of paper, they distort the shapes and sizes of land masses and oceans.

The kind and amount of distortion depend on the **map projection** used. A map projection is a way of drawing Earth on a flat surface. There are many kinds of map projections. Each fills a different need.

Each map projection either tears or stretches Earth in some way to show it flat. (The same thing happens when you either tear or stretch a whole orange peel to make it lie flat.) On some maps, the shapes of things are fairly true, but their sizes are not. On other maps, distances are fairly true, but directions are not.

Three map projections of the world are shown on the facing page. As you can see, the shapes and sizes of things look slightly different on each projection.

The first projection is a **Mercator projection**, named after its inventor, a European mapmaker of the 1500s. It was favored by navigators of that time because it gives a fairly reliable picture of the shapes of landforms, and shows north-south directions as straight up and down.

A Mercator projection is not useful for comparing the sizes of land masses because it enlarges the size of areas in the higher latitudes. This happens because the meridians do not bend toward the poles, as they do on a globe.

What effect does this have? Look at Greenland. It appears to be larger than South America. If you look at those places on a globe, you will see that South America is about eight times the size of Greenland.

The second projection is a **Peters projection**. The Peters projection distorts shapes and distances in order to give a consistent representation of relative sizes of land areas. Peters's way of doing this is clear. When he shows lines of longitude as straight verticals, he is making the space between them *wider* than it should be in the high latitudes. In those places, he makes the gap between lines of latitude *shorter*. This keeps the overall area (height times width) consistent.

What effect does this have? Look at Alaska. If you flew high enough over Alaska while holding a Peters map, you might think the mapmaker had squished the state. The Mercator projection gives a better picture of Alaska's shape. But you might notice later that Mexico (762,000 square miles) is quite a bit larger than Alaska (587,000 square miles). Mercator made Alaska, at its high northern latitude, look larger. Peters gives a fairer idea of size.

The oval projection is a **Robinson projection.** Note that the meridians on this map do bend toward the poles, just as they do on a globe. Size, shape, and distance are all a bit distorted, and directions are inconsistent. Still, relative sizes of continents are more accurately rendered than on the Mercator projection, shapes are more accurate than on the Peters projection, and distances are more accurate than on either of the others.

Each projection distorts shapes, sizes, distances, or directions.

**MERCATOR
PROJECTION
OF THE WORLD**

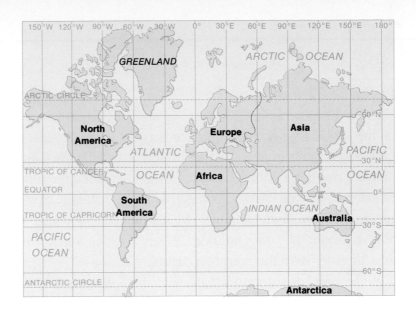

**PETERS
PROJECTION
OF THE WORLD**

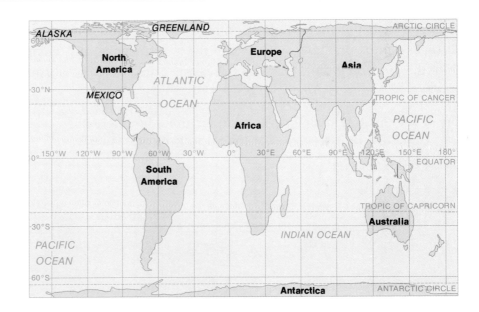

**ROBINSON
PROJECTION
OF THE WORLD**

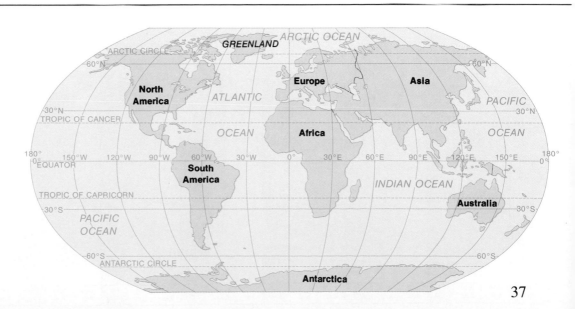

World Time Zones

It is never the same hour of the day in all parts of the world at any one time. Earth is divided into 24 time zones. In the United States alone, there are 6 time zones. In the Soviet Union, there are 11 time zones. Each zone represents one hour of time. In land area, that is about 15° of longitude. When the sun is directly over the meridian that divides a time zone, it is noon in that zone.

All time zones are measured from the prime meridian, in Greenwich, England. As you move west from Greenwich, the time in each time zone is one hour *earlier* than the time in the preceding time zone. To the east of Greenwich, each new zone's time is one hour *later* than the time in the preceding zone.

The first time zone in the United States is called the Eastern time zone. It begins at the Atlantic Coast. Eastern time is five hours earlier than Greenwich time. That means that when it is noon in Greenwich, England, it is 7 A.M. in New York City. In which time zone do you live?

Look at the world time-zone map below. Imagine that you are in Tokyo, Japan, and that you want to make a telephone call to someone in London, England. If it is noon in Tokyo, what time is it in London?

You can use this time-zone map to compare times in different cities. At 9 A.M. in Moscow, what time is it in Buenos Aires?

WORLD TIME ZONES

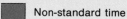 Non-standard time

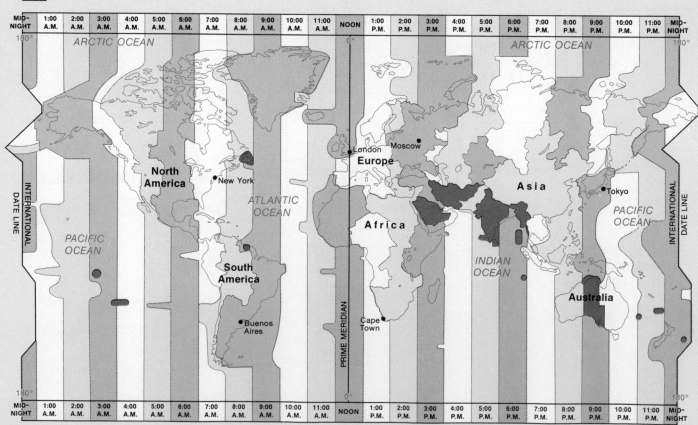

Special-Purpose Maps

Many maps indicate the locations of mountains, rivers, and countries. Other maps may show you where certain crops are grown or how to travel from place to place.

Some maps that help you to travel are road maps. There are other maps that are used for traveling, too. If you flew to Mexico City and had no car, you might be grateful for the metro, or subway, map on this page.

This map shows seven subway lines. Each line is represented by a different color and is identified by a circled number at either end of the line. Along the lines are small squares with names next to them. These indicate the subway station stops.

As with any subway or bus map, you must first find the stop that is nearest to you. Then, find the stop that is nearest to where you want to go. Trace the shortest route between the two places with your finger. That is the route that you should take.

To find out which train to take, look for the line numbers at the ends of the route that you have traced. If you were going to travel from Santa Anita station to Martin Carrera station, for example, you would take Line #4 all the way to the end. If you want to go from Santa Anita station to Politecnico station, you will need to take two trains.

To determine how to take two trains is easy with this map. You can see that one station is on Line #4 and that the other station is on Line #5. You can also see that these lines cross at Consulado station. So, you can leave the #4 train at Consulado station and board the #5 train that goes toward Politecnico station.

Maps such as this are sometimes called special-purpose maps. Many cities have such maps to help people to use the local transportation systems. Knowing how to read these maps is a useful skill. Have you ever used such a map?

Other special-purpose maps may show bicycle paths and hiking trails that can be found in parks, walking tours that may be taken in historic areas, or the exhibit rooms that are in museums. When you go on your next trip, see how many special-purpose maps you can collect.

Which trains would you take to get from Martin Carrera to the Observatorio?

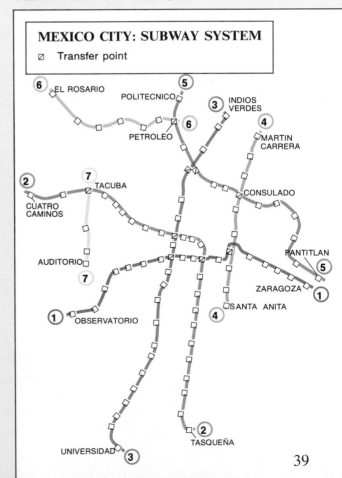

Forms of the Land

Introduction

"Stop right here, son....Where in the world do you think you're going in this blizzard? Are you crazy?"

The scene: A country store.

The characters: The country-store regulars who are sitting around a wood-burning stove, and a young man who has just come in from a storm.

The young man takes a deep breath and gives the answer that he has given hundreds of times during the past months.

"Well, sir, my name's Peter Jenkins. I'm walking across America."

"Why would you want to do a thing like that?" asks one of the regulars.

"To get to know the country," the young man replies.

Peter Jenkins had begun a hike that was to become a 5,000-mile (8,046.5-km), five-year, living geography lesson. He hiked across the Appalachian Mountains, up and down the Cumberland Hills, and across the plains that rim the Gulf of Mexico. Then he moved into the high country of Texas, onto the plateaus of the Southwest, through the Rocky Mountains and the Pacific Coast mountains to the Pacific Ocean.

This incredible hike introduced Peter Jenkins to many different people and to practically every kind of terrain that the country provides. In this chapter, you, too, will be introduced to Earth's many forms of land in all parts of the world.

Yosemite Valley in Yosemite National Park in California is seen from Half Dome, a large rock outcropping there.

Lesson 1

MOUNTAINS

Once a year, in summer, the trappers met at a place that they had chosen the year before. Buyers from as far away as the East Coast came to purchase the furs that the trappers had collected during the past months. For a few days, talk and laughter rang through the clear air. Then, the buyers left, and the trappers returned one by one to the wilderness.

The trappers were the "mountain men" of the Rocky Mountains, American fur hunters who roamed the West in the early 1800s. "Only with reluctance does a trapper abandon his dangerous craft," wrote one observer, "and a sort of serious homesickness seizes him when he retires from his mountain life to civilization." For these rugged men a life in the mountains offered a special kind of magic. Even today that special magic still moves countless other people all over the world.

Mountains are one of the four major **landforms** on Earth's surface. A landform is a distinctive feature, or form, of the land. Geographers define the four major landforms in terms of their height. Look at the diagram. What other major landforms are shown there?

Across Earth, the level of the oceans—**sea level**—is about the same. The heights of land surfaces, however, vary a great deal. A land surface can be lower than sea level, as it is in California's Death Valley. It can also rise miles above sea level, as it does on Earth's tallest mountains in the Himalayas in South Asia.

The height of a land area in relation to sea level is called **elevation**. A land area that is just above sea level has a low elevation. On the other hand a mountain peak has a high elevation.

This cross-sectional diagram shows how geographers use both elevation and relief to identify the four major landforms.

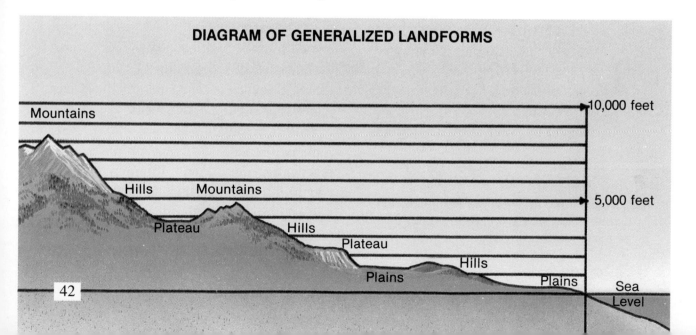

DIAGRAM OF GENERALIZED LANDFORMS

Mountains

10,000 feet

Hills   Mountains

5,000 feet

Plateau   Hills

Plateau

Plains   Hills

Plains   Sea Level

42

The cross-sectional drawing on page 42 shows the elevations of the four main landforms. The difference in height between two related land surfaces is called **relief**.

On the cross section, the difference in height between the first plain and the first stretch of hills is small. Thus, this is an area of low relief. The difference in height between the stretches of hills and their nearby mountains is much greater. This is an area of high relief. Take a look at both the map and the diagram on this page to see how relief is shown on a map.

What Is a Mountain?

A **mountain** is a landform that is characterized by high relief and by steep slopes. It rises at least 2,000 feet (609.6 m) above its neighboring area. The angle of its rise, or slope, averages about 25°, but sometimes reaches 50° to 60°. In rare, spectacular cases, a mountain can rise at a 70° angle.

Mountains cover about one-fifth of Earth's land surface. That means that about one in five square miles of land is mountainous. For their inhabitants, mountains present special problems. Rough surfaces and steep slopes make mountain travel difficult. Their elevation makes mountains colder than surrounding areas. (You will learn why in Chapter 6.)

Most mountains do not stand alone. They are usually grouped together in mountain ranges. A mountain range is a chain of mountain peaks, ridges, and valleys. The

MAP SKILLS: Compare the drawing of Madagascar above to the contour map below. On the map, lines connect places that lie at the same elevation.

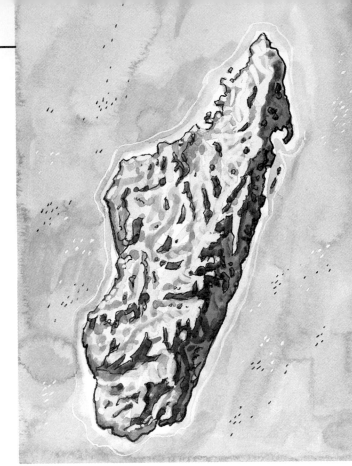

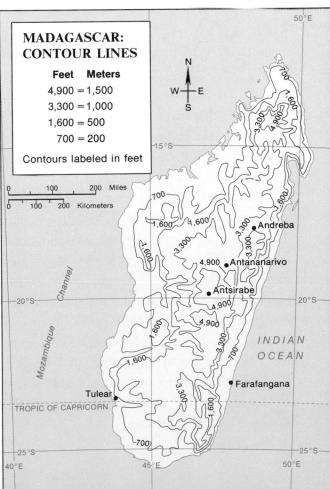

MADAGASCAR:
CONTOUR LINES

Feet	Meters
4,900	= 1,500
3,300	= 1,000
1,600	= 500
700	= 200

Contours labeled in feet

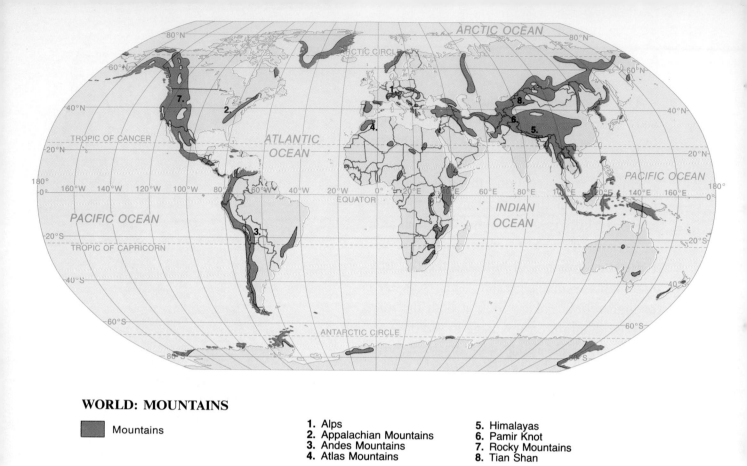

WORLD: MOUNTAINS

▮ Mountains

1. Alps
2. Appalachian Mountains
3. Andes Mountains
4. Atlas Mountains
5. Himalayas
6. Pamir Knot
7. Rocky Mountains
8. Tian Shan

MAP SKILLS: This map shows the worldwide distribution of mountains. Which continents are the least mountainous?

mountains that are found within a range are generally alike in their form. The reason for this is that they have been created by the same process.

Mountain ranges are often joined to form an even larger group, a mountain system. The map shows some of the major mountain systems in the world. The Rocky Mountains on the North American continent are an example of a mountain system. The Brooks Range of Alaska, the Selkirk Mountains of Canada, the Sawtooth Mountains of Idaho, the Teton Range of Wyoming, and the San Juan Mountains of Colorado are only a few of the ranges that combine to make up the Rocky Mountain system.

The Mountains of Earth

Notice the distribution of mountains on the map. Can you find the Pamir Knot in central Asia? Three of Earth's great mountain systems stretch out from this region.

One arm of mountains reaches southeastward. Its major system consists of the Himalayas of southern Asia. It then extends south through the archipelagoes of the Asian continent and reaches, underwater at times, to Australia. You will learn more about underwater mountains in Chapter 4.

Another giant arm stretches first northeastward through Asia and then across the Pacific Ocean to North America. There, it curves south along South America's Pacific

Can You Imagine?

In 1977, a group of 10 women decided to climb the eleventh-tallest mountain in the world—Annapurna I in the Himalayas. They wanted to be the first Americans to reach its peak. Imagine your having been with them.

You would have carried a 46-pound (20.9 kg) pack during the 2-month climb. Your climb to the first camp would have taken you 16,500 feet (5,029.2 m) up the mountain. From there, you would have scaled 2,000 feet (609.6 m) of ice to reach the second camp.

On your climb to the third camp, you would have inched your way up 70° slopes of ice and snow. Heavy snows all around you would have threatened to bury you under avalanches. Yet, somehow, step after agonizing step, you would have reached the top. Imagine planting your flag there.

Mountain climbers come from all over the world to challenge the steep, treacherous slopes of the lofty Himalayan peaks.

coast. Among its mountain systems are the Tian Shan of China, the Rocky Mountains of North America, and the Andes Mountains of South America.

The third arm curves westward through southwestern Asia, across Europe, and into Africa. It includes the Carpathians, the Alps, and the Pyrenees in Europe and the Atlas Mountains in northern Africa.

Within these three arms of mountains, ranges and systems vary a great deal. The most spectacular and the highest are the Himalayas. (The word *Himalaya* means "abode of snow.") Among the peaks of the Himalayas stands the tallest mountain in the world, Mount Everest.

The soaring Himalayas form an almost impassable barrier between the countries that they border. Even air travel is difficult. "When you fly, even high, over the Himalayas," wrote one traveler, "the cold comes through the floor of the plane and shoots up your leg like an electric shock."

The Andes are the second-highest mountain system in the world. They were the home of the Inca. Before the Europeans came to America, the Inca ruled much of Peru and neighboring regions.

45

An English poet called the Alps "palaces of nature." This great mountain system covers much of both Switzerland and Austria and extends into several other countries as well. Among its snow-covered peaks lie beautiful lakes, such as Lake Como in Italy. Writers, artists, and photographers have made people throughout the world familiar with Alpine sights—flower-dotted meadows, sturdy wooden chalets, farmers rounding up cows from mountain pastures, and trams that take throngs of skiers to mountaintop resorts.

Isolated Mountains

As you can see from the map on page 44, not all of the world's mountains are part of the three giant arms that swing out from the Pamir Knot. For instance, the Appalachians of eastern North America form an independent system. Age has worn down these mountains into rounded slopes. ("Younger" mountains, such as the Himalayas, have taller, more jagged peaks.)

Some unusual mountains soar alone into the sky. Usually, these mountains have been formed by eruptions of volcanoes.

Using Mountain Land

Rough terrain, cold climates, and steep slopes discourage people from settling in mountains. Only a small fraction of Earth's people live in mountainous regions.

What do people do in mountainous regions? Some people farm. For example, tea plantations dot the lower slopes of the Himalayas. Some people raise sheep and cattle. The people of mountainous areas live in valleys where they are sheltered from winds and where the soil—worn down from the valley walls—is suitable for farming.

Minerals such as gold, silver, and copper are often found in abundance in mountainous regions, and so, mining has been common there. The Rocky Mountains, for instance, formed the scene of a great gold strike in the 1800s, after the days of the "mountain men." More recently, mountains have struck a new kind of gold—tourism. Skiing and climbing attract thousands of visitors to mountains every year.

Lesson 1 Review

Recalling Information
1. How does elevation differ from relief?
2. What percentage of Earth's land is covered by mountains? Why do relatively few people live there?

Interpreting Information
3. Describe the three arms of mountains that stretch out from the Pamir Knot.
4. Summarize three ways in which mountain land is used.

Applying Information
5. Which are the closest mountains to you? What might you do there?
6. Which characteristics of mountains would discourage you from settling in them? Which would attract you?

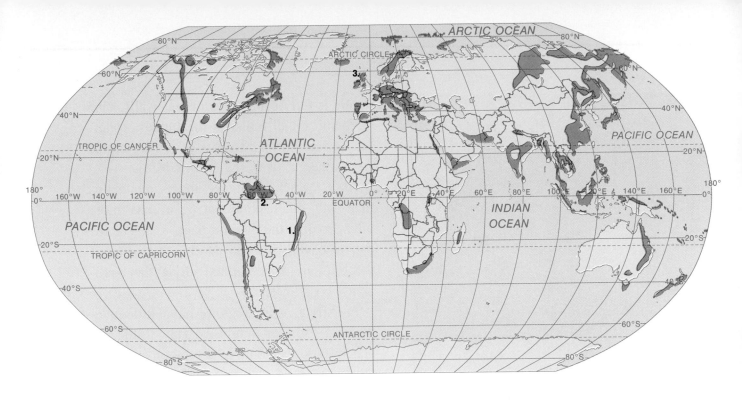

WORLD: HILLS

Hills

1. Brazilian Highlands
2. Guiana Highlands
3. Scottish Highlands

MAP SKILLS: Compare this map with the map on page 44. Which of the hilly regions that are shown here are probably foothills? Explain.

Lesson 2

HILLS

What is the difference between a mountain and a **hill**? A hill has sloping land, like a mountain, but it has lower relief. Geographers usually classify a hill as a landform that rises anywhere from 500 feet (152.4 m) to 2,000 feet (609.6 m) above the land around it.

The Distribution of Hills on Earth

As you can see from the map on this page, hilly regions exist on all the continents except Antarctica. Hills may exist on Antarctica, too, but the deep snow and ice make it impossible to tell.

Often, hills lie at the foot of a mountain range. These are called foothills. In the eastern United States, the Appalachian Mountains are bordered by hilly regions. The same is true of the Andes in South America. Foothills lie between the Pacific Ocean and the soaring peaks of the Andes.

Another kind of hilly region, known as **highlands**, consists of hills and mountains together. One such area, the Guiana Highlands, is located in northern South America. Most of it lies in Venezuela. Because of sharp drops from one level to another, the

47

region is full of magnificent waterfalls. One of them, Angel Falls, is the highest waterfall in the world. Streams of water tumble from a height of 3,212 fcct (979 m).

Asia, which contains more mountains than any other continent, also has more hills. Look at the map on page 47 to see the pattern of hills in Asia. Notice that many of the hills are concentrated along the continent's coastlines.

In Africa, hilly regions have little relationship to mountains. The hills lie generally to the south of the mountains, and they border coastal waters and ring other landforms.

Hilly regions cover large areas of Europe, especially in the south, around the Mediterranean Sea. Hills also cover much of the British Isles. One well-known hilly area is the Scottish Highlands in northern Scotland. A region more unlike the Guiana Highlands would be hard to find. The hills of the Scottish Highlands are covered with gnarled trees, low shrubs, and purple heather. Gray skies and cold winds make visitors glad that they can buy the heavy woolen cloth, known as tweed, that was first woven in these highlands.

Using Hilly Land

As you might expect, more people live in hilly regions than in mountainous ones, for hills are neither as high nor as cold as mountains. Grazing is also possible in many of the world's hilly regions.

By building terraces, farmers in the Philippines turn rugged hills into valuable farmland. How else are hilly areas used?

Some farming is possible, but fields are often small because of the terrain. In the hills of Ireland, farmers mainly grow potatoes. In much of the Mediterranean area, grapes and olives are grown.

Terracing is a way of creating level land in hilly areas. Many farmers in Asia and in Europe have created farmland by building steplike terraces in the hills.

Hilly lands often yield timber and minerals. The Guiana Highlands, for instance, contain important stands, or areas, of standing cedar and mahogany trees, as well as mines that contain gold and diamonds.

Lesson 2 Review

Recalling Information

1. What are foothills? Name two areas in which they are found.
2. What are highlands? Name two important highlands.

Interpreting Information

3. How does the relief of a hill compare to that of a mountain?
4. Why do more people settle in hilly regions than in mountainous ones?

Applying Information

5. Do you live in a hilly area? If so, how do hills influence your life? If not, how do you think that hills might change the way in which you live now?
6. What characteristics of hills might encourage you to settle in them? What characteristics might discourage you?

PLATEAUS

Take another look at the cross-sectional drawing on page 42, and find the **plateaus** that are illustrated on it. From the diagram, you can discover two important features of plateaus. First, they tend to be flat. Second, they are generally located at high elevations. Plateaus can most often be found at elevations above 3,000 feet (914.4 m). Using these characteristics you can develop a definition for this landform: A plateau is a fairly flat area at a fairly high elevation. Many plateaus lie between or at the base of mountains.

Coming upon a plateau can be a dramatic experience. You might be driving across an area of flat land when a sheer cliff, called an **escarpment**, comes into view. Atop the escarpment is another area of flat land; yet, it may be hundreds of yards higher than the land that you are driving on. This is one kind of plateau, the kind in which at least one side rises up sharply from the surrounding land.

Another kind of plateau rises up sharply on all sides from the surrounding land. If it is large, it is called a tableland, and if it is small, it is called a mesa (the Spanish word for *table*). At one time, a tableland may have been a part of a much larger plateau. Streams of water cut across many plateaus. Over the centuries, these streams may have cut deeply into the plateau surface, carving it into several tablelands. If you have ever visited the Grand Canyon in Arizona, you have seen what the cutting power of a river

The spectacular Grand Canyon is located in the Arizona section of the Colorado plateau.

can do. There, the Colorado River has cut a gorge in the Colorado Plateau more than 1 mile (1.6 km) deep and 200 miles (321.9 km) long.

The Distribution of Plateaus

Plateaus cover about 40 percent of Earth's land surface, as the map on the facing page shows. You can see that Africa contains the most plateaus. In fact, the entire continent is often described as one immense plateau. Plateaus are the dominant landforms in Africa. Their elevations usually range from 500 feet to 3,000 feet (152.4 m to 914.4 m).

The Sahara, the great desert of northern Africa, is situated on a plateau. In eastern Africa, the plateaus are cooler and drier and are covered with grass. These grass-covered plateaus are the homes of the big game animals—elephants, lions, tigers, hippopotamuses, and rhinoceroses.

Look at the map, and find the major plateau areas of North America. Most of these areas are located in the western part of the country. They usually lie between mountain areas.

South America has some very big plateaus. The largest of the South American plateaus is in Brazil. This Brazilian plateau drops off sharply in an escarpment to the east. As a result, this plateau region has hindered travel to and from the interior of the country.

Another plateau in South America is a region that is known as Patagonia, in southern Argentina. Patagonia covers about 260,000 square miles (673,000 sq km). Its highest region, at the base of the Andes Mountains, lies at about 3,000 feet (914.4 m) above sea level. Like many other plateaus around the world, Patagonia is windy and cold. One recent traveler described its appearance this way: "The landscape had a prehistoric look, the sort that forms a painted backdrop for a dinosaur skeleton in a museum: simple, terrible hills and gullies; thornbushes and rocks; and everything smoothed by the wind."

Asia has several important plateaus. One covers almost the entire Arabian Peninsula, a broad desert area. Find this peninsula on the atlas map on pages 488 and 489. Part of this plateau is so uninviting that it is called the Empty Quarter. To the northeast, the

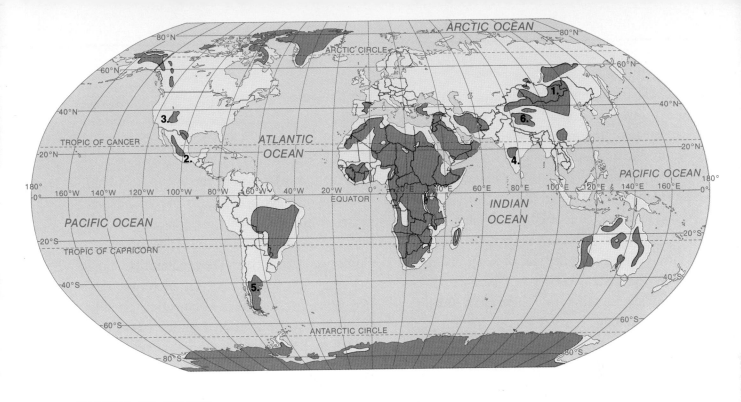

WORLD: PLATEAUS

 Plateaus

1. Central Asia Plateau
2. Central Plateau (Mexico)
3. Colorado Plateau
4. Deccan Plateau (India)
5. Patagonia
6. Plateau of Tibet

MAP SKILLS: This map shows the worldwide distribution of plateaus. Which continent has virtually no significant plateaus?

Central Asia Plateau extends as far east and west as the entire United States. Covering a large part of it is the great Gobi Desert of Mongolia.

South of the Gobi, in the midst of the Himalaya Mountains, lies what has been called the highest, bleakest, coldest, remotest, most inhospitable country in the world—the Tibetan Plateau. Known as "the roof of the world," its average height is 14,000 feet (4267.2 m). Its valleys are higher than the summits of the Alps. The biggest plateau on Earth, the Tibetan Plateau covers about 530,000 square miles (1,372,700 sq km)—almost twice the size of Texas.

Icy plateaus is the term that is used to describe most of Greenland and Antarctica. Whatever the shape of the land below them, their snow-and-ice surface creates a plateau effect. After endless miles of flat expanse, these surfaces drop off suddenly down icy cliffs to the sea. Antarctica's neighbor to the north, Australia, is almost half covered by very different kinds of plateaus. Australia's western plateau is mainly composed of hot desert.

Using Plateau Land

In general, plateaus are not heavily populated. They tend to be dry, and so, they are not good for farming. One of the few

51

plateaus that contains a large population is the Central Plateau of Mexico. It lies between two mountain ranges, the Sierra Madre Occidental (Western) and the Sierra Madre Oriental (Eastern). This plateau of more than 5,000 feet (1,542 m) occupies more than 50 percent of the country and is the home of most Mexicans. It supports many farms and is the site of Earth's largest urban area, Mexico City.

Plateaus at fairly low elevations are useful for grazing. Vast flocks of sheep graze in Patagonia and in Australia. Plateaus also yield minerals. The plateau region of the western United States is the world's largest producer of copper.

Lesson 3 Review

Recalling Information

1. What are the two main features of plateaus?
2. How much of Earth is covered by plateaus?

Interpreting Information

3. Compare Patagonia and the Tibetan Plateau in terms of both size and elevation.
4. Compare life on plateaus with life on mountains.

Applying Information

5. If you wanted to buy land for farming, why might you avoid a plateau?
6. Which major plateau area of the world might you most like to visit? Why?

Lesson 4

PLAINS

Find the **plains** on the cross-sectional drawing on page 42. Plains are broad and gently rolling areas that are generally lower than the land around them. Like plateaus, plains are fairly flat. They generally show less than 500 feet (152.4 m) of relief. Unlike plateaus, however, plains are usually found at lower elevations, under 1,000 feet (304.8 m). Because of their low relief and low elevation, plains are often called lowlands. All continents have lowlands.

Many people associate plains with grass. In the United States, this is generally true. Some plains, however, are covered with sand and gravel—the desert plains of Australia, for example. Some glisten with snow and ice, like the Arctic Coastal Plain. Others are swampy, like a broad area of western Siberia in Asia, for example. Still others are covered with forests.

Study the map of world plains on the facing page. Note that some plains areas are found around the edges of continents, where land meets ocean. These are coastal plains. Note the plains areas in the middle of North America, South America, and Eurasia. These are interior plains.

Both coastal and interior plains can be formed out of silt, a fine sediment that is deposited by rivers. Such plains are known as alluvial, or flood, plains. Much of the southern coastal plain in the United States is an alluvial plain that formed over the centuries as the mighty Mississippi River periodically overflowed its banks.

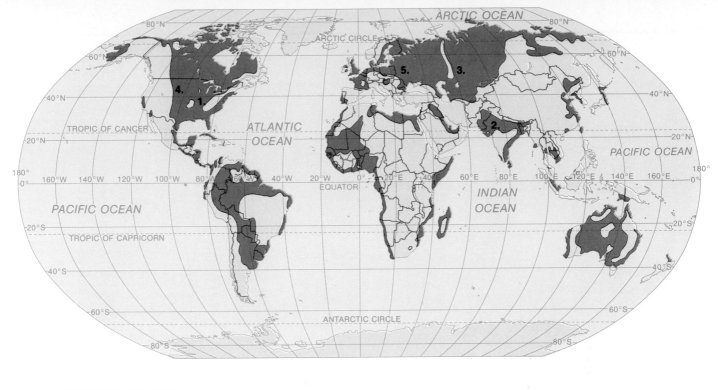

WORLD: PLAINS

 Plains

1. Central Plain
2. Ganges Plain
3. Great Lowland Plain
4. Great Plain
5. North European Plain

MAP SKILLS: Are coastal plains dominant on the Atlantic or the Pacific side of North America and South America?

The Distribution of Plains

American Indians in feather headdresses, vast herds of buffaloes, cowhands roping cattle—all of these sights used to be part of life on the Great Plains of North America. This interior plain of western Canada and the United States, about 500 miles (804.7 km) wide at its widest, extends more than 2,000 miles (3,200 km) from north to south.

Although dry and treeless, the Great Plains are noted for their fields of waving grass. The thousands of miles of tall grass indicates the deep richness of the soil. Some of the nation's richest farmland is to be found here. Many of the first farmers who settled there built houses of sod—chunks of grass-covered earth. Now, the houses are made of wood, but they are few and far between, for the farms on the Great Plains are very large. Giant farm machines crawl across the flat land, cultivating the fields and harvesting crops.

Other plains areas in North America are the Central Plain, which is east of the Great Plains, and a big coastal-plains area that curves east and north from the Gulf of Mexico to New England.

Find South America on the map above, and locate the plains areas there. This continent's largest interior plain extends from the *pampas*, a Spanish word meaning "plains," and the great plains of Argentina

53

**On the rolling, grassy plains of Inner Mongolia in China,
nomadic herders graze sheep, goats, and horses.**

(in the south) northward to the Amazon Plain. The Amazon Plain gets its name from the river that it surrounds. If you were to travel the entire length of this great interior plain, you would never be more than 900 feet (274.3 m) above sea level. On your journey northward, you would cross grassy, treeless areas, swamps and marshes, and, finally, the dense forests around the Amazon.

Europe and Asia share a region that is called the Great Lowland Plain. Twice as wide as the entire United States, it covers much of northern Europe and extends around the Ural Mountains to include much of the Asiatic part of the Soviet Union, too.

Another big plains area of Asia is located in northern India. About 200 miles (321.9 km) long, it stretches in a broad band about 1,500 miles (2,414 km) from east to west. It is called the Ganges Plain after the Ganges River, which runs through it. Two other rivers that cross this plain are the Brahmaputra (*brah∗mah∗POOT∗rah*) and the Indus rivers, and all three rivers deposit soil there. As a result, the Ganges Plain is the largest alluvial plain in the world.

The rich, moist soil and the warm climate of the Ganges Plain support a large population. Indian farm families of the plain live in mud houses that are clustered in small villages which are surrounded by tiny plots of land. If you were to travel through this region, you would see thousands of white-clad men working in the fields with hoes or with wooden plows drawn by oxen.

As the map on page 53 shows, plains areas cover very little of Africa. Only in northwestern Africa and in isolated coastal areas are there plains.

Australia is another story. An interior plain covers much of its center. This plain does not contain fertile soil such as that of the North American or Eurasian interior plains, however. The Australian interior plain is mainly dry. Where else in Australia are there plains?

Using the Plains

Plains, with their low elevations and low reliefs, are the most heavily populated landforms on Earth. Although plains cover only about 40 percent of Earth's land surface, they are home to 80 percent of Earth's people. Why? First, farming is easier on fairly level land than it is on areas of high relief. Second, it is easier to build transportation routes such as railroads and highways, or to use rivers for transport, over level land than over any other landform.

The importance of plains as population centers is nothing new. More than 5,000 years ago, early people began to settle in the alluvial plains around four big river systems. In later chapters, you will read more about people who lived along the Nile River of Egypt, the Tigris and the Euphrates rivers in western Asia, the Indus River of southern Asia, and the Huang He of China.

Other plains areas are also good for farming. The interior plains of the United States and Canada produce much of the world's wheat. In the Soviet Union, wheat is grown on the Great Lowland Plain. Plains farmers also grow bumper crops of corn, soybeans, rice, and cotton.

Because plains areas make transportation easy, they stimulate city growth, too. Among plains cities in the United States are Chicago, Illinois, a manufacturing and transportation center on an interior plain, and New York City, a financial and port city on a coastal plain.

Lesson 4 Review

Recalling Information
1. How does a plain differ from a plateau?
2. Explain what is meant by an interior plain, a coastal plain, and an alluvial plain, and give an example of each.

Interpreting Information
3. Compare the Great Plains area of the American West to the Ganges Plain of India.
4. Africa is a continent of low crop production. How might you explain this low production?

Applying Information
5. Which areas, if any, of your state are covered by mountains? By hills? By plateaus? By plains?
6. If you were a manufacturer, in which region would you prefer to settle? Why?

Special People
Ibn Batuta

Ibn Batuta was a great Moroccan traveler of the 1300s. His journeys took him through Africa and Asia and to parts of Europe. He crossed deserts, plains, plateaus, hills, and mountains. He forded mighty rivers and sloshed through swamps. Some of his journeys took years to complete. It is estimated that he traveled 75,000 miles (120,697.5 km)—a distance equal to three times around the world.

At the age of 22, Ibn Batuta made a pilgrimage to the holy city of Mecca in Arabia. It was on his way across North Africa that he developed his passion for travel. In later years, Ibn Batuta journeyed across Asia to the court of the emperor of China. He crossed the Sahara desert to visit the city of Timbuktu and the Mandingo empire. On his travels, Ibn Batuta met many kinds of people. He was shocked at the violent way of the sultan of Delhi, in whose territory he spent eight years. On the other hand, he was impressed by the just laws and customs of the peoples of Mali.

After his travels, Ibn Batuta wrote his famous book, *Rihlah* (Travels), describing his many adventures. The book is a valuable source of information about the political, social, and cultural life of much of the world in the 1300s.

Chapter **2** *Review*

Summary of Key Facts

In this chapter, you learned that

- the height of a land area above sea level is its elevation.
- the difference in height between two related land surfaces is called relief.
- most of Earth's great mountain systems curve out in three great arms from central Asia.
- hills have sloping land and lower elevations than mountains.
- highlands include mountains and hills.
- plateaus are fairly flat areas at high elevations.
- plateaus cover one-third of Earth's land surface.
- plains are flat or gently rolling areas of low relief.
- plains are the most heavily populated of Earth's landforms.

Using Vocabulary

On a separate sheet of paper, write the term that will correctly complete each sentence.

sea level	elevation
relief	plateau
escarpment	plains

1. Coastal _____ are flat, low-lying areas on the edges of continents.
2. In an area of low _____ , the difference in height between related landforms is small.
3. A plateau may end in a sheer _____ .
4. A tableland may be formed by streams that cut deeply into a large _____ .
5. A landform that is slightly above sea level has a low _____ .
6. _____ is used in measuring elevation.

Discussing the Chapter

1. Why are most mountain regions sparsely populated?
2. Compare hills and plateaus in terms of human use.
3. Why are plains regions particularly suitable for human settlement?
4. Describe one of Earth's continents in terms of the four major landforms.
5. What kind of landform is most widely distributed on Earth? What kind of landform is least common?

Chart and Graph Handbook

You live in an "information age." You get information from books and newspapers, television and movies, radio and videos. This mass of information is not organized, so it is not always easy for you to understand and to use it.

Some of the ways in which information might be organized are shown in this handbook. Graphs, charts, timelines, and diagrams organize facts so that you can understand their relationships. Knowing how to use these aids is an important skill.

Use data from this chart to estimate the world's total land area.

THE GREAT LANDMASSES

Name	Area
Asia	17,012,000 square miles (44,060,000 sq km)
Africa	11,785,000 square miles (30,522,000 sq km)
North America	9,400,000 square miles (24,347,000 sq km)
South America	6,883,000 square miles (17,828,000 sq km)
Antarctica	5,100,000 square miles (13,209,000 sq km)
Europe	4,071,000 square miles (10,545,000 sq km)
Australia	2,966,000 square miles (7,682,000 sq km)

How does this pie graph show you the relative sizes of Earth's continents?

LANDMASSES AS A PERCENTAGE OF THE EARTH'S LAND SURFACE

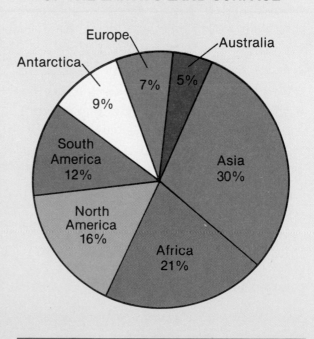

Europe 7%
Australia 5%
Antarctica 9%
South America 12%
North America 16%
Asia 30%
Africa 21%

Charts

The chart on page 58 shows information about the continents. Notice that information on a chart is arranged in rows and columns. When you read a chart, always check the title and the labels on the rows and columns first. What facts are given here?

Pie Graphs

The graph on page 58 is known as a pie graph, or a circle graph. This graph shows information about the world's continents, too, but the information is presented in a different way. The whole pie stands for 100 percent of the landmasses of Earth, or all Earth's landmasses combined. Each "slice" of the pie stands for one of Earth's continents. The numbers printed on each slice of the pie give you percentages, or parts of the whole.

Line Graphs

A line graph shows trends, or how something changes over a period of time. On this kind of graph, a line goes up to show an increase or goes down to show a decrease.

A double-line graph, such as the one on this page, compares the trends of two things. Read the title and the labels on the line graph. What is being compared? What color is the line for the United States? What color is the line for Japan? Is the trend for the United States up or down?

(Above) In what year did Japanese TV production begin to increase steadily? (Below) Which two of these countries produce about the same amount of rice?

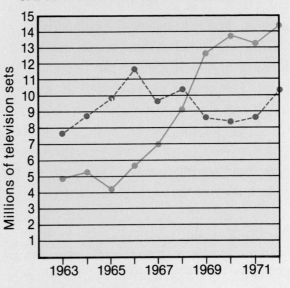

TELEVISION SETS PRODUCED IN JAPAN AND IN THE UNITED STATES

Millions of television sets

United States ----- Japan ———

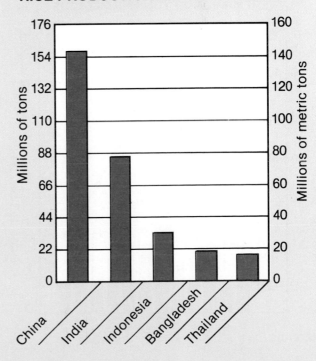

RICE PRODUCTION IN FIVE COUNTRIES

Millions of tons — Millions of metric tons

China, India, Indonesia, Bangladesh, Thailand

Bar Graphs

The bottom graph on page 59 is called a bar graph. It is useful for comparing information. The title names the comparison.

You can read a bar graph quickly by looking at the length or the height of the bars. The graph on page 59 shows how much rice was grown in 1980 in five countries. By looking at the scale on the left, you can find out how many metric tons of rice each country grew. The scale on the right tells you the amount in short tons.

Metrics

In many places in your book, numbers are followed by other numbers in parentheses.

How do weather conditions in Moscow compare with those in your city or town?

MOSCOW CLIMOGRAPH
Elevation 735 feet (224 m)

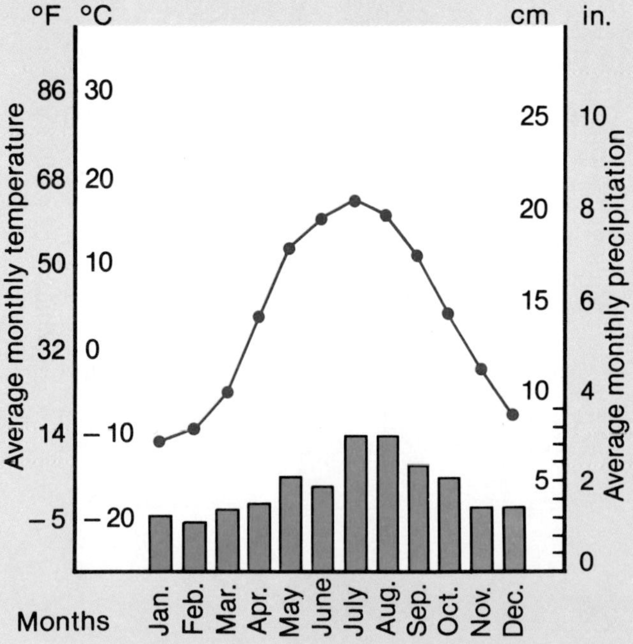

For example, the elevation of Moscow, in the Soviet Union, might be shown like this: 735 feet (224 m). The number in parentheses expresses in meters the same value as 735 feet. A meter is a unit of measurement in the metric system. This is a system of measuring that is based on the number 10. For example, a kilometer is one thousand meters.

You also will see the metric system used to measure such things as weight, volume, and temperature. In the United States, we are becoming more familiar with the metric system. Most of the other major countries already use this system.

Maps, charts, and graphs often show measurements in both systems. The graph on this page is an example of this. Which measurements in the graph are given in the metric system?

Climographs

The graph shown at left is known as a climograph. A climograph shows two kinds of information, in this case, temperature and precipitation.

A climograph uses both a line graph and a bar graph. On this climograph, the red line shows the average monthly temperature in Moscow. The temperature scales at the left show the United States units and the metric units for temperature. The *F* in the scale stands for *Fahrenheit* and the *C* stands for *Celsius*.

On the right of the climograph is a scale that shows average monthly precipitation. The abbreviation *in.* stands for *inches*, and *cm* stands for *centimeters*. Which unit of measure is used in the metric system?

News Cartoons

News cartoons are sometimes called editorial cartoons because they present an opinion about something in the news. Often, news or editorial cartoons express humorous points of view about some serious subjects.

Such cartoons often use some common symbols to represent ideas. For instance, the figure of Uncle Sam is a symbol of the United States.

Look at the cartoon on this page. It presents one cartoonist's opinion on environmental protection. The rabbit represents the rapid rate at which the environment is being harmed. The turtle with Uncle Sam on its back shows the cartoonist's view of the government's progress in environmental protection. What is that view?

Picture Graphs

You can get information from pictures and symbols in many ways. For example, the picture graph on this page makes use of symbols to represent a quantity of something. What is the symbol that is used on this picture graph? What does this symbol represent?

You can also compare information by using a picture graph. According to the picture graph on this page, which country had the most telephones in 1980? Which of the six countries shown in the picture graph had the fewest telephones in 1980?

What statement does the cartoon make about "Uncle Sam's" environmental policies?

Which of the listed nations had about 25 million telephones in 1980?

"LET'S PUT A MOVE ON IT"

NUMBER OF TELEPHONES: 1980

United States	☎☎☎☎☎☎ ☎☎☎☎☎☎ ☎☎☎☎☎☎
Japan	☎☎☎☎☎☎
United Kingdom	☎☎☎
France	☎☎
Canada	☎☎
Mexico	☎

☎ = 10,000,000 telephones

Diagrams

A drawing that shows how something works or how it is made or formed is called a diagram. One kind of diagram is a cross section. A cross section shows what something would look like if part of it were cut away and you could see its inside.

The diagram on this page is a cross section of a modern dike. For centuries, dikes have been used along the coast in the Netherlands to hold back the sea. Much of the coastal land in the Netherlands is very low, and floods have caused great destruction there.

Dikes have allowed the Netherlands to protect its land. The areas of lowland that are reclaimed from the sea are called polders. The soil in polders is good for farming. Thus, by building dikes, the people of the Netherlands have increased the land area that is suitable for agriculture. Compare the level of the polder to the level of the sea. What would happen to the polder if there were no dike?

When you read a diagram, look at all the labels. You may find a word that you do not know and must look up. Look at the diagram again. What materials are used to make a modern dike? What is the purpose of the ditch near the polder?

Using this diagram, describe how you think a dike is built. Why do you think each material is used as it is?

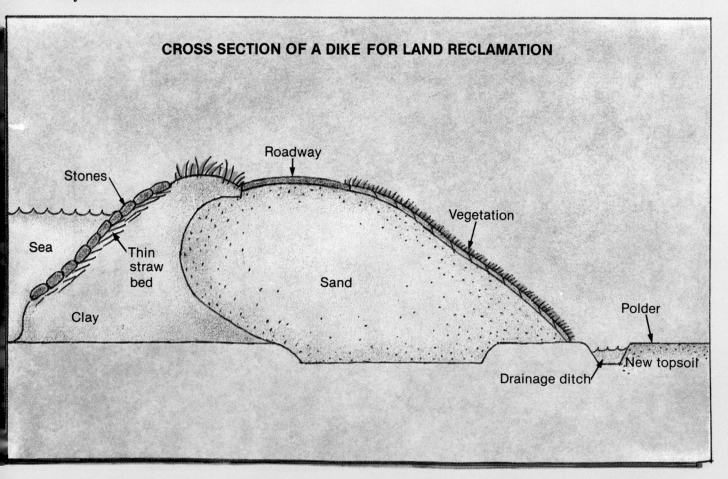

CROSS SECTION OF A DIKE FOR LAND RECLAMATION

Roadway

Stones

Sea

Thin straw bed

Clay

Sand

Vegetation

Polder

Drainage ditch

New topsoil

Measuring Time

A timeline, such as the one on this page, shows the chronological order of historical events. It shows how events are related to each other, whether they took place in a single year or over a period of many years. A timeline can be made to be read either vertically or horizontally.

Find the letters *B.C.* and *A.D.* on the timeline. *B.C.* refers to all the years before the birth of Jesus Christ. *A.D.* stands for the Latin term *anno Domini,* which means "in the year of the Lord." *A.D.* refers to all the years after the birth of Jesus. What is the date shown at the top of the timeline?

The time period covered by the timeline on this page is from 3500 B.C. to A.D. 2000. This is a total of 5,500 years. Notice that this timeline is divided into 500-year sections.

Look at the timeline, and find the year in which sails were invented. The *c* in front of this date stands for *circa*, which is a Latin word that means "about." This *c* means that historians are not sure of the exact date of the invention of sails. You will often see a *c* before dates for which there are no exact records of the events that took place.

Read the timeline to find 1954. What important event happened on this date? Note that there is no *c* in front of it. This date is exact because it happened recently enough in history for historians to have precise records.

The people of Cretan civilization (c.3000-1400 B.C.) were the first to build a fleet of trading ships. What do you suppose their vessels looked like?

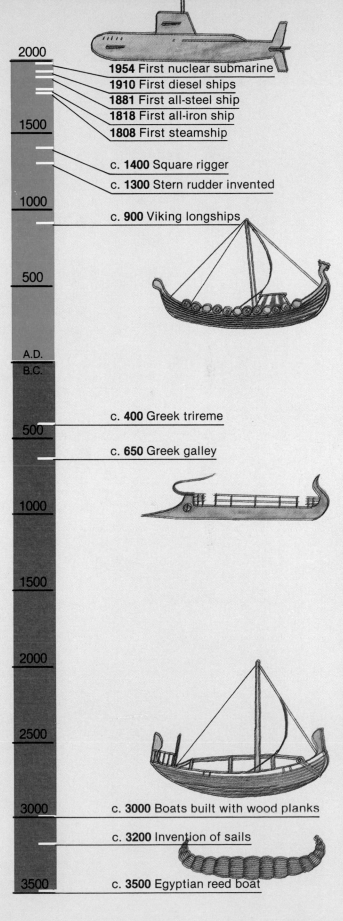

2000
1954 First nuclear submarine
1910 First diesel ships
1881 First all-steel ship
1818 First all-iron ship
1808 First steamship

1500

c. **1400** Square rigger

c. **1300** Stern rudder invented

1000

c. **900** Viking longships

500

A.D.
B.C.

c. **400** Greek trireme

500

c. **650** Greek galley

1000

1500

2000

2500

3000   c. **3000** Boats built with wood planks

c. **3200** Invention of sails

3500   c. **3500** Egyptian reed boat

The Shaping of Earth's Crust

Introduction

Eric Meola had been a photographer for 10 years. He had been waiting patiently for a chance to photograph an eruption of Kilauea (*kee*low*AY*uh*), a huge volcano on the island of Hawaii. Finally, on a spring day in 1983, while perched on the rim of the gaping crater, Meola's patience paid off.

Suddenly, a fountain of fiery lava shot up from deep within the crater. Kilauea was erupting for the first time in a decade—and Meola was there.

"I had my camera on the tripod," he recounted later. "Everything was bluish and moody looking. Although it was quite dark, there was just enough light to make out things."

For several days, Meola scurried across blackened mountain slopes and between glowing rivers of lava. He never stopped taking pictures.

Later, he said of his time at Kilauea: "I think it's maybe the only experience where I've felt that close to nature. It's one thing to go into the woods and spend a weekend camping. It's another to see what literally amounts to the formation of the earth."

Erupting volcanoes reshape Earth's surface by adding to it. Molten rock from deep within Earth rises to the surface and spreads over the land, forming a new landscape. Earth's crust is continuously changing. In this chapter, you will read about other forces that build and shape our planet.

Earth changes slowly, but the violence of Mount St. Helens on May 18, 1980, made great, sudden changes in the land.

Lesson 1

BUILDING UP EARTH

Workers use huge machines to prepare the foundation of a new skyscraper. With bulldozers and with cranes, they dig out and remove tons of rock and soil. What would they find if they dug below the level of the foundation? What is Earth like hundreds and thousands of miles beneath its hard, rocky surface?

No one has ever ventured or dug down more than a few miles into Earth. Even so, scientists today, using computers and mod- ern technological equipment, have been able to make many discoveries. They have greatly increased their knowledge about Earth's structure. By studying the rocks, the landforms, and the processes that act *on* Earth's surface, scientists can determine what lies *below* the surface.

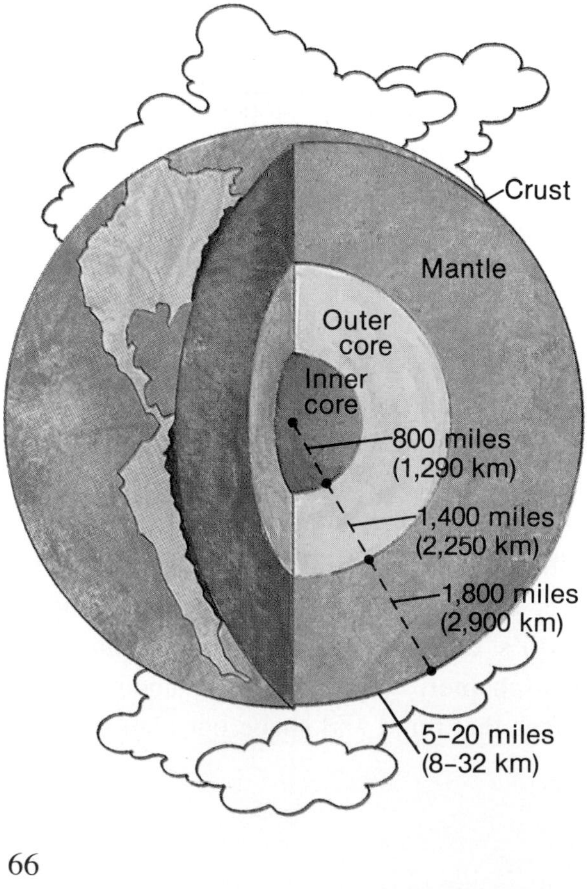

The Layers of Earth

If you could slice Earth in half, what would you see? Scientists have learned that Earth consists of several layers, as shown in the diagram on this page.

The outer layer is Earth's crust. It in- cludes the continents and the vast ocean floors. This rocky "skin" is the thinnest layer of Earth. It extends from 5 miles to 20 miles (8 km to 32.2 km) deep. Tempera- tures deep in the crust can reach 1,600°F (871.1°C).

Beneath the crust lies a layer of softer, partially melted rock that is known as the mantle. The mantle reaches to a depth of 1,800 miles (2,896.7 km). **Magma**, or molten rock, rises from the mantle through cracks in the crust and forms volcanoes, such as Kilauea in Hawaii. Hawaii is in a part of Earth where many volcanoes occur.

Deeper into Earth and hotter than the mantle is the core. The outer core, which is made of molten iron and nickel, lies at a depth of 3,200 miles (5,149.8 km). Tem- peratures there reach an astonishing 9,000°F (4,982.2°C). Earth's dense, solid inner core, 4,000 miles (6,437.2 km) beneath the crust, is as hot as the outer core. There, however, intense pressure keeps the iron and the nickel from melting. The inner core of the Earth is a totally solid mass.

This diagram shows Earth's internal structure. Which of the layers are partially melted rock? Which is solid?

A CROSS SECTION OF EARTH

Crust

Mantle

Outer core

Inner core

800 miles (1,290 km)

1,400 miles (2,250 km)

1,800 miles (2,900 km)

5–20 miles (8–32 km)

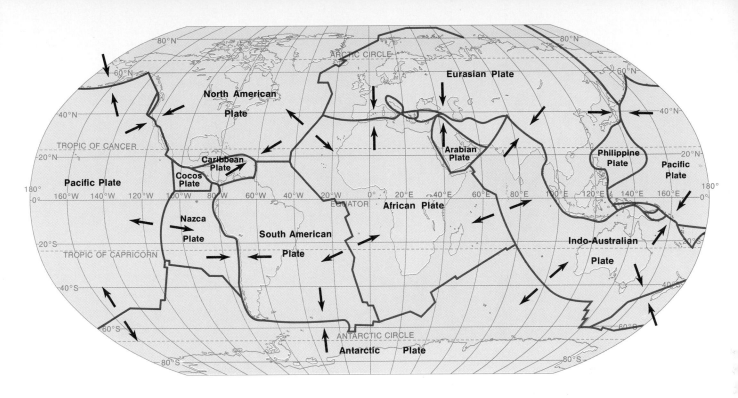

WORLD: TECTONIC PLATES

—— Plate boundary

——▶ Direction of plate movement

MAP SKILLS: Use the map to locate places where Earth's tectonic plates are either colliding or pulling apart.

Pieces of Crust

Earth's hard crust is not a single, solid piece. Instead, it is broken up into a number of smaller pieces, called **tectonic plates**. Scientists say that there are about 8 major tectonic plates and about 18 smaller ones.

Plates float on the softer rock of the mantle beneath them. The plates are continuously in motion, sometimes pulling away from and sometimes colliding with one another. The arrows on the map show the direction of their movement. Tectonic plates move at a snail's pace—up to 8 inches (20.3 cm) a year.

Even slight plate movements can have devastating results. When two neighboring plates grind past each other, great cracks appear in the crust where they meet. A movement of only a few inches can trigger earthquakes and landslides that are severe enough to destroy entire towns. Damaging earthquakes in San Francisco in 1906, in Japan in 1923, and in Alaska in 1964 were probably caused by shifting plates.

The movement of tectonic plates can result in the creation of land. The volcanic islands of Hawaii, for example, were created when plates pulled apart in midocean. Magma poured up through the openings in the ocean floor and built up layer upon layer of lava. Enough layers were finally deposited to raise the level of the ocean floor

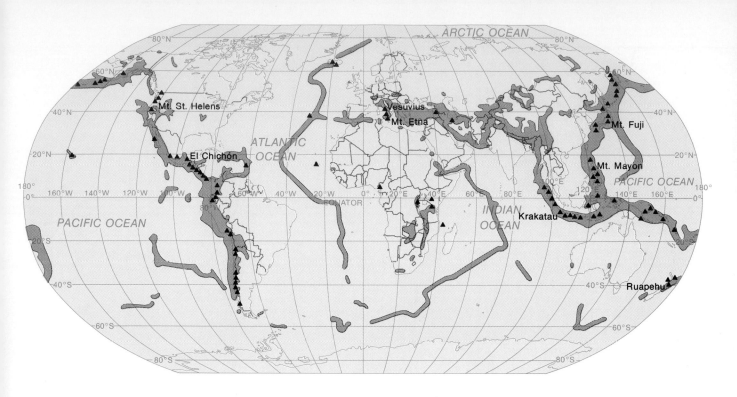

WORLD: EARTHQUAKES AND VOLCANOES

Earthquake region

▲ Volcano

MAP SKILLS: Compare this map with the map on page 67.
Where do most earthquakes and volcanoes occur? Why?

around each of the openings. The result was a new chain of islands.

Faults and Folds

John Muir, one of the first Americans to call for the protection of nature, once wrote, "Climb the mountains and get their good tidings." Today, many people all over the world are taking Muir's advice. Each year, hikers, skiers, tourists, and adventurers flock to such spectacular mountain ranges as the Rockies and the Alps. They are drawn to the scenic delights and the recreational challenges that only rugged, snow-capped peaks can provide.

How were these majestic mountains formed? Many scientists believe that, like volcanoes, mountains may have developed from the movement of tectonic plates.

Imagine a head-on collision between two plates. When these massive slabs of Earth's crust are pressed together, the pressure that is created is great enough to **fold**, or buckle, solid rock. As crust is folded and thrust upward, mountains are built. Scientists think that the Alps were formed by repeated collisions of the African and the Eurasian plates. They think that the collision of the plates that carry India and Eurasia produced the Himalayas.

Other kinds of plate movements also have probably contributed to the formation of mountains. Shifting plates can cause long breaks, called **faults**, in Earth's crust. When a fault opens, large blocks of crust on one side of it sink down, and blocks on the opposite side may be pushed up. California's Sierra Nevada was formed in this way. The western flank of this range has steep, sheer slopes that mark the edge of an old, enormous fault.

Plate movement cannot build mountains overnight. The Himalayas have taken 45 million years to develop, and scientists believe that they are still growing.

Lesson 1 Review

Recalling Information
1. What is magma? How does it contribute to the shaping of Earth?
2. What is a tectonic plate?

Interpreting Information
3. What practical value might be provided by knowledge of Earth's tectonic plates and of their movements?
4. What other landforms might be the result of faulting?

Applying Information
5. What evidence do you have from your own experience that Earth's crust is rocky?
6. Think of mountains that you have seen in pictures. Do you think that they were the result of faulting, of folding, or of volcanic activity? Why?

WEARING EARTH DOWN

Rain falls on a rolling hill. It trickles into a small stream, which splashes down the hillside. The stream empties into a sluggish river that winds lazily across broad, windswept plains on its way to the ocean. High in nearby mountains, snow falls. A new layer is added to a large block of ice that is slowly inching down the steep slope.

You may not notice it, but all around you, wind, rain, snow, and ice are gradually reshaping Earth's surface. As you learned in the last lesson, Earth's major features, such as mountains and continents, are built up by the motion of tectonic plates. In this lesson, you will discover that equally powerful forces are hard at work, wearing down Earth's crust and reshaping it.

Weathering

Where do the boulders, stones, gravel, sand, and soil that cover so much of Earth's land areas come from? Each of these is a product of a process known as **weathering**. Weathering is the process of breaking down Earth's hard, solid rock crust into smaller parts. Soil is produced when fine, heavily weathered particles of rock combine with the decayed remains of both plants and animals. You will read more about soil production in Chapter 8.

Some weathering is the result of chemical reactions. Carbon dioxide, a gas in the air, can, for example, combine with water to produce a mild acid. Over time, this acid can break rock down and cause it to crumble into smaller pieces of rock.

Other kinds of weathering are caused by physical agents such as wind and water. Water breaks down rock in several ways. It may seep into a rock's cracks and crevices and then freeze. Because water expands when it freezes, the ice may break apart the rock. Rain, too, causes weathering. It can seep into soft parts of rocks and flush these soft parts out. Eventually, the whole rock crumbles.

What happens to stones when water flows over them? They crash into each other as they are pushed forward. The impact can cause them to break up. This is another example of how water weathers rock.

How does wind cause weathering? As winds blow over dry land, they pick up particles of rock, sand, and dust. Driven by the wind, these hard, sometimes sharp particles can slowly grind down and scrape away exposed rock surfaces.

Erosion

Weathering breaks down rock. **Erosion** removes the products of weathering and deposits them elsewhere. Through the action of water, wind, ice, and gravity, the particles of Earth's surface are eroded, or worn away and moved to another place.

Much erosion results from the pull of Earth's gravity. For example, landslides and avalanches occur when weathered material that has collected on a steep slope becomes too heavy. Gravity pulls this material down the slope until it settles at a lower level. Landslides remove rock and soil from the slopes of mountains and of hills. Often, this debris is deposited on valley floors making them suitable for farming.

Gravity also gives water the power to erode. When rain falls, it drains from the land into streams and rivers that flow downhill. Particles of sand, soil, and clay, which is called silt, are washed off the land and carried downstream. Large rivers, therefore, may transport huge quantities of silt as well as water. The Mississippi River carries as much as two million tons of silt to the Gulf of Mexico every day.

Streams and rivers cut deep channels into the land that they cross. They play a major role in shaping the land. Particles of rock and sediment that are picked up by a stream increase the stream's power to erode. These particles roll along the stream bed, pushing along other particles and grinding against the underlying rock. Like miniature power tools, these particles chip away Earth's crust. As you learned in Chapter 2, this is how the Colorado River carved the Grand Canyon. During a period of millions of years, the mighty river dug a gorge more than 1 mile (1.6 km) deep.

Water Deposits

The particles worn away by streams come to rest in many different places. For example, as rivers flow to the sea, they lose some of the sediment that they had carried. Often, this sediment is deposited in ways that create landforms. In Chapter 2, you read about one of these landforms—the alluvial, or flood, plain. These plains are formed when a river overflows its banks and deposits layers of silt on nearby lands. Silt deposits can improve the quality of the soil for farming.

A levee is another landform that is created by the repeated flooding of a river. Levees are long, natural walls that are built up along a river's banks from deposits that were left by floodwaters. Near New Orleans, Louisiana, the Mississippi River has levees that are 5 feet to 10 feet (1.5 m to 3 m) higher than the surrounding land and about 1 mile (1.6 km) wide.

Large deposits of sediment that form where a river meets a shallow sea or a lake are called **deltas**. The triangular deposits at the mouth of the Nile River, which look like the Greek letter *delta* (Δ), gave this landform its name. Not *all* deltas are triangular, however.

Another kind of delta, called an alluvial fan, occurs in mountainous areas. Alluvial fans form where steep, swift mountain streams suddenly empty onto broad, flat plains. There, the stream quickly loses speed, causing it to leave fan-shaped deposits like those shown here.

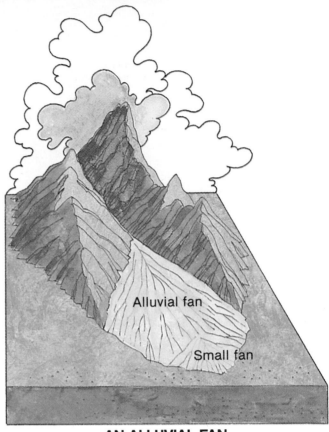

AN ALLUVIAL FAN

Alluvial fans are most common in dry regions. A fan can be many miles wide.

Glacial Erosion

Huge, dense masses of snow and ice that are called **glaciers** also cause erosion. Today, glaciers are found mostly in polar regions or on the cold upper slopes of large mountains. A single glacier may be thousands of feet thick and may weigh thousands of tons. Mountain glaciers, which are dragged downhill by gravity, move slowly, rarely more than a few feet each day. Still, their power is awesome. As they inch forward, they dig through Earth's crust like unstoppable bulldozers. They scoop up enormous rocks and carry them along, hollowing or flattening everything in their path. Thousands of years ago, a glacier carved the deep, U-shaped Yosemite Valley in California.

During ice ages that ended thousands of years ago, glaciers were more widespread than they are today. As the map on page 72 shows, glaciers once covered vast areas of North America, Europe, and Asia. As the glaciers advanced, they reshaped the land. One dug great hollows into parts of central North America. When Earth warmed and the glacier melted, the hollows filled with water and formed the Great Lakes. The fjords of Norway—arms of water that reach far inland from the sea—were formed in a way that is similar to this.

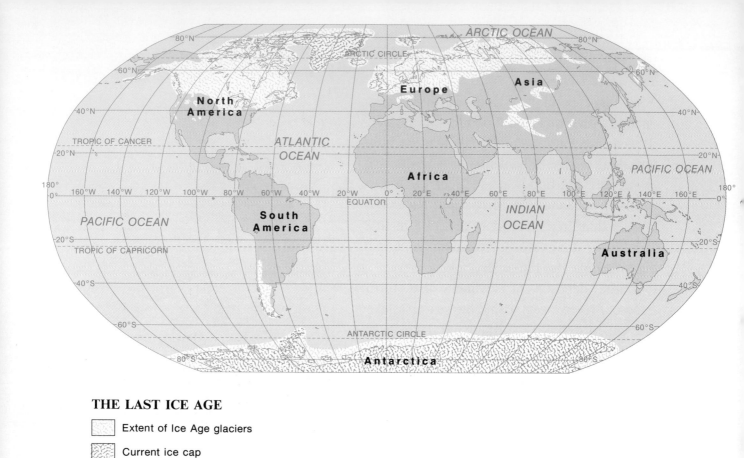

THE LAST ICE AGE

▢ Extent of Ice Age glaciers

▨ Current ice cap

MAP SKILLS: The glaciers that were formed during Earth's last Ice Age have retreated. How near to the equator do they extend today?

Glacial Deposits

An advancing glacier is a powerful shaper of the land. As it moves, it sweeps along huge amounts of rock and debris. When a glacier melts and recedes, it deposits this debris, creating landforms. A terminal moraine is a long, low ridge of debris deposited along the front edge of a shrinking glacier. Part of Cape Cod, an arm of land that extends from Massachusetts into the ocean, is a terminal moraine that was formed during the last Ice Age.

Wind Erosion

Have you ever been caught in a wind that was so strong that it stopped you in your tracks? If you have, you know that winds, although invisible, have great power. Sand-filled wind can weather rocks; winds can also erode land. The blowing of strong winds along the ground can hollow out bowl-like depressions in the land that are often several miles wide. Wind-blown sand can also help to sculpt, to polish, and to wear away areas of standing rock. Examples of wind erosion in the western desert areas are often striking.

Wind Deposits

When a strong wind dies down, it drops whatever rock, sand, and dust that it had been carrying. Winds have deposited large quantities of fine-grained sediment on some areas of Earth. This yellowish-brown sediment, called loess (LEHS), is valuable because it enriches the soil on which it has been deposited.

In deserts and on sandy beaches, wind erosion and deposition can build large hills of sand, called **dunes**. They form where an obstacle stops a sand-carrying wind, causing the wind to deposit its load of sediment. If this process is repeated, the dune grows. Winds can also move a dune by blowing sand over the top of the dune and down the other side. This movement is typical of some deserts, which often seem like oceans of endlessly shifting sands.

Lesson 2 Review

Recalling Information
1. What is weathering?
2. What is erosion?

Interpreting Information
3. Frost can cause weathering in rock. Why do you suppose that this is so?
4. Can the same force both weather and erode land? Explain.

Applying Information
5. Where in your area can an example of erosion by water be found?
6. Where in your area can an example of erosion by wind be found?

Winds carve new contours almost daily in the dry sands of the Arabian landscape.

HOW WAVES CREATE A CLIFF

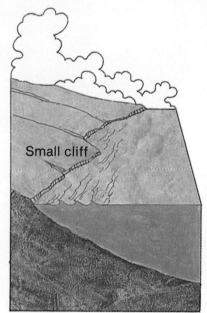

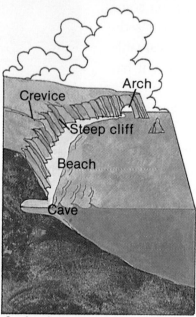

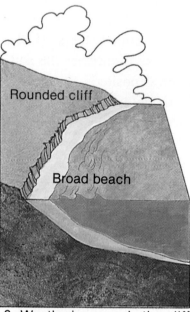

1. A small cliff is first cut by the waves.

2. As the waves continue to cut, the cliff grows higher and many details appear — an arch, a beach, a cave, and a crevice.

3. Weathering rounds the cliff and a broad beach is created below it.

Coastlines are shaped by erosion. In addition to arches and sea stacks, what other land features can pounding waves carve?

Lesson 3

COASTLINES CHANGE

Would you like to live on a beautiful piece of land that overlooks the ocean? Would you build a house there, even if you knew that the land was disappearing?

In the last lesson, you learned that Cape Cod was formed from debris that was left by a glacier. Today, this long, lovely stretch of land is a popular vacation resort. However, Cape Cod is shrinking. Since the end of the last Ice Age, the Cape has lost a strip of land almost 2 miles (3.2 km) wide. Scientists say that if erosion continues at its present rate, Cape Cod will disappear completely in 4,000 to 5,000 years. You are likely to be safe living on the Cape today, but your descendants might have to find someplace else to spend their vacations.

Tides and Waves at Work

Cape Cod, like other worldwide coastal areas, is being whittled away by the action of waves. Waves are powerful agents of erosion. An 18-foot (5.5-m) storm wave can easily shift a 10-ton (9.1-MT) boulder.

Breaking waves that carry gritty sediment can cut into rock. Waves that pound the rocky cliffs of Nantucket Island (near Cape

Cod) can remove 6 feet (1.8 m) of rock from the island's edge in a year.

The diagram on page 74 shows how waves cut into land and change the coastline. The middle picture shows the results of this process, the creation of a steep cliff that is called a headland. Note also the sea stack and the arch near it. They are also carved by the action of waves.

The motion of **tides** contributes to the erosion of coastlines. Tides are the regular rising and falling of the water level of oceans, of seas, and of large lakes. At high tide, the ocean level rises at the shoreline. At low tide, the ocean level recedes. Tides are caused by the gravitational pull of the sun and of the moon. Tides remove material from beaches and from shores and deposit it in deep water.

Coastline Deposits

Waves and tides do not only wear down coastlines; they also change the shape of coastal areas by depositing sand and rock along them. Sediments that are carried from the land to the ocean by rivers are carried back to the shore by waves and tides, forming sandy beaches.

In a similar way, the action of waves can create sandbars. Waves may erode a strip of shoreline that juts into the ocean. The waves then carry the eroded material into open water and deposit it there. As this process continues, a sandy, bar-shaped deposit is slowly built up.

In Canada's Bay of Fundy, tides may rise and fall up to 50 feet. These pictures show the same boat at high tide and at low tide.

Barrier islands may grow to be more than 200 miles (321.9 km) long. This one, off the coast of North Carolina, is a popular vacation spot.

Some bars grow so high that they form a barrier that protects the coast from ocean waves. These bars may continue to grow broader and longer over time. They can stretch for great distances, separated from the mainland by a body of water called a sound. The islands that meet at Cape Hatteras off North Carolina are examples of such barrier islands.

Lesson 3 Review

Recalling Information

1. What causes tides?
2. How do waves erode?

Interpreting Information

3. Why are the forces of erosion stronger at high tide than at low tide?
4. How does the action of waves that are directed against a coastline create both erosion and deposition?

Applying Information

5. Think of a coastline that you have seen. Where along this coastline might erosion occur fairly quickly? Why?
6. Where along a coastline have you seen evidence of deposition?

Special Feature
Technology: Learning with Landsat

In the early 1900s, people who were loaded down with supplies searched the backwoods of the American West for gold deposits. Today, such searches are easier. *Landsat*—a satellite in the sky—can help to find gold.

Four *Landsat* satellites were launched from 1972 through 1982. These satellites search the surface of Earth to find minerals and to monitor crop conditions. In addition, *Landsat* can transmit information about changes that are taking place on Earth.

Every 25 seconds, *Landsat* scans an area that is bigger than Maryland. The satellite measures heat, moisture, and sunlight that has been absorbed by objects. It uses these measurements to detect conditions on Earth.

A healthy forest appears to be bright red in a *Landsat* picture. A city, on the other hand, will show up blue.

Skills for Thinking

GETTING AND USING INFORMATION

There were very few people lucky enough to receive a formal education 500 years ago. If you had been one of those fortunate students, your teacher might have given you this assignment.

"Between now and late adulthood, read all the books that have ever been printed in English. Make notes, and organize the facts that you learn."

Impossible? At that time, if all the books that had been printed were available, it would have been possible to carry out the assignment. Few printed books existed. By reading books for only a few hours each day, a person could learn in an average lifetime all the important facts that had been written about our world.

Today, of course, such an assignment would be impossible to carry out. Not only are there millions of books in print, but information is also stored in many other media. Computers, films, newspapers, records, and tapes contain important information that you may want to know.

Learning How to Learn

Try this assignment as a trial run. Find the population of your state for the years 1920, 1940, 1960, and 1980. You might begin by making a list of sources from which you can get this information. For example, you could check population maps of your state, almanacs, encyclopedias, and state history books. As you consult each source, make notes.

Once you have collected the information, you could use it in one of several ways. You might note whether the population of your state has increased or decreased during the last 60 years. You might compare the population figures for your state to those of another state. You might estimate what will happen to your state's population in the next 20 years. Complete the assignment by listing two ways in which you might use the facts that you have found. Try to include one way that is not suggested in this assignment.

In the "Skills for Thinking" pages that follow each chapter of this book, you will learn many ways to find information. You will also learn how to use this information. The purpose of these pages is to help you to "learn how to learn." Your thinking skills will serve you well in school, outside of school, and throughout your life.

Chapter 3 Review

Summary of Key Facts

In this chapter, you learned that

- Earth is a series of layers that extend from the outer layer, or crust, to the mantle, the outer core, and the inner core.
- the crust is broken up into plates that are in constant motion and float on the softer rock of the mantle.
- magma from Earth's mantle shoots out to the surface through volcanoes.
- movements of the plates cause mountains to form.
- weathering is a process that wears down Earth's crust.
- erosion is a process that contributes to the reshaping of Earth's crust.
- water, wind, and ice all contribute to the processes of weathering and of erosion.

Using Vocabulary

On a separate sheet of paper, write the term that will correctly complete each sentence.

tectonic plates	magma
glacier	erosion
delta	fault

1. _____ is liquid rock.
2. Pieces of Earth's crust are called _____ .
3. A _____ is a break in Earth's crust.
4. _____ is the breaking down of the rock of Earth's crust.
5. A _____ is a great body of ice and snow.
6. A _____ is formed by silt at a river's mouth.

Discussing the Chapter

1. Describe the four layers of Earth.
2. How do the movements of tectonic plates affect the surface of Earth?
3. How do wind and running water change the surface of Earth?
4. How do glaciers change Earth's surface?
5. What effects do tides have on coastlines?

Reviewing Skills

Make a list of four sources that you would use to discover the locations, the activity, and the heights of the world's volcanoes.

Earth's Waters

Chapter 4

Introduction

You and your father have been on the lake since dawn. It is a misty morning, and the breeze makes you shiver. You forget about the weather quickly because the fish are biting. You and your father have caught three perch.

Your rowboat is drifting close to shore. As you look out over the gray water, you remember some of the things you have read about this lake. The Iroquois named it *Seneca* after their mightiest group. It is one of New York's Finger Lakes, which were formed at the end of the glacial period when the great ice sheet melted.

The Seneca fished where you are fishing today. When the Europeans arrived, they used the long, narrow lake as a pathway for settlement. Steamboats plied its waters. Canals were built to link the lake and nearby rivers and to provide a route to market for products from the frontier.

As time passed, railroads and highways replaced the steamboats and the canals. Lake Seneca began to attract tourists, who came to swim, to boat, to water-ski, and, like you, to fish.

Lakes have been important to humans throughout history. So have other bodies of water. In this chapter, you will see how all bodies of water—oceans, seas, lakes, rivers—are part of Earth's important water system, a system that serves the needs of plants, of animals, and of humans.

Underwater formations such as Molasses Reef, in the Florida Keys, support an amazingly large variety of life forms.

THE WATER CYCLE

Think about the water that you have already used today. Did it come from a well, a river, or a lake? Was it rainwater or melted snow? No matter where it came from, you benefited from using it.

Water covers more than 70 percent of Earth's surface. The amount of water on Earth never changes. What does change, however, is the location of the water—where it can be found on Earth at a particular time. Its physical state—whether it is a solid (ice), a liquid, or a gas (water vapor)—changes, too.

The same water molecules have been moving over, in, and throughout Earth since they were formed. The system through which the molecules move is known as the **hydrologic** (*heye∗druh∗*LAHJ∗*ihk*) **cycle**. *Hydros* is Greek for water.

Let us trace the path of a molecule of water through the system.

Our molecule of water is on the surface of the ocean. The ocean is both the main supplier and the main destination of water. It is a hot day. Our molecule is being changed from a liquid to a gas. This is done

Through a process that is called transpiration, plants and trees return water to the air by evaporation through their leaves.

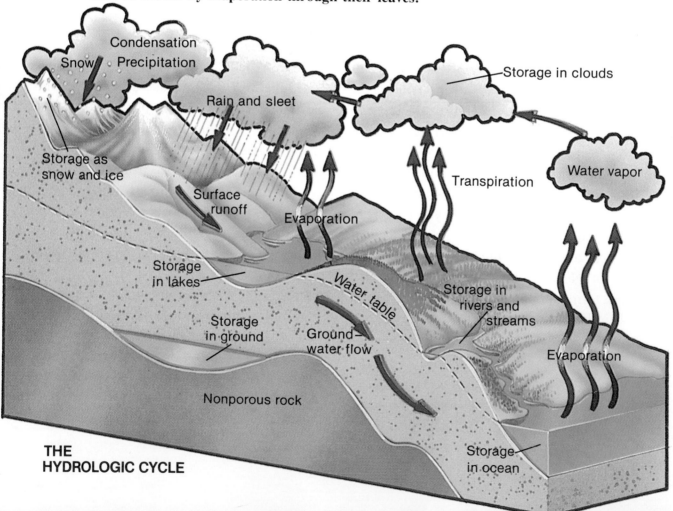

THE HYDROLOGIC CYCLE

Water that this hiker drinks in New Hampshire may once have irrigated a field in Egypt. How?

in a process that is called evaporation (*ih∗vap∗uh∗*RAY∗*shuhn*). The sun's heat is the source of the energy that will change the molecule of water to a gas and will lift it from the ocean into the air. Because the molecule is part of the air, it is called water vapor. Next, as it floats over the surface of the water, the water vapor cools and condenses, or changes into a denser form. It becomes part of a cloud.

Eventually, our molecule will cool further and will fall to the ground as **precipitation**—rain or snow, sleet or hail. Then, it may seep into the earth, or it may become part of a stream, a river, or a lake. Underground or overland, the water will flow in response to gravity. Eventually,

it will return to the ocean. It may take hundreds or thousands of years, but the same water molecule that was evaporated from the ocean will return to it.

Detours Along the Way

There can be many detours along the hydrologic cycle. Ice caps and glaciers are water in solid form. They keep much of Earth's water "locked up."

Animals and plants, too, are retreats for water as it moves about Earth. Living things need water to survive. There is water in blood and water in sap. The human body is about three-fourths water.

Lesson 1 Review

Recalling Information

1. What energy powers the hydrologic cycle?
2. Where is most of Earth's water found?

Interpreting Information

3. What is the difference between water in a cloud and water in an ocean?
4. How do ice caps and glaciers keep fresh water "locked up?"

Applying Information

5. Where does the water that you use at home come from? What, if anything, is done to it before it is ready for you to use?
6. If the water supply to your home were cut off for six hours, how would your life be affected? For one day? For one week?

OCEAN WATERS

Earth's giant water system contains about 326.5 million cubic miles (1.4 billion cu km) of water. Ninety-seven percent of this water is found in the oceans. You can probably begin to understand how vast the oceans are. Now, you are ready to ask the next question—what are oceans like?

Full of Substances

Along the ocean shore, the smell of salt is strong. Ocean water contains salt and many other substances. Present in ocean water are 73 of the 92 natural elements that are found on Earth. Salt is the most common mineral that is found in ocean water.

Ocean water also contains gases and valuable minerals. It contains metals, including calcium, potassium, and even gold. Except for salt, however, most of the minerals have been so diluted by the water that it is usually too expensive to remove them.

Always Moving

Ocean water is always moving. Some of the most obvious and best-known ocean movements are the tides. As you know,

Past and Present

For centuries, people have wanted to explore the ocean depths. Even without equipment, divers in warm waters have been able to reach depths of 150 feet to 200 feet (45.7 m to 61 m). After about two minutes underwater, they have brought back pearls, coral, and sponges.

By the nineteenth century, "diving bells" were used to raise sunken goods. Getting enough air to breathe was a problem for divers who used these bells. One way in which a diver could receive air was through a hose that reached to the surface.

The best diving bells and the hard-hat diving suits that were based on them permitted underwater work at about 300 feet (91.4 m). Something better was needed.

For a while, that something better was the bathysphere (BATH*uh*sfeer). A bathysphere was a strong steel ball that had windows for vision. It was large enough to hold at least one person. In 1938, William Beebe dived 3,028 feet (nearly 1 km) in his bathysphere.

The next step was a bathyscaphe (BATH*uh*skaf), a kind of submarine that is intended only for deep-ocean exploration. In 1960, the bathyscaphe *Trieste*, with two people aboard, touched bottom in the Mariana Trench, 35,800 feet (10,911.8 m) deep. That is an astounding depth of almost 7 miles (11.3 km).

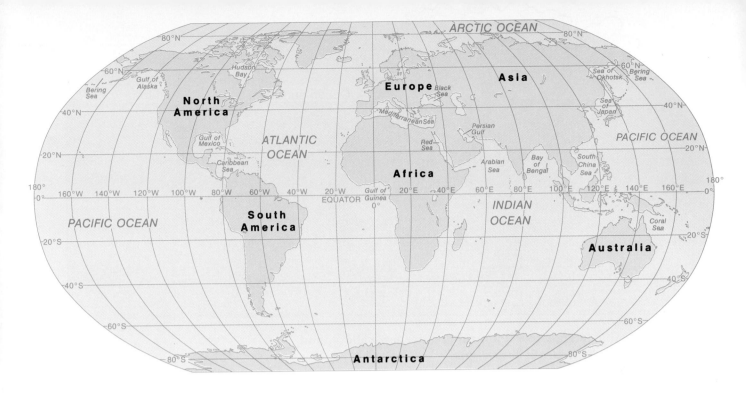

WORLD: OCEANS AND SEAS

MAP SKILLS: Most of the continents are almost completely surrounded by water. Which oceans and seas border Africa?

tides are the regular rise and fall of the ocean's surface in response to the pull of both the moon's and the sun's gravity.

Oceans also contain streams of moving water, called **ocean currents**. Some ocean currents move fast; others move slowly.

For centuries, sailors have made use of rapid ocean currents to speed up their journeys. One such current, the Gulf Stream, was used to reduce travel time between the American colonies and Great Britain. In some places, the surface flow of the Gulf Stream is 6 miles (9.7 km) per hour.

Currents vary in width and in temperature as well as in speed. Some are warm; others are cool. The Gulf Stream is a warm cur-

rent. Varying in width between 50 miles and 150 miles (80.5 km and 241.4 km), it is among the largest and the strongest currents on Earth.

The Gulf Stream, like all currents, follows a definite path. Warmed by both the Caribbean Sea and the Gulf of Mexico, the Gulf Stream heads north along the East Coast of the United States. Then, off North Carolina, it begins its turn eastward toward the British Isles. In Unit 2, you will learn about how wind and ocean currents work together to affect Earth's giant weather system. Find the Gulf Stream and several other ocean currents on the map on page 131 in Chapter 6.

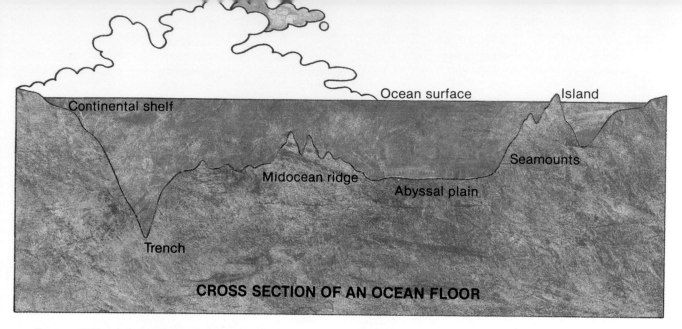

Some of Earth's longest mountain ranges, deepest valleys, and broadest basins lie beneath the oceans.

Landforms Under the Ocean

In the 1850s, an American businessman named Cyrus Field was planning to lay a transatlantic telegraph cable from Newfoundland to Ireland. When he began, he believed that there was an almost flat surface under the ocean, a so-called Telegraph Plateau, on which the cable could rest. After many years and many failures, his 2,350-mile (3,781.9-km) cable was laid. Field discovered that 400 miles (643.7 km) of extra cable had been required just to follow the contours of the ocean floor. It was not a plateau at all.

Human beings have faced serious problems in trying to explore beneath the surface of the ocean. They need air to breathe, light to see, protection against the cold, and armor against the enormous pressure that builds up as depth increases. Because of this, the deep ocean floor has not been mapped as well as the surface of the moon.

Some people consider the ocean floor to be Earth's last frontier. Many of its mysteries have yet to be solved. Many resources have yet to be developed for use.

We do know some things about the ocean floor. We know that undersea landforms are not much different from those that are above water. The ocean floor contains high mountains, broad plains, and deep valleys which are called trenches. We know, too, that it is useful to divide underwater landforms into three main regions.

Continental Shelf

Suppose that you own a modern bathyscaphe for exploring the depths of the ocean. You intend to take a journey that follows the route of Cyrus Field's original telegraph cable. You will travel along the ocean floor from Heart's Content, Newfoundland, to Valentia, Ireland.

At first, you think that you are following a Telegraph Plateau. For many miles—the average depth is about 106 feet (170.6 m)—you see a gently sloping, fairly flat stretch of land. This is known as the **continental**

shelf. Every continent is surrounded by a continental shelf. Scientists believe that continental shelves were once part of dry land.

Continental Slope

Soon, you reach the eastern edge of the continental shelf of North America. You are about 600 feet (182.9 m) underwater. In front of you, a cliff drops steeply. This is the **continental slope**. You go thousands of feet down the slope to the next region of your journey—the **ocean basin**.

The Ocean Basin

On the ocean-basin floor, you find a broad, flat plain that is sometimes called the abyssal plain. It is made up of layers of sediment that lie over other landforms. The sediment has been smoothed and flattened by ocean currents. This plain is much wider than the continental shelf.

As you head eastward, you begin to notice other landforms that exist on the plain. Underwater, volcanic mountains rise from the ocean floor. Hundreds of miles to the south of you, the Azores rise high enough to become islands. In the South Pacific, the Hawaiian Islands form a chain of such peaks. Thousands of these mountains dot the underwater plain.

Midocean Ridge

Eventually, you reach what looks like an endless mountain range. It is a midocean ridge. In the Atlantic, this midocean ridge runs like the seam of a baseball all the way from the northern polar region to the southern polar region.

In a way, the midocean ridges are kinds of seams. The new sea floor—actually, the new Earth's crust—forms there, where tectonic plates meet. Lava pushes up from inside Earth at this point, building on itself and forming a ridge. These ridges contain narrow rifts, or depressions, that run down their centers. Rifts may result from the movement of the tectonic plates.

Past the midocean ridge, you descend once again to the ocean-basin floor. You continue until you reach the steeply rising continental slope off Europe. When your bathyscaphe reaches the top, you are on Europe's continental shelf. One hundred miles (160.9 km) or so farther, you emerge from the ocean at the end of Cyrus Field's cable. You have surfaced just off the western coast of Ireland.

Seas, Gulfs, Bays

Sometimes, the ocean is referred to as the sea. A true sea, such as the Mediterranean, is part of the ocean, but it is cut off from the rest of the ocean by land. A sea, then, is a large body of salt water that is almost surrounded by land. Many seas are found on Earth. The Mediterranean Sea, a part of the Atlantic Ocean, is almost entirely surrounded by southern Europe, Asia Minor, and North Africa.

The Caribbean is a sea that lies south of Florida. The Caribbean Sea, like the Mediterranean, is also a part of the Atlantic Ocean. The Caribbean Sea is almost entirely surrounded by the West Indies, Central America, and South America. Locate both seas on the map on page 85.

Like seas, gulfs and bays are part of the

world's oceans. Gulfs and bays are similar to each other: Both are indentations in the shoreline. A gulf, however, is usually bigger and deeper than a bay. Which bay seems to be an exception to this rule?

The Gulf of Mexico is one of the largest gulfs in the world. An even larger one is the Gulf of St. Lawrence in Canada. The Persian Gulf, which lies between Iran and the Arabian Peninsula, is a gulf that has often been in the news in recent years. Can you guess why, from observing its location on the map?

A bay can also occur along the shoreline of a lake. Find the labeled bays on the map on page 85, and describe their locations and their size.

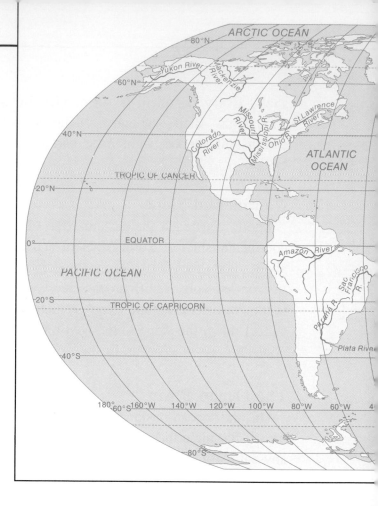

Lesson 2 Review

Recalling Information

1. What difficulties have been experienced in exploring the depths of the ocean?
2. What are two features of the ocean-basin floor?

Interpreting Information

3. What materials can ocean water provide for people?
4. What do scientists learn by studying the ocean floor?

Applying Information

5. What part of the ocean floor might you like to explore? Why?
6. Where would you set up an underwater colony in the ocean? Why?

Lesson 3

RIVERS

Rivers have always been very useful to humans. From the beginning of history, rivers have provided easy transportation for both people and goods. Rivers are an important source of fresh (unsalty) water. Rivers supply two-thirds of the water that is used in the United States. Throughout the world, rivers are harnessed for irrigation and for electrical power. Rivers powered industry even before electricity was in use. River valleys are often important farming areas and are the sites of large centers of trade—cities.

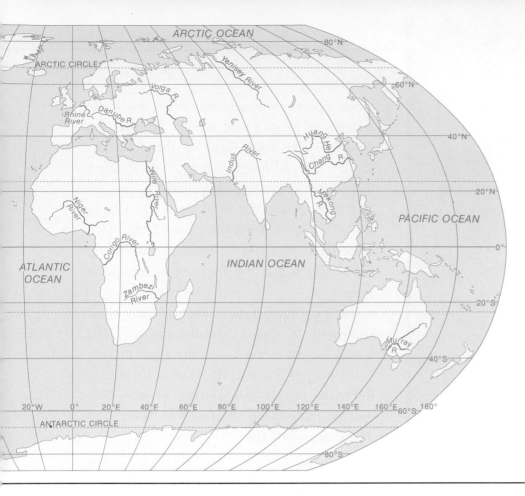

ARCTIC OCEAN
ARCTIC CIRCLE
80°N
Yenisey River
60°N
Volga R.
Rhine River
Danube R.
40°N
Huang He
Indus River
Chang R.
Nile River
20°N
Niger River
Mekong R.
PACIFIC OCEAN
Congo River
0°
INDIAN OCEAN
ATLANTIC OCEAN
Zambezi River
20°S
Murray R.
40°S
20°W 0° 20°E 40°E 60°E 80°E 100°E 120°E 140°E 160°E 60°S 180°
ANTARCTIC CIRCLE
80°S

MAP SKILLS: Major river systems can be found on almost all of the continents. Name the major rivers of Asia and of North America.

Rivers and Their Tributaries

What is a river? A river is a moving stream of water flowing in a channel that it has eroded in the earth. As soon as a raindrop strikes soil or rock, erosion begins. The place where a river begins is called its source. Water is pulled downhill by gravity until it reaches the level of the oceans. Water that runs downhill toward another body of water is called runoff. Runoff moves through channels that have already been cut, or else it creates new channels.

The direction of runoff depends on the direction of the slope of the land. In North America, east of the Appalachian Mountains, the rivers flow east toward the Atlantic Ocean. However, west of the Rocky Mountains, rivers flow west toward the Pacific Ocean.

A river system consists of a main river and its **tributaries**. Tributaries are streams that "contribute" water from other places, such as mountain streams and smaller rivers, to a main river.

Look at the map on this page. You can see that some of the tributaries of major rivers are actually large rivers in their own right. The Mississippi-Missouri river system is the third-longest river system in the world. Some of the major tributaries of the Mississippi-Missouri system are the Arkansas, the Ohio, and the Red rivers. All three

Glacier

Spring

Stream

Brook

Waterfall

Rapids

Tributaries

Floodplain

River

Delta

A RIVER SYSTEM

Large river systems often begin as networks of mountain brooks, streams, and springs.

rivers are among the principal rivers of Earth. In fact, even some of *their* tributaries are major rivers.

A river system includes all the land that a river drains. To *drain* means to "carry away the runoff." The land area that is drained is called a drainage basin, or a watershed.

The World's Great Rivers

The Nile is the longest river on Earth. From its source in equatorial Africa, it flows 4,145 miles (6,670.5 km) north to the Mediterranean Sea. Other great rivers of Africa include the Zaire and the Niger.

In South America, the Amazon drains a vast area. The Amazon and its 1,100 tribu-

taries contain enough miles of navigable waterways to go twice around Earth at the equator. The total flow of the Amazon, Earth's second-longest river, is 11 times that of the Mississippi-Missouri.

The longest river in Asia is the Chang River of China. Its source is in Tibet. Two other rivers that rise in Tibet are the Huang He of China and the Mekong of Southeast Asia.

Europe's important rivers are fairly short compared to those already named. The Volga, which empties into the Caspian Sea, is the longest. Next is the Danube, which is linked by canals to a number of other European rivers—the Rhine, the Main, the Tisza, and the Oder.

Lesson 3 Review

Recalling Information
1. What is a river? How are rivers formed?
2. What is a tributary? Name three tributaries of the Mississippi River.

Interpreting Information
3. What is the function of a drainage basin?
4. In what ways are rivers important?

Applying Information
5. Which large river is the closest to where you live? What is its importance to you?
6. If you could explore any river on Earth, which one would you choose? Why?

Lesson 4

LAKES AND GROUNDWATER

In Scotland, a **lake** is called a loch. One small loch is known throughout the world. Called Loch Ness, it is 22 miles (35.4 km) long and 700 feet (213.4 m) deep. For more than 50 years, people have been waiting to find out if there is a "monster" in Loch Ness. There have been many reports of a strange, large animal in Loch Ness, but so far, the deep waters of the lake have yielded no answer.

Few, if any, lakes have monsters. Many lakes, including Loch Ness, are scenic. All lakes are useful. Many furnish fresh water for plants, for animals, and for people. Many lakes, as you will learn in later chapters, provide homes for both plants and animals as well, and they affect the world's weather.

What is a lake? A lake is a body of water that is completely surrounded by land. Most lakes contain fresh water. Some contain salt water.

Although lakes exist throughout the world, they are found especially in high and mountainous areas. Canada alone has almost half of the world's lakes. Minnesota calls itself the Land of 10,000 Lakes. Actually, it has more than 11,000. Are there many lakes in your area?

The highest lake in the world is Lake Titicaca on the border between Bolivia and Peru. It is 12,507 feet (3,812.1 m) above sea level. In contrast, the Dead Sea is 1,310 feet (399.3 m) below sea level. The Dead Sea is the lowest spot on Earth.

Although called a sea, the Dead Sea is really a lake. The Caspian Sea, located between the Soviet Union and Iran, is a lake, too—the largest in the world. Both are saltwater lakes. A saltwater lake in the United States is the Great Salt Lake of Utah.

The second-largest lake in the world, one that contains fresh water, is Lake Superior. It is located between the United States and Canada. Lake Superior is the largest of the 5 Great Lakes, but all 5 are among the 15 largest lakes in the world. Can you name the other Great Lakes?

Lakes vary greatly in depth. Lake Eyre (AIR) in Australia is often dry. When it is filled with water, its greatest depth is about 4 feet (1.2 m). At the other extreme is Lake Baikal (*beye*∗*KAHL*), the largest lake in Eurasia. With a maximum depth of more than 1 mile (1.6 km), it is the deepest lake in the world.

"Invisible Water"

Groundwater, or water that is underground, was once considered a mystery. Now, we know something about it. We know, for instance, that about one-sixth of Earth's fresh water is underground and out of sight.

Groundwater enters Earth as rainfall. It passes through air spaces in the soil and also through any layers of rock that have spaces that permit passage. Rock that water can seep through is called permeable (PER∗*mee*∗*uh*∗*buhl*). When water reaches a level of rock through which it cannot pass, it begins to back up into the permeable rock like water behind a dam. The

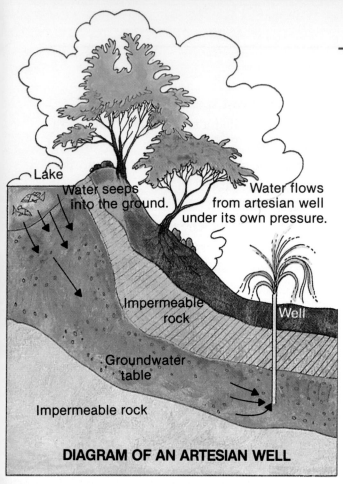

Lake

Water seeps into the ground.

Water flows from artesian well under its own pressure.

Impermeable rock

Well

Groundwater table

Impermeable rock

DIAGRAM OF AN ARTESIAN WELL

As this cross-section diagram shows, an artesian well taps the groundwater that flows downhill between layers of impermeable rock.

Water is flowing between two layers of rock which are not permeable. When this water reaches a natural opening or when a well is dug, pressure exerted by the inflowing water causes the water between the two layers to rise to the surface. This kind of well is called an artesian (*ahr∗TEE∗zhuhn*) well.

As you can tell by studying the diagram on page 82, groundwater is part of Earth's water cycle. Groundwater moves slowly through the ground. Water that is not tapped by people flows into rivers and eventually returns to the sea or to lakes. What happens to it then?

Lesson 4 Review

Recalling Information

1. What is a lake? Which country has the most lakes?
2. Why is the Dead Sea, a lake, called a sea?

Interpreting Information

3. What could make the water table rise? If the water table rises in a place where it is at the ground's surface, what will be the result?
4. How can there be spots of green in a desert?

Applying Information

5. Which lake is most important to you? Why?
6. Why would the pollution of groundwater concern you even if you were miles away?

level that it reaches as a result of this backing-up process is called the water table. Find the water table that appears in the diagram on page 82.

In some areas, the water table may be close to the surface of the ground. In other areas, it may be many feet under the ground.

Some of Earth's driest places actually have underground water supplies. By drilling wells, people can reach the water and pump it to the surface.

In some areas, groundwater is under pressure and does not require a pump to get it to the surface. Look at the diagram above.

Skills for Thinking

UNDERSTANDING WORDS IN CONTEXT

As you study written materials, you often come across words that are new to you or words whose meanings you do not know. If you have a dictionary or a glossary, you can look up these words. You can often also get a good sense of a word's meaning by studying the context in which it is used. The context of a word consists of the phrase, the sentence, and the paragraph in which it appears.

Read the following description of a famous river. Pay special attention to the underlined words. If any of these words is unfamiliar to you, use context to help you to determine the meaning of the word.

Near Mount Marcy, the highest peak in the Adirondack Mountains, is a body of water that is called Tear of the Clouds, which is surrounded by land. From this little <u>lake</u> flow many <u>brooks</u>. One of these brooks, or streams, which is joined at numerous <u>forks</u> by <u>tributaries</u>, grows large enough in its southward flow to be called a river. It is the Hudson River.

After cutting eastward for many miles through meadows to the city of Glens Falls, the Hudson turns and follows a deep <u>channel</u> southward. There, hundreds of miles from its <u>source</u> in the Adirondacks, the <u>floor</u> of the Hudson is below sea level. That is why incoming ocean <u>tides</u> can wash up into the river. When sea water and fresh water meet, the steady southward <u>current</u> of the river seems to change. At times, the river almost seems to be moving backward or uphill.

Melted snow from Mount Marcy (below) feeds streams that combine in the Hudson River.

The mighty Hudson continues to move toward its <u>mouth</u>, however. There, where the river ends, it meets Lower New York Bay. The <u>bay</u>, a small arm of the ocean, provides a safe <u>harbor</u> for large ships.

Which Word Clues Will Help Me?

Suppose that you did not know what the word *lake* meant. The description that you just read gives you clues. It tells you that a lake is a body of water that is surrounded by land. *Lake Tear of the Clouds* is one example of such a clue.

Now, try your own skill at understanding words in context. Match each of the following words to one of the definitions. Then, write the words or the phrases that give clues to each meaning.

source   channel
harbor   current
tributary

a. continuous onward movement
b. stream that flows into a larger stream
c. deep path of a river
d. protected body of water where boats can anchor
e. where a river begins

Write the letters *A* to *D* on a piece of paper. Then, find each letter on the map. Next to each letter, write the word that best identifies that place on the map.

fork   brook
bay   lake

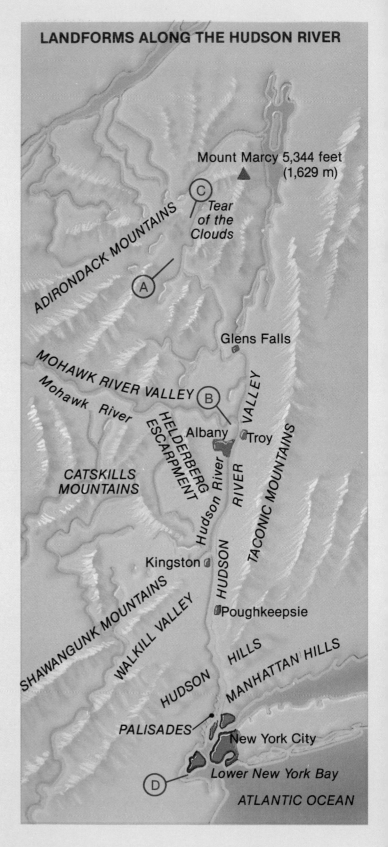

LANDFORMS ALONG THE HUDSON RIVER

Mount Marcy 5,344 feet
(1,629 m)

C Tear of the Clouds

ADIRONDACK MOUNTAINS

A

Glens Falls

MOHAWK RIVER VALLEY   B   VALLEY

Mohawk River

HELDERBERG ESCARPMENT

Albany   Troy

CATSKILLS MOUNTAINS

Hudson River

HUDSON RIVER   TACONIC MOUNTAINS

Kingston

SHAWANGUNK MOUNTAINS   WALKILL VALLEY   HUDSON   Poughkeepsie

HILLS   MANHATTAN HILLS

PALISADES   New York City

D   Lower New York Bay

ATLANTIC OCEAN

Chapter 4 Review

Summary of Key Facts

In this chapter, you learned that

- water on Earth is constantly cycled from one place to another and from one physical state to another.
- the ocean is both the main supplier and the main destination of water.
- 97 percent of all water is in the ocean.
- the ocean can be divided into three landform regions—the continental shelf, the continental slope, and the ocean basin.
- the ocean basin consists of mountains, plains, and valleys.
- a river system consists of a main river and its tributaries; it also includes all the land that a river drains.
- lakes are bodies of water that are surrounded by land.
- about one-sixth of Earth's fresh water is groundwater.

Using Vocabulary

On a separate sheet of paper, write the number of each term and then its meaning.

1. hydrologic cycle   underwater mountains
2. continental shelf   stream that feeds a larger stream
3. midocean ridge   water source that is created by internal pressure
4. tributary   movement of parts of Earth's water supply
5. artesian well   flat land between the coast and the ocean basin

Discussing the Chapter

1. What are some common detours in the hydrologic cycle?
2. Describe the three landform regions of the oceans of the world.
3. How do seas, bays, and gulfs differ?
4. How is a river formed?
5. In what ways do lakes vary?
6. How does groundwater enter Earth?

Reviewing Skills

Use the context to choose the correct meaning of each underlined word.

1. The headwaters of the Hudson River rush down from the Adirondacks.
   a. large lakes
   b. source streams
   c. saltwater rivers
2. Sandbag levees prevent flooding.
   a. deep wells
   b. human-made embankments
   c. traditional sailboats

Unit 1 Review

Summary of Key Facts

In this unit, you learned that

- Earth is one of nine planets in a solar system that is located in a galaxy which is called the Milky Way.
- oceans and other bodies of water cover 70 percent of Earth's surface.
- Earth has seven continents.
- Earth's major landforms—mountains, hills, plateaus, and plains—differ in elevation and in relief.
- Earth's layers are the crust, the mantle, the molten outer core, and the inner core.
- the movement of tectonic plates causes faults, folds, earthquakes, and volcanoes.
- the surface of Earth is shaped in part by weathering, deposition, and erosion that are caused by wind, water, and ice.
- ocean landform regions include the continental shelves, the continental slopes, and the ocean basin.
- rivers, lakes, and groundwater supply most of Earth's fresh water.

Discussing the Unit

1. How are our lives affected by Earth's revolution and rotation?
2. Using examples, describe the relief, the location, and the use of mountains, hills, plateaus, and plains.
3. How do tectonic plates cause earthquakes and volcanoes?
4. How are deltas, alluvial fans, terminal moraines, and sandbars formed?
5. Describe the hydrologic cycle.
6. Describe some landforms under the ocean. How are they formed?

Activities

1. Choose one of the planets other than Earth or another kind of body in space. Do research to prepare a report to the class on that body. Include information on how it differs from Earth.
2. Collect several magazine articles that have to do with the natural forces that shape Earth, such as volcanoes or earthquakes. Summarize each article, and put them together in an Earth Newsletter to share with the class.

Test

Using Vocabulary

On a separate sheet of paper, write the sentence from each pair that uses the underlined term correctly.

1. Greenland and Borneo are <u>continents</u>. Australia and Africa are <u>continents</u>.
2. The <u>environment</u> is the study of Earth. The <u>environment</u> is composed of physical surroundings.
3. <u>Mountains</u> have high elevations. <u>Mountains</u> have low reliefs.
4. <u>Hills</u> have sloping land. <u>Hills</u> are steep escarpments.
5. Shifting <u>tectonic plates</u> cause severe rainstorms. Shifting <u>tectonic plates</u> cause severe earthquakes.
6. <u>Weathering</u> means "affecting the outcome of the weather." <u>Weathering</u> is the wearing away of Earth's surface.
7. <u>Deposition</u> creates volcanoes. <u>Deposition</u> creates sand dunes.
8. The <u>hydrologic cycle</u> begins and ends in the ocean. The <u>hydrologic cycle</u> is the continual rise and fall of the ocean's tides.

The Big Question

What are Earth's main landforms, what are the processes that have shaped them, and how do these processes unify Earth?

Write your answer in complete sentences. Draw upon the information in this unit to write a good answer.

Using Map Skills

Use the map on page 38 to complete this exercise.

1. If the sun is directly overhead at the prime meridian, what time is it along most of the international date line?
2. How many time zones are there in Australia?

Identifying a Geographic Theme

Think about the geographic themes of **location** and **place** as you complete this exercise.

1. Give two examples of how a map is used to determine location.
2. From each chapter in the unit give an example of a physical or human characteristic of a place.

Unit 2

Patterns in the Atmosphere

Have you ever, in the middle of a heat wave, toward the end of a bitterly cold winter, or on the day of a rained-out picnic, wished that there were no such thing as weather? Life would certainly be much simpler in a world without weather.

The layer of air that protects us from the freezing cold of outer space and from some of the sun's scorching rays clings to Earth and travels with it as the planet rotates each day. This layer of air is never at rest. Its shifting and ever-changing patterns bring us warm breezes on one day and chilling rain on another. These patterns are our weather.

Concepts

weather   latitude zone
climate   troposphere

The Big Question

What determines the climate of an area?

Focus on a Geographic Theme

In this unit you will study the geographic theme of **region**. A region is an area defined by certain human or physical characteristics. A region may be as small as your neighborhood or as wide ranging as the Rocky Mountains.

Perth Bay, Australia. How else have we put the atmosphere to work?

Weather

Introduction

Whoosh! A blast of flame heats the air in our balloon, and we begin to rise. What a great way to spend the holiday! It's the Fourth of July, and all over the United States, people are celebrating with parades, picnics at parks and at the beach, fireworks, and even hot-air balloons.

Near Kansas City, Kansas, it's pleasantly warm, but it's raining. That's not so good for parades and picnics, but the farmers are happy. The corn looks good this year.

Nome, Alaska, is warm, too—warm for Nome, that is. Some people aren't even wearing sweaters or jackets because the temperature has climbed into the mid-50s.

In Vermont, a family is enjoying a picnic under a clear blue sky. The temperature is a comfortable 72°F (22.2°C).

At the southern tip of South America, scientists are studying the local wildlife. The penguins are having fun, but the scientists are shivering. It's well into winter here, and snow is falling.

Half a world away, in a small farming village in India, a woman looks at her dry fields and shakes her head. The hot sun beats down on the dusty soil. The summer rain is late this year. There won't be enough rice to feed the family this year, she thinks.

It seems as though everyone all over the world is thinking about the weather.

◀ **A mountain, a hot-air balloon, and the sky between—atmospheric conditions connect and affect them all. How?**

Atmospheric particles created these sunbeams. Can you explain how?

Lesson 1

EARTH'S ATMOSPHERE

We're back in our balloon now. It has risen so high that we can almost touch the clouds.

"Wow," we say, "we'll be above the weather if we go much higher."

"Not really," the balloonist replies. "We couldn't breathe that high up."

"How high does the air go?" we ask.

"Air that is enough for breathing doesn't go much higher than our mountain peaks, but the **atmosphere** goes a lot higher than we can go."

What Is the Atmosphere?

The atmosphere, an ocean of air that surrounds Earth, extends for hundreds of miles above Earth's surface. The atmosphere is made up of various gases. Near Earth's surface, about 78 percent of the atmosphere is nitrogen, an element that is needed by nearly all forms of life. Another 21 percent of the atmosphere is composed of oxygen, the gas that people and animals need to breathe. The remaining 1 percent is made up of carbon dioxide and about a dozen other gases, most of them in amounts almost too small to measure.

In addition to these gases, the atmosphere contains varying amounts of water vapor, dust, and all the things that we call pollution. Except for the pollution, these things are natural and necessary to life.

As you learned in Chapter 4, most of the water vapor in the atmosphere comes from the oceans. When the vapor turns to precipitation, rain or snow falls.

Even the dust in the atmosphere is important. Without it, there would be no precipitation. The water vapor forms raindrops or snowflakes by clinging to tiny dust particles.

Humans add numerous polluting substances to the atmosphere. Car exhausts, factory smokestacks, incinerators, and other means of burning garbage are some of the things that are responsible for atmospheric pollution.

Four Layers

Meteorologists, or scientists who study the atmosphere, divide the atmosphere into four main zones, or layers. Each layer wraps around Earth like layers of an onion.

The **troposphere** is the layer of the atmosphere that is closest to Earth. The troposphere is called the weather layer. It is in this layer that clouds form, storms brew, and warm and cold air mix to create our changing weather patterns. About 90 percent of the atmosphere and most of the water vapor and dust are contained in the troposphere.

The air in the troposphere appears to be blue. The sun's rays contain all the colors of the spectrum. Blue rays vibrate quickly. As they move, they strike molecules and dust particles that are in the air. This causes the blue rays to go out in all directions, creating the appearance of a blue sky.

If our balloon rose all the way through the troposphere, you would notice two things. First, you would have trouble breathing because the air becomes thinner and thinner as you rise above Earth. Second, the higher you go, the colder it becomes. The temperature in the troposphere is colder as you go up.

Had our balloon been able to leave the troposphere and enter the stratosphere, we would have been exposed to a temperature of about -50°F (-45.6°C). The air here is too thin to hold a plane up. To go much higher, we would have had to ride in a rocket.

If we could travel through the stratosphere, we would eventually notice that the temperature stops falling. It remains about

Between which atmospheric layers does a 747 jet fly? How would the air feel at this altitude? Could you breathe it?

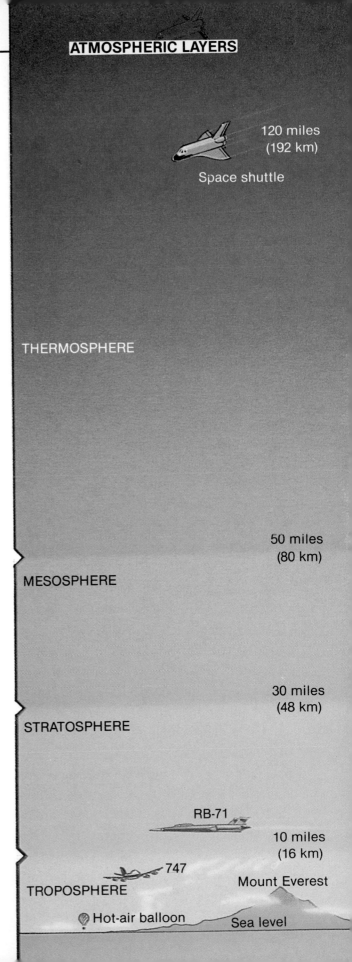

ATMOSPHERIC LAYERS

120 miles (192 km)
Space shuttle

THERMOSPHERE

50 miles (80 km)
MESOSPHERE

30 miles (48 km)
STRATOSPHERE

RB-71

10 miles (16 km)

747

TROPOSPHERE

Mount Everest

Hot-air balloon   Sea level

the same for a while and then begins to rise as we go higher.

Beginning in the troposphere and extending into the upper stratosphere is a layer of ozone, a special form of oxygen. This **ozone layer** is important. The ozone layer protects life on Earth from the dangerous ultraviolet rays of the sun by absorbing most of them. This imperfect process of absorption causes the rise in temperature. Some ultraviolet light does manage to get through the ozone layer. That's how people get sunburns. If it weren't for the ozone layer, however, so much ultraviolet light would reach Earth's surface that people wouldn't dare go outdoors.

Above the stratosphere is the mesosphere. The temperature changes again in the mesosphere. From the bottom to the top of this layer, where the temperature is about -120°F (-84.4°C), it falls steadily.

The temperature begins to rise again in the fourth and highest level of the atmosphere. This level is known as the thermosphere. The temperature rises rapidly at first and then more slowly.

As in the upper stratosphere, something that is going on here accounts for this rising temperature. In the stratosphere, the absorption of ultraviolet rays by ozone creates heat. In the thermosphere, a reaction called ionization produces heat. The sun's rays strike particles of oxygen and nitrogen and change them into electrically charged atoms called ions. This chemical change transforms some of the sun's energy into heat. The thermosphere, or part of it, is called the **ionosphere** (eye*AHN*uh*sfeer) because of this reaction.

The electrically charged ions can reflect some radio waves back to Earth. If you have a shortwave radio, you can sometimes pick up broadcasts from halfway around the world because of this bouncing of radio waves off the ionosphere.

The thermosphere is the source of the glowing or flickering green and red lights that are seen in the sky in spring and fall. In the Northern Hemisphere, this striking phenomenon is known as the aurora borealis (aw*RAWR*uh bawr*ee*AL*ihs). In the Southern Hemisphere, when these same lights glow, they are called the aurora australis (aw*STRAY*lihs). These lights are believed to be caused by atomic particles that hurtle into the thermosphere, where they collide with atmospheric particles at speeds of thousands of miles a second. More familiar to us is the light of the stars. Stars seem to shine and twinkle because their light is reflected off the particles that are found in the Earth's atmosphere.

Only 1 percent of all the air in the atmosphere is contained in the thermosphere. The thermosphere starts at about 50 miles (96.6 km) high and extends to the edge of outer space. Scientists don't usually pick any one height at which the thermosphere ends. The air gradually becomes thinner and thinner until, at about 600 miles (965.6 km), only very small amounts of a few light gases are left.

A Protective Shield

The atmosphere is a shield that protects living things on Earth. You have already seen how the ozone level and the ionosphere absorb some of the sun's harmful rays. As you will see in the next lesson, the atmosphere also absorbs or reflects back into space much of the sun's heat.

The atmosphere also conserves, or saves, part of the sun's heat. At night, Earth does not lose all of its heat. Instead, some of the heat remains trapped in the atmosphere.

The atmosphere protects Earth from meteors, too. Millions of these solid bodies from outer space fall toward Earth's surface every day. Most are burned up as they fall through the atmosphere, becoming the "shooting stars" that you sometimes see at night. This is the result of friction.

Lesson 1 Review

Recalling Information
1. What are the four layers of the atmosphere? Which is the weather layer?
2. What gases make up the largest part of the atmosphere? What else is present?

Interpreting Information
3. Suppose you *could* rise about 60 miles (96.7 km) into the atmosphere in a balloon. From what would you have to protect yourself?
4. What would Earth be like if it had no atmosphere? Explain.

Applying Information
5. What are some of the ways in which people pollute the atmosphere?
6. What are some things that you and other people can do to help to hold down air pollution?

Forecasters throughout the country use maps to explain weather patterns.

Lesson 2

FEATURES OF WEATHER

"And now the weather. At noon, the temperature was 87 degrees Fahrenheit—that's 30.6 degrees on the Celsius scale. The relative humidity was an uncomfortable 76 percent, and winds were southwest at 12 miles per hour. The forecast calls for continued hot and muggy weather today, with a high in the low 90s."

This is the kind of short weather report that you might hear on radio or television. Everyone is interested in the weather. A

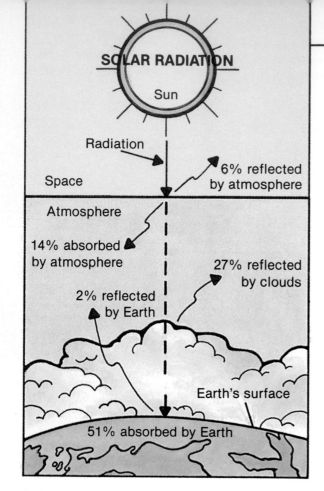

SOLAR RADIATION

Sun

Radiation

Space

6% reflected by atmosphere

Atmosphere

14% absorbed by atmosphere

27% reflected by clouds

2% reflected by Earth

Earth's surface

51% absorbed by Earth

How might a long cloudy period affect temperatures on Earth?

weather forecast can help you to plan your day. Should you take your raincoat or umbrella to school? Will it be a good day for a cookout in the backyard?

There are four main elements in the weather forecast that you read, although one of them was not directly stated.

These four weather factors—temperature, moisture, air pressure, and wind—combine to produce weather.

Temperature

Temperature is a measure of the amount of heat in the atmosphere. As you saw in the last lesson, the temperature in the atmosphere varies considerably. However,

when we think about weather, we're not really too concerned with how warm or how cool it is in the upper atmosphere. We want to know what it's like outside. We want to know what the conditions arc in the part of the atmosphere that is nearest to Earth's surface.

As you know, not all of the sun's energy gets all the way through the atmosphere. Almost half of it is absorbed by dust and clouds or is reflected away from Earth. The diagram shows what happens to the sun's radiation. The radiation that does reach Earth's surface heats the air near the surface only slightly. Instead, most of the sun's energy passes through the air until it reaches the ground and the waters of Earth. This heat is then transferred back into the air by Earth's surface.

Different parts of Earth receive and absorb different amounts of heat. An area that is near the North Pole, for example, receives less heat than an area that is near the equator. (You'll see why in the next chapter.) An area that is covered by fresh snow is heated less than an area that is covered by a forest. The white snow reflects much of the sun's radiation back toward space. Land and water heat at different rates, too.

The heated land and waters of Earth radiate their heat away from the surface. Much of this heat, however, does not get back into space. Some of the heat energy is used up in evaporating water from oceans and other bodies of water. Some of it is reflected back to Earth. Enough of it remains in the lower atmosphere to keep most of Earth warm.

Moisture

The atmosphere, you remember, contains varying amounts of water vapor, most of it in the troposphere. The amount of water vapor in the air is referred to as humidity.

Relative humidity is the kind you hear about in a weather forecast. Relative humidity, which is given as a percentage by forecasters, is a ratio of the amount of moisture that is in the air compared to the amount of moisture that the air *can* hold at the same temperature. In the weather forecast at the beginning of this lesson, for example, the temperature was said to be 87°F (30.6°C), and the relative humidity was 76 percent. This means that the air contained 76 percent of the amount of moisture that it can hold at that temperature.

If the temperature remained the same but the air became more moist, the relative humidity would rise. When it reached 100 percent, the air would be saturated. In other words, the air would contain all the moisture that it could hold at that temperature. This saturation point is called the dew point. If you've ever seen dew on the grass in the early morning, you've seen the result of air that has exceeded its dew point. The extra moisture, which the air can now no longer hold, condenses. It turns into water on any handy surface, such as blades of grass and leaves of trees.

Warm air can hold more moisture than cold air. If the temperature falls, therefore, the relative humidity would increase because the air would be closer to being saturated.

There is always some moisture in the air at the weather level, but usually we don't notice it. It comes to our attention mainly when the moisture turns to precipitation or when the humidity is very high.

High humidity can make you feel uncomfortable because it interferes with the body's natural air-conditioning system. When it's warm, you perspire. The beads of perspiration on your skin evaporate, especially if there's a bit of wind to help them along. The evaporation cools your body. If the air around you was already close to the saturation point, it now resists taking on more moisture.

Precipitation is water vapor that condenses into liquid or ice and falls to Earth. Rain and snow are the most common forms of precipitation. Hail and sleet are other forms.

Sleet is the icy rain that coats streets and sidewalks. Sleet begins as cold rain. It only freezes into ice when and if it comes into contact with an even colder surface at the level of the ground.

Hail is the result of very unusual weather conditions. Very strong winds inside a rain cloud blow frozen raindrops up and down. Each time a frozen hailstone moves upward, it gathers more moisture around its surface. The new moisture freezes and adds to the size of the hailstone. Finally, hailstones become so large that even strong winds cannot hold them up any longer. They fall to the ground as stones of ice. Hailstones that are as large as baseballs have been observed.

Dew and fog are not forms of precipitation. They form near ground level rather than higher in the atmosphere. Dew, as you

CAUSES OF PRECIPITATION

have seen, is condensation that forms on a surface near the ground. Fog is the condensation of water into tiny droplets that hang in the air, held up by the slightest wind or rising air. A fog is a ground-level cloud.

The diagram on this page shows several ways in which precipitation can form. A map showing average yearly precipitation around the world appears on page 114. In what areas of the world is it the rainiest?

Lesson 2 Review

Recalling Information
1. Define *temperature* and *humidity*.
2. What happens when the relative humidity reaches 100 percent?

Interpreting Information
3. A mass of moist, warm air moves toward a mountain and begins to rise. As it rises, the air cools. What is likely to happen? Why?
4. In which city would you feel more uncomfortable? Why?
   Phoenix—(32.2°C), 36 percent humidity.
   Houston—(29.4°C), 92 percent humidity.

Applying Information
5. How do temperature and humidity affect your life? Give an example or two.
6. Give a weather report that you could have heard yesterday.

Frontal lifting means a weather change. Convectional lifting brings thunderstorms. Orographic lifting is discussed more fully in Chapter 6.

AIR PRESSURE, WIND, AND WEATHER

Small ripples of surface water move across a pond. Huge ocean waves crash against rocks along the shoreline. Leaves flutter gently in a tree. A palm tree bends over, its top almost touching the ground. Then, it is pulled out by its roots and hurled against a house. A sailboat, its sails hanging loosely, sits motionless in water that is so still that it looks like the surface of a mirror. These are some of the effects of **air pressure** and wind, two more factors that make up weather.

Air Pressure

"Light as air," people say to describe something that has almost no weight at all. Although air is light, there is quite a bit of it above us. All that air adds up to something that has considerable weight. The weight of the atmosphere pushes down on the surface of Earth and everything on it. We call this weight air pressure.

Right now, at sea level, about 15 pounds of air are pressing down on every square inch (1.1 sq kg per sq cm) of your body. You don't feel it, of course. Your body has developed the strength to withstand it. Only if this weight suddenly vanished would you notice it. Airplanes that fly high into the atmosphere, where there is less air overhead, have pressurized cabins to keep the air pressure close to what it would be on the ground.

The weight of 15 pounds per square inch (44 km per sq cm) is an average. The air pressure is not the same everywhere in the world. Many different factors cause air pressure to change, whether by day or by season. Changes and differences in air pressures, are key factors in weather patterns.

Warm air expands and rises. A large mass of rising warm air has less weight, or pressure, than a mass of sinking cold air. The air over the icy poles is cold. The poles, therefore, are covered by permanent high-pressure areas. Along the equator, where it is always hot, there is a permanent belt of rising warm air, a low-pressure area. Smaller high- and low- pressure areas are found all over Earth. Some of them are almost always in the same places. Others move around the surface of Earth. The maps on page 110 show the air-pressure patterns on Earth for January and July.

An important weather rule is that air flows from a high-pressure area into a low-pressure area. This movement creates wind.

Wind

Wind is the movement of air from one place to another. It is a result of differences in air pressure. Since some high- and low-pressure air masses are permanent, some winds always blow in the same general direction. Such winds are called **prevailing winds**. The map on page 110 shows the six major belts of prevailing winds on Earth.

Notice that these prevailing winds do not blow directly north or south, from the permanent highs at the poles to the permanent low at the equator. The rotation of Earth affects the direction of the winds. The effect of rotation on wind patterns is called the

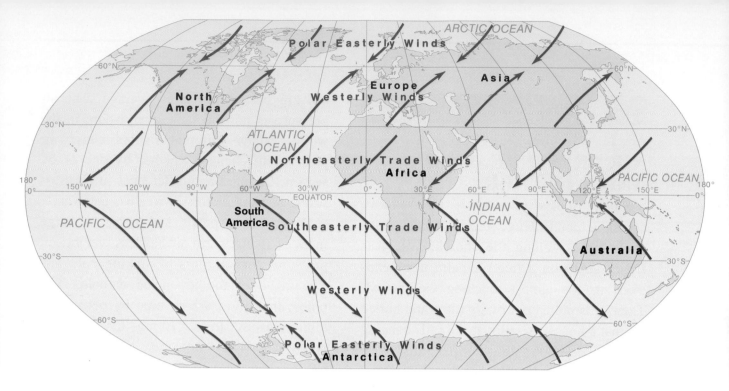

WORLD: WIND CURRENTS

MAP SKILLS: Find two belts of trade winds on the map above. Are they high- or low-pressure systems? Why? Compare the maps on pages 110 and 111. How do high pressure belts differ?

Coriolis (*kawr*ee*OH*lihs*) effect, which was named after the person who first described it.

To understand the Coriolis effect, imagine a pair of giants who are playing catch. One giant stands at the North Pole; the other stands at the equator. The one at the pole throws a ball to the other player, aiming it directly at the catcher and forgetting that the planet is rotating. At the equator, the ground is moving from west to east at about 1,000 miles (1,609.3 km) per hour. By the time that the ball reaches the target, the catcher is no longer there.

To the catcher, it looks as though the ball is curving to the left. Actually, the ball was thrown in a straight line, but the ground and the catcher moved away from the path of the ball.

Thus, the rotation of Earth changes the movement of air over its surface. Winds curve as Earth rotates. In the Northern Hemisphere, winds turn in a clockwise direction. In the Southern Hemisphere, they move in a counterclockwise direction.

If all the winds on Earth moved exactly as they are shown on the map, weather forecasting would be an easy job. However, there are variations in wind patterns. The prevailing winds *usually* flow in the same

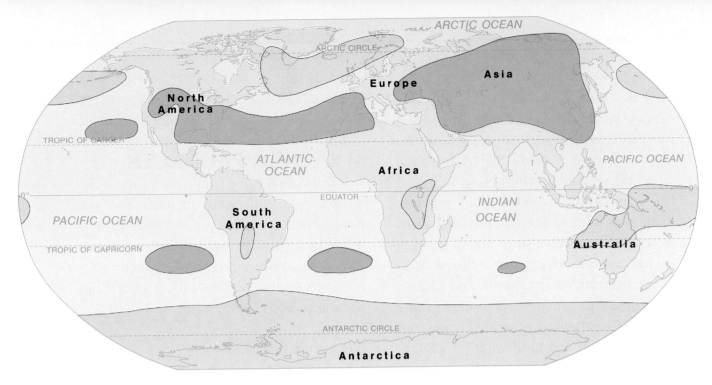

WORLD: JANUARY AIR PRESSURE

- ▬ High pressure
- ▬ Low pressure

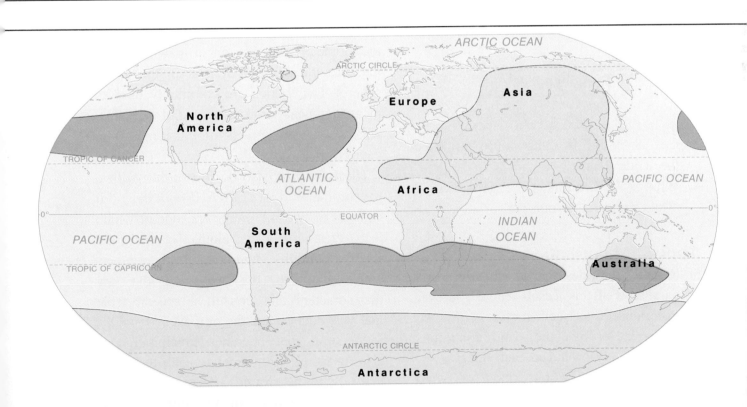

WORLD: JULY AIR PRESSURE

- ▬ High pressure
- ▬ Low pressure

direction, but they can vary. Seasonal changes in temperature cause changes in high- and low-pressure systems and the winds that result from them. In some places, the prevailing winds blow in one direction in summer and in the opposite direction in winter. The unequal heating of land and water areas also results in changes in wind patterns. High land areas, such as mountains, can deflect winds and change their direction. These and other factors break up the pattern of prevailing winds into secondary winds and local winds. Such factors make weather so changeable.

Lesson 3 Review

Recalling Information
1. What is air pressure?
2. What is a prevailing wind?

Interpreting Information
3. Can a change in temperature influence the wind? How?
4. What is the Coriolis effect? How does it affect prevailing winds?

Applying Information
5. Reread the description in the first paragraph of this lesson. Have you ever experienced or seen pictures of such effects? Describe the wind conditions that probably produced each one.
6. When do the worst kinds of wind conditions occur where you live?

Lesson 4

WEATHER PACKAGES

Put the factors of temperature, moisture, air pressure, and wind together and you have a weather package. Whether it turns out to be a package that you can regard as a gift or as something that you would rather not have depends on how these ingredients come together.

Measuring the Weather

In order to describe weather or to predict what it will be, we need instruments that measure the factors that make up weather. Some instruments are extremely modern and complex. The four listed here, however, are fairly simple in their design.

You are probably most familiar with the thermometer, the instrument that is used to measure the amount of heat in the atmosphere. Two scales are commonly used to measure heat—Fahrenheit and Celsius, which are both named after the men who devised them.

Humidity can also be measured—with a psychrometer (*seye*KRAHM*uh*ter*). It consists of two thermometers, one of which is covered with a wet cloth. To obtain the relative humidity, you compare the temperatures in both the wet and the dry thermometers and consult a special table that was devised for the purpose.

Moisture that becomes precipitation is also measured. Containers collect the water that falls to the ground. If snow or ice falls, it is melted to find out how much water it contains. Amounts of precipitation are given in inches or centimeters. The map on page 114 shows the varying amounts of precipitation that fall yearly in different parts of the world.

A barometer measures air pressure. The mercury in a long tube rises or falls, depending on how much air pressure is acting upon it. The units that are used are inches or centimeters of mercury. The higher the reading, the higher the air pressure is.

Wind is described by its direction and its speed. A weather vane is a simple device for obtaining wind direction. Winds are named for the direction from which they have come. A southwest wind, for example, blows from the southwest toward the northeast. Wind speed is measured in miles or kilometers per hour. Bad storms can bring winds of over 100 miles (160.9 km) per hour.

Air Masses

An **air mass** is a huge area of air that has the same general characteristics of heat and humidity. That is, all the air has approximately the same temperature and the same amount of moisture. Since its temperature is either warmer or cooler than that of the air that surrounds it, the air mass is either a high-pressure area (cooler) or a low-pressure area (warmer). A small air mass may cover an area of more than 1,000 square miles (2,590 sq km). A large one may be as big as a continent.

An air mass formed over the ocean contains a lot of moisture picked up from the waters below it. One formed over land is dry. Similarly, an air mass formed closer to the poles contains cold air, one formed

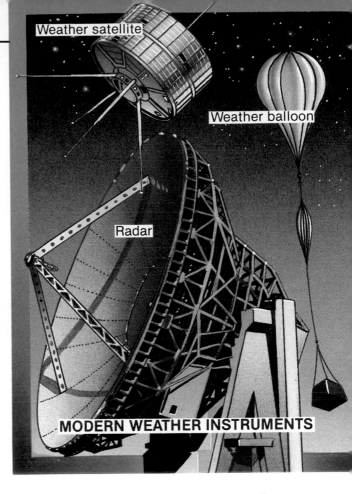

MODERN WEATHER INSTRUMENTS

Scientists use many instruments to study weather at all atmospheric levels.

nearer to the equator contains warm air.

Beneath a dry air mass, people are likely to be enjoying sunny weather. It may be warm or cold, depending on the air temperature. Under a moist air mass, cloudy conditions are most likely. Some of the moisture condenses into clouds.

Air masses are not still. They move from areas of high pressure to areas of low pressure. Cold high-pressure masses, therefore, tend to move away from the poles. Their movement sets warmer low-pressure masses moving as well, but cold air masses are generally stronger and move more rapidly than warm air masses. As an air mass

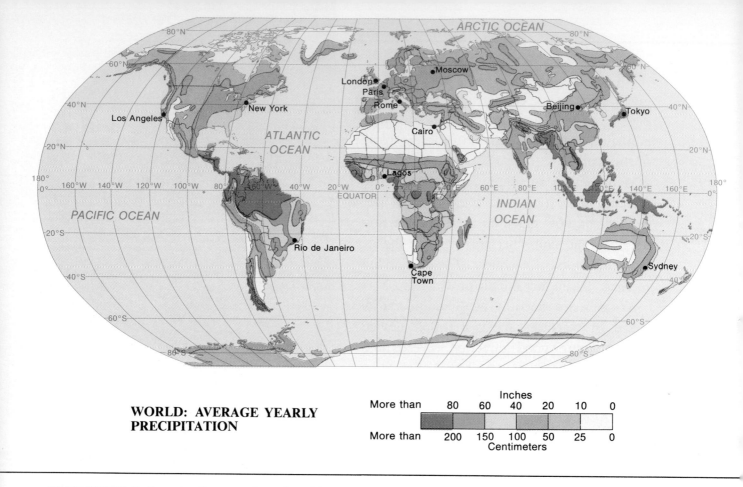

WORLD: AVERAGE YEARLY PRECIPITATION

	Inches					
More than	80	60	40	20	10	0
More than	200	150	100	50	25	0
			Centimeters			

MAP SKILLS: Locate three regions in which annual precipitation is between 10 and 20 inches (25 and 50 cm).

moves from one place to another, the temperature or the humidity of the air that is in it may change. A moist air mass that moves from over the ocean to over a continent, for example, may lose some of its moisture to the land. Because they are so huge, however, air masses tend to resist changing very much.

Changes are far more likely to take place around the edges of an air mass than within the air mass itself, particularly when two different air masses meet. The boundaries between two different air masses that come together are known as **fronts**. People who study the weather identify these fronts by measuring the differences between the tem-

peratures, the air pressures, and the wind directions of the two approaching masses.

Warm and Cold Fronts

A warm, moist air mass in the Atlantic slowly drifts to the northwest, approaching the East Coast of the United States. A cool, dry air mass that covers most of the United States moves to the southeast in a path to meet it. A natural event is soon to affect the lives of many people. Along the coast, people are informed of the expected change in weather. In some areas, heavy storms are predicted. In other areas, the forecasters predict a fine, sunny day. Two weather packages are going to meet.

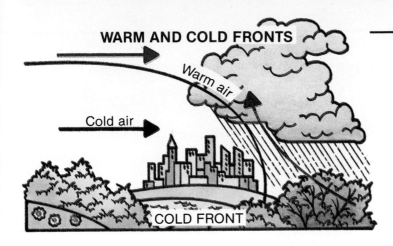

WARM AND COLD FRONTS

Warm air

Cold air

COLD FRONT

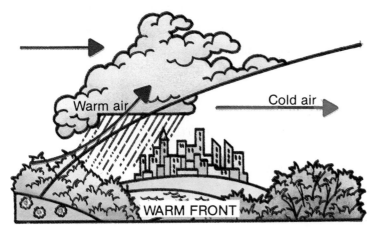

Warm air

Cold air

WARM FRONT

Although cold fronts and warm fronts cannot be seen, they bring weather changes. Which kind of front brings precipitation?

The meeting of two air masses is like a battle. Each mass tries to resist the other. If the cold front is stronger, it pushes itself under the warm air of the warm air mass. The warm, moist air that is forced to rise soon begins to cool as it moves higher into the atmosphere. The cooling air then releases much of the moisture which it carries as precipitation—either heavy rain or snow, depending on the temperature of the cold air front. Cold fronts usually bring brief periods of heavy storms, followed by cooler and drier weather.

If the warm front is stronger, it advances over the cooler air of the cold air mass. The air in a warm front cannot push the cold air up because the cold air is heavier. Again, as the warm air rises, it cools and releases precipitation. In this case, the precipitation is more likely to be characterized by steady rain or snow rather than by the sudden storms that accompany a cold front. The precipitation may last for a day or more as the slow-moving warm front continues to pass over the cooler air of the cold front. The kind of precipitation that is brought by a warm front will be followed by clear weather and by warmer temperatures.

Lesson 4 Review

Recalling Information

1. In what important way does an air mass that forms over an ocean differ from one that forms over land?
2. What is a front? What happens when a cold front and a warm front meet?

Interpreting Information

3. For days, your barometer has stayed at about 29.7 inches (76.2 cm). Then, the reading falls rapidly. What is likely to happen to the temperature? Why?
4. The temperature is 32°F (0°C), and a low-pressure air mass is moving toward you. Should you plan on skiing tomorrow? Explain.

Applying Information

5. How does the weather where you live affect what you might do on a summer and a winter vacation in your area?
6. What is the worst kind of weather that you might get in your area? Describe it.

Skills for Thinking

READING A WEATHER MAP

Suppose that you had a chance to work at a local television station. If you were asked to stand in for the person who gives the weather report, could you do it? Could you read the weather map, or would it confuse you?

Television and newspaper weather reports use weather maps that contain symbols. To understand a weather report, you should know what these symbols mean.

What Does the Map Mean?

Look at the map and the key on this page. Find the symbols for *high* and *low*. You remember that high pressure usually brings sunny or clear weather and low pressure usually brings clouds or storms.

Find the symbol for a front. You recall from the chapter that a front brings together opposing systems.

Study the map to find the direction in which the weather systems are moving.

Now, use the map to answer the following questions.

1. What is the weather in Helena, Montana? How should people dress there?
2. Where is there a high-pressure area? What is the weather probably like?
3. Find the tiny arrows on the map key. What do you think they mean?
4. What is the weather in Washington, D.C.? What would you need if you went outdoors there?
5. Look at the key. Tell what you think happens at a stationary front.

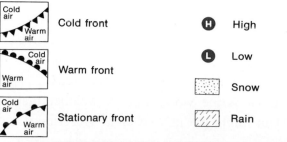

UNITED STATES: WEATHER

Cold air / Warm air	Cold front	**H**	High
Cold air / Warm air	Warm front	**L**	Low
Cold air / Warm air	Stationary front		Snow
			Rain

Chapter 5 Review

Summary of Key Facts

In this chapter, you learned that

- the atmosphere is a layer of air that protects life and creates weather.
- the four layers of the atmosphere are the troposphere, the stratosphere, the mesosphere, and the thermosphere.
- weather is a combination of temperature, moisture, air pressure, and wind.
- wind is the movement of air from a high-pressure area to a low-pressure area.
- an air mass is a huge area of air that is at the same general temperature and has about the same amount of humidity.
- weather changes when the fronts of two different air masses meet.

Using Vocabulary

On a separate page, write the term that will correctly complete each sentence.

ozone layer   air mass
relative humidity   prevailing wind
air pressure   front

1. The weight of the atmosphere is called _____ .
2. The amount of moisture that the air can hold at a certain temperature is its _____ .
3. The place where air masses meet is a (an) _____ .
4. A wind that always blows in a certain direction is a (an) _____ .
5. Some dangerous rays of the sun are absorbed by the _____ .

Discussing the Chapter

1. Describe three ways in which the atmosphere protects us.
2. Describe the way in which a change in temperature can lead to precipitation.
3. How does air pressure create winds?
4. How can winds affect precipitation?

Reviewing Skills

Use the map on page 116 to answer the questions below.

1. What kind of front is moving toward Miami, Florida? How will the weather change?
2. Where is there a low-pressure area? What is the weather there like?

What Determines Climate?

Introduction

In just an hour, the weather can change dramatically in a place. Imagine the desert on a bright, sunny day. Air and soil are hot and dry. Only a slight breeze relieves the heat. Suddenly, the wind picks up. Clouds form and the sky turns dark. A cloudburst dumps several inches of rain. Then, as quickly as the clouds came, the sky turns bright again.

You could not make a general statement about the average weather of the desert based on your observations of this particular day. Such storms are rare in a desert. Several months could pass before another drop of rain falls.

The sun and the seas are major determinants of climate. What measures have these people taken against the cold?

Only if you observe the weather patterns of a region for a long period of time can you describe the average weather there. Then, you can make a general statement about the **climate** of the place. Climate is the condition of the atmosphere in a place over a period of years. Weather, as you know, is the condition of the atmosphere over a brief period of time.

Climates vary throughout the world. Many factors work together to create varied climates.

Think about the features of the area in which you live. How far north or south of the equator is it? Is it near or far from the ocean? How high above sea level is it? Is the land nearby flat, hilly, or mountainous? All these factors influence climate, as you will learn in this lesson.

119

CLIMATE AND THE SUN

The sun provides the energy that heats Earth. Some places on Earth receive more heat from the sun than others. Thus, some places are warmer than others. This condition alone is enough to cause there to be different climates on Earth. Other factors, however, are also important.

Differences in temperature cause huge masses of air and water to move over Earth. These movements, too, affect climate, and it all begins with the uneven heating of Earth. Reasons for the uneven heating in-clude Earth's shape, its movements through space, and the tilt of its axis.

What land regions do the sun's most-direct rays strike? What type of weather would you expect to find there?

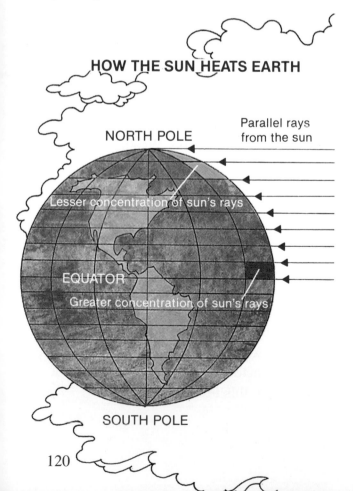

HOW THE SUN HEATS EARTH

NORTH POLE

Parallel rays from the sun

Lesser concentration of sun's rays

EQUATOR

Greater concentration of sun's rays

SOUTH POLE

Earth's Shape

Earth is a sphere. Its round shape is partly responsible for the fact that some places receive more of the sun's heat than others. On a sunny summer day, the sun shines the brightest at noon. That is the time when the sun is high in the sky and its rays strike Earth most directly. Late in the afternoon, the sun is lower in the sky. Its rays then strike at an angle.

The angle at which the sun's rays strike Earth determines the amount of heat that an area of Earth's surface receives. To see how the sun affects climate, look at the diagram on this page. You can see that in areas near the equator, the sun's rays strike Earth most directly. Closer to the poles, the sun's rays hit Earth at an angle. In addition, the rays must spread over a wide area. Each polar area gets less solar energy than areas at or closer to the center. Thus, polar areas are colder than the equator.

Tilted and Ever Moving

Recall what you learned about Earth in Chapter 1. Earth *rotates*, or spins on its axis, at a speed of over 1,000 miles (1609.3 km) per hour at the equator. At the same time, Earth revolves around the sun at an even greater speed. Of course, you don't really feel these movements, but you do feel them indirectly in a great many ways.

As you know, the rotation of Earth affects the movement of air. It also affects the movement of water. Can you explain how? These movements of air and water, in turn,

EARTH'S ORBIT AROUND THE SUN

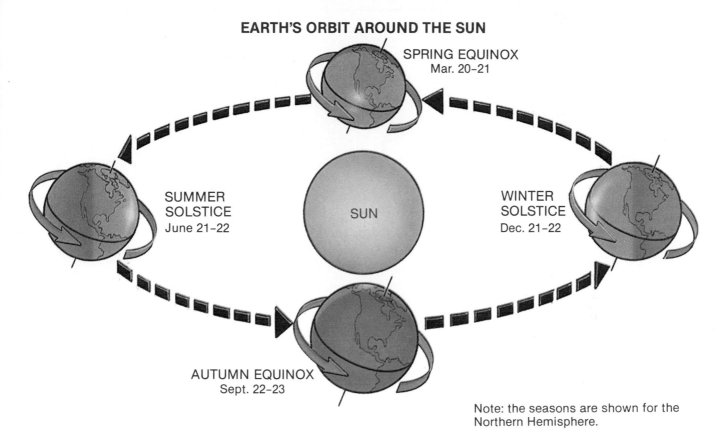

SPRING EQUINOX
Mar. 20–21

SUMMER
SOLSTICE
June 21–22

SUN

WINTER
SOLSTICE
Dec. 21–22

AUTUMN EQUINOX
Sept. 22–23

Note: the seasons are shown for the
Northern Hemisphere.

**Which two Earth motions are illustrated here? Which motion
causes the seasons to occur?**

influence climate. Earth's rotation also causes night and day, the length of which influences climate. How? When days are long, the sun has a long time in which to heat Earth. On short days, there is less time for solar heating. The duration of sunlight changes in many places as the seasons of the year change because of the tilt of Earth's axis.

The tilt of Earth always stays the same: 23 1/2°. The North Pole always points toward the North Star. As Earth revolves around the sun, however, the position of the poles changes in relation to the sun. For six months of the year, the North Pole leans toward the sun, while the South Pole leans

away from it. After Earth has completed half an orbit, the North Pole leans away from the sun for six months, while the South Pole leans toward it.

If the axis were not tilted, areas at the equator would receive the sun's direct rays all year. Areas near the poles would never receive the sun's rays. Thus, near the equator, it would always be hot, while near the poles it would always be cold. Temperatures between the equator and the poles would reflect how far north or south a place is. They would, however, be the same throughout the year.

The diagram on this page shows the relationship between Earth and the sun for a full

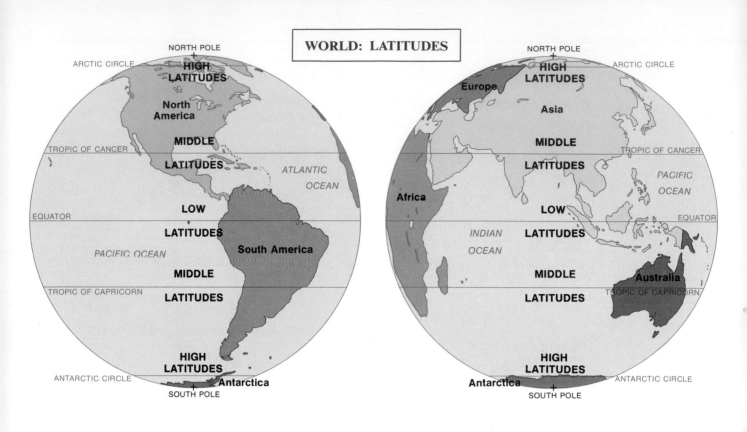

WORLD: LATITUDES

MAP SKILLS: In which climate zone are the Tropic of Cancer and the Tropic of Capricorn?

year. The seasons labeled are for the Northern Hemisphere. The seasons are just the opposite in the Southern Hemisphere. At the summer **solstice** (SOHL*stihs*), or the first day of summer, the direct rays of the sun reach farther north than they do at any other time of the year. The sun is directly over anywhere within the Tropic of Cancer (23 1/2°N) at noon. Places in the Northern Hemisphere have more hours of daylight on this day than on any other day of the year. North of the Arctic Circle (66 1/2°N), the sun shines all day long. There is no night.

Summer continues for the next three months in the Northern Hemisphere as

Earth moves in its orbit. During these months, the direct rays of the sun reach farther south until, at the autumn **equinox** (EE*kwuh*nahks*), they are directly over the equator. The autumn equinox is the first day of autumn. On this day, all parts of Earth have 12 hours of day and 12 hours of night.

Through the autumn months and into winter, daylight in the Northern Hemisphere gradually lessens. At the winter solstice, the sun's rays move south toward the Tropic of Capricorn (23 1/2°S). The winter solstice is the beginning of winter and the date on which the Northern Hemisphere has the fewest hours of daylight. The sun's rays strike the Northern Hemisphere at an angle. The area north of the Arctic Circle is completely dark. There is no daylight.

Through the winter months, Earth moves toward the position of the spring equinox. At the same time, daylight in the Northern Hemisphere gradually increases. Then, once again, the sun shines directly over the equator, and day and night are of equal duration all over Earth.

Latitude Zones

You have seen that the Tropic of Cancer, the Tropic of Capricorn, the Arctic Circle, and the Antarctic Circle are indicators of climate. These four lines of latitude, therefore, are used to divide Earth into three major climate, or **latitude, zones**.

The zone between the Tropic of Cancer and the Tropic of Capricorn is called the **tropical zone,** or the low-latitude zone. (It is called low because its latitudes range from 0° at the equator to 23 1/2° north and south of the equator.) Areas in this zone receive the direct or the almost direct rays of the sun all year long. At sea level, this zone always has a hot or a warm climate. The lands within this zone are often referred to as the tropics.

North of the Arctic Circle and south of the Antarctic Circle are two zones called the **frigid** (cold) **zones**, or the high-latitude zones. (They are called high because their latitudes range from 66 1/2° to 90° north or south.) The high latitudes never receive the direct rays of the sun; sometimes they receive no sunlight at all. The high latitudes have cool or cold climates. The high latitude zones are also called the polar zones.

Between the low latitudes and the high latitudes are the **temperate zones**, or the middle-latitude zones. These zones are hot at some times and cold at other times. It is here that the greatest seasonal changes take place. The sun's rays never strike Earth directly in the middle latitudes. They come closest to being direct rays in the summer.

The maps on page 124 show the average January and July temperatures around the world. Note how they differ in the middle latitudes. You will read more about all climate zones in Chapter 7.

Lesson 1 Review

Recalling Information

1. How does Earth's shape influence climate?
2. How do Earth's tilt and rotation around the sun affect climate?

Interpreting Information

3. Even in summer, it is cooler in Boston, Massachusetts, than in Miami, Florida. Why?
4. When it is summer in the Northern Hemisphere, what season is it in the Southern Hemisphere?

Applying Information

5. In which latitude zone do you live? Describe each season in your latitude zone.
6. What is your favorite season? Where would you travel to find that season all year long?

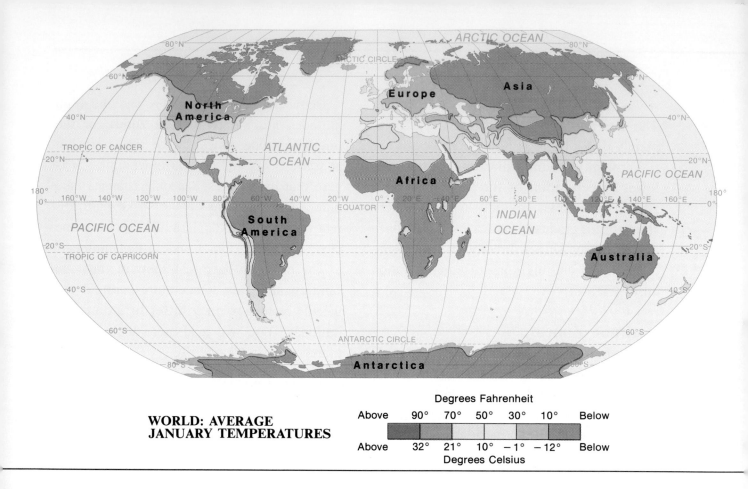

**WORLD: AVERAGE
JANUARY TEMPERATURES**

Degrees Fahrenheit

| Above | 90° | 70° | 50° | 30° | 10° | Below |

| Above | 32° | 21° | 10° | −1° | −12° | Below |

Degrees Celsius

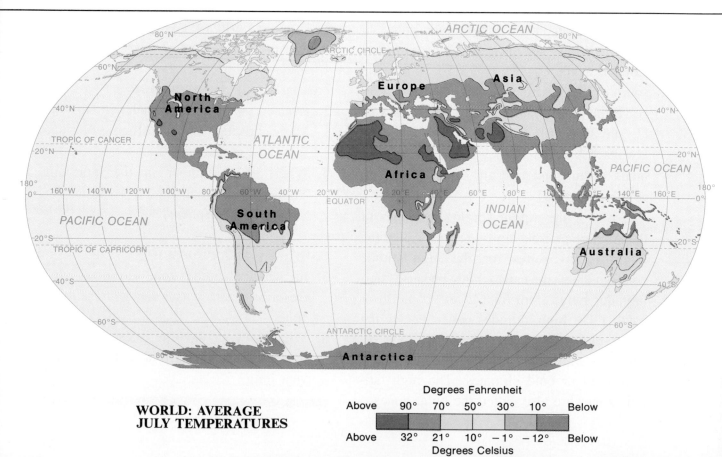

**WORLD: AVERAGE
JULY TEMPERATURES**

Degrees Fahrenheit

| Above | 90° | 70° | 50° | 30° | 10° | Below |

| Above | 32° | 21° | 10° | −1° | −12° | Below |

Degrees Celsius

Lesson 2

CLIMATE AND ALTITUDE

Knowing the latitude zone of a particular area would give you a good idea of its climate. You would, however, have to consider other factors that affect climate. Suppose, for example, that you wanted to find a warm, pleasant place for a winter vacation. You might choose a city such as Tampa, Florida, or San Diego, California. Both cities are about 30°N latitude, close to the tropical zone.

Mount Everest, the world's highest mountain, is also located at about 30°N latitude. Few people, however, would care for a winter vacation there. Even in summer, the mountain is topped by snow.

The great difference in temperature between Tampa and Mount Everest—both located at the same latitude—is the result of differences in **altitude**. Tampa is at sea level. Mount Everest rises to over 29,000 feet (8,839.2 m).

The words *altitude* and *elevation* refer to the same thing, to distance above sea level. *Altitude* refers to the height of an object in the air, and *elevation* refers to the height of an area of land. Thus, for example, you might say that a jet airplane is flying at an altitude of 20,000 feet (6,096 m) and that Houston, Texas, is at an elevation of 49 feet (14.9 m). In this lesson, we will use the word *altitude* for both kinds of height.

<u>MAP SKILLS:</u> **Average temperatures for summer and winter are useful for studying climate. Where is it the coldest in January? What is the average July temperature there?**

Altitude and Temperature

If you have taken a trip to the mountains, you may have noticed that it becomes cooler as you go up. Take a look at the diagram on page 126. In general, temperatures fall about 3.6°F (2°C) for every 1,000 feet (304.8 m) in elevation. There can be quite a temperature difference between a lowland area and a nearby highland area. You can see this by comparing average temperatures for July in Charleston, South Carolina, and Asheville, North Carolina. Although the cities are only a few hundred miles apart, Charleston is at sea level, and Asheville is located more than 2,000 feet (609.6 m) up in the Appalachians. The difference in altitude is not great, but there is as much as an 8°F (4.4°C) difference in the average temperatures of the two cities.

Keep in mind, though, that the drop in temperature that is associated with altitude is only a general rule. Other factors such as wind, the amount of sunlight, and the amount of plant growth influence temperature. If you rise straight upward in a hot-air balloon, you might experience a regular drop in temperature. If you climb the side of a mountain, you might discover that other factors come into play.

As you saw in Chapter 5, the atmosphere gradually thins above Earth. At the top of a high mountain, the air is thinner than at sea level.

The air at high altitudes also contains less moisture, dust, and other kinds of pollutants. Therefore, the sun's rays can pass through the atmosphere and penetrate Earth with greater intensity at high altitudes. This does not mean that high altitude areas are

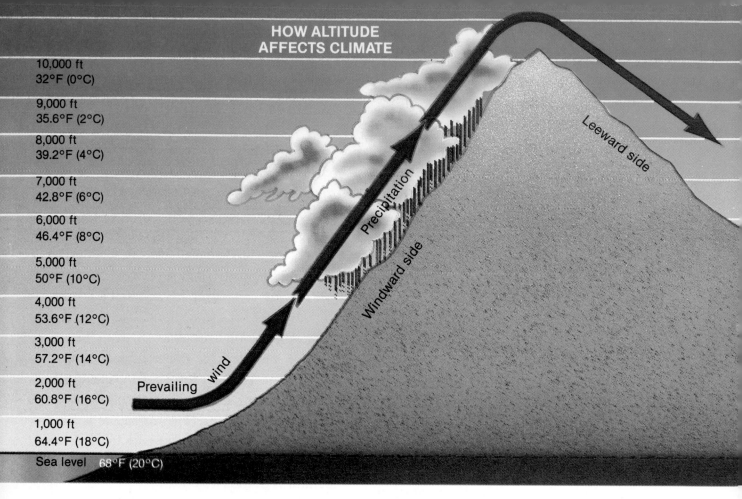

10,000 ft
32°F (0°C)

9,000 ft
35.6°F (2°C)

8,000 ft
39.2°F (4°C)

7,000 ft
42.8°F (6°C)

6,000 ft
46.4°F (8°C)

5,000 ft
50°F (10°C)

4,000 ft
53.6°F (12°C)

3,000 ft
57.2°F (14°C)

2,000 ft
60.8°F (16°C)

1,000 ft
64.4°F (18°C)

Sea level   68°F (20°C)

Prevailing wind

Precipitation

Windward side

Leeward side

**How would the flow of air differ if the mountain were not
there? Would the air still be full of moisture? Explain.**

warm, though. Land heats quickly, but the thin air does not hold heat very long after the sun stops shining or on a cloudy day. Land cools rapidly, which is the reason why differences in day and night temperatures can be very great at high altitudes.

The shape of mountains also affects high-altitude climates. One side of a mountain is sunny, and the other side is shady. The sunny side is warmer than the shady side.

Wind and Precipitation

Areas at high altitudes are generally windier than the surrounding lowlands. At the foot of a mountain, you might feel a gentle breeze. As you climb a mountain,

you will notice that the wind has become stronger.

These winds have an influence on climate and precipitation. Winds blowing across a lowland area toward a mountain range follow the level of the rising land and flow upward. As the air that is carried by the wind gains altitude, it begins to cool. As you read in Chapter 5, cool air holds less moisture than warm air. As the air continues to rise and to cool, it cannot hold all of its moisture. The moisture condenses, and the air begins to release precipitation.

Prevailing winds that blow toward mountains release most of their moisture on the windward side—the side of the mountain

126

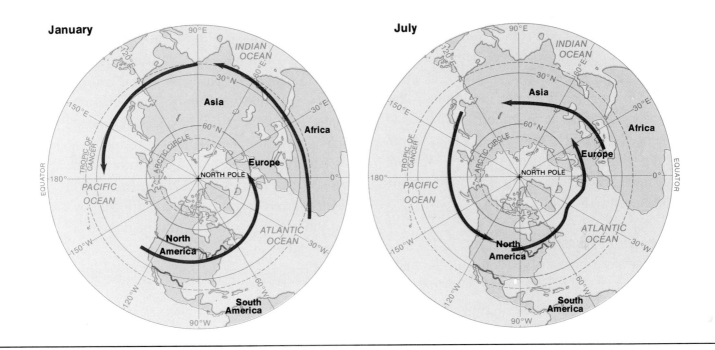

WIND CURRENTS: JET STREAMS

→ Jet stream

January

July

MAP SKILLS: Which symbols show the jet stream's path?
Describe the changes in its path between January and July.

facing the wind. After passing over the mountain peaks, the winds lose their force over the leeward side—the side away from the direction of the wind. As it loses altitude, the air, having released much of its moisture, begins to warm again. Now, it begins to soak up moisture from Earth on the leeward side of the mountain.

This process highlights another feature of mountain climate. The windward side is usually wetter than the leeward side. One side may have heavy precipitation, and the other side may be desert dry. As you can see, mountain climate is unique and conditions change frequently, depending on altitude, sunshine, and wind direction.

The Jet Stream

We have been examining winds that blow close to the surface of Earth. There is another kind of wind that occurs only at very high altitudes, between 5 and 9 miles (8 to 14.4 km) above Earth. This is a strong wind that is called a **jet stream**. Jet streams occur in the troposphere.

When airplanes first began to fly at very high altitudes, pilots noticed something unusual. Across North America and Europe, they could fly a distance from west to east faster than they could fly the same distance from east to west. A jet stream pushes them along as they fly eastward and holds them back as they fly westward.

127

The path of a jet stream influences the weather below it. The North Pole jet stream forms a kind of border between warm, tropical air moving north and cold, arctic air moving south. The weather south of the jet stream tends to be warm because it is influenced by air coming from the tropics. The weather north of the jet stream, which is influenced more by the arctic air, is cool. What probably happens often to weather patterns when the North Pole jet stream shifts north? South?

Freakish Weather

Imagine a blizzard in Miami in the middle of July or a heat wave in Montreal, Canada, in January. Such thoughts seem farfetched but no more so than some of the unusual and destructive weather that affected much of the world at the end of 1982 and the beginning of 1983.

Severe droughts created dust storms in such places as southern Africa and Australia. Torrents of rain ruined crops and caused mud slides in Ecuador and Peru. Unusually high tides and frequent storms sent huge waves crashing against the West Coast of the United States, destroying beaches and homes.

This freakish weather was caused by a change in the pattern of a Pacific Ocean weather system called El Nino. El Nino is a system of winds and ocean currents that controls weather over about one-quarter of Earth. Its normal pattern includes easterly winds that blow over the Pacific and that drive a warm ocean current west toward the Indian Ocean.

Every few years, however, as happened in 1982 and 1983, the system breaks down. Changes in air pressure cause winds to blow toward the east instead of the west. The ocean current changes direction and pushes abnormally warm water toward South America. The extra warm, moist air causes heavy rains and flooding. The pressure change over parts of the ocean blocks moist winds over other areas. Drought results.

Meteorologists are not quite sure what causes these changes in El Nino. However, scientists from countries that are affected by El Nino's severe changes are beginning a 10-year study to find out.

Lesson 2 Review

Recalling Information

1. How does altitude affect temperature?
2. How does the jet stream affect climate?

Interpreting Information

3. What danger faces climbers who have to spend a night on a mountaintop?
4. Mount St. Helens, an active volcano in southwest Washington, erupted in 1980, spewing thousands of tons of ash. Much of this ash rose to the level of the jet stream. What do you think happened to it after that?

Applying Information

5. At what altitude do you live? How did you find the answer?
6. If you were going to move from an area at sea level to the mountains, how different would your life be in your new home?

Lesson 3

LAND, WATER, AND CLIMATE

Both land and water influence climate, but in different ways. This in part is because they absorb heat and transfer it differently.

Land and Water Contrasts

When the heating rays of the sun fall on the ocean, they pass through the water. Thus, the sun heats not only the water's surface but also the water below the surface. Land, however, is denser than water. The sun's rays heat only the land's surface, and the heat does not spread out as it does in water.

Water is a fluid that is always in motion. Water that is heated by the sun mixes easily with colder water from the lower layers of the ocean. This continuous mixing spreads the heat. As the heat is spread, the temperature of the surface water is reduced.

The mixing of warm and cold does not take place on land. Because land is solid, only the parts that receive the sun's rays receive heat. Land, however, absorbs heat faster than water. It takes more energy to heat a given amount of water than it takes to heat the same amount of land.

These three contrasts between land and water all lead to the same result. Water heats slowly but absorbs more heat and holds it longer than land does.

Land areas reach their highest and their lowest temperatures about one month after the solstices. Thus, the land in the Northern Hemisphere becomes the warmest around

Would the land or water be warmer in the northeastern United States in October? Which would be warmest in April? Why?

late July and the coldest around late January. Bodies of water reach their maximum and their minimum temperatures about one month later. The maximum and minimum water temperatures, in turn, affect the temperature of the air near the water.

The difference in the heating and the cooling rates of land and water has an important effect on climate. An example will illustrate this effect. The average temperature during July in San Francisco, California, is 59°F (17.2°C). The average temperature during July in Springfield, Missouri, is 78°F (25.6°C). Latitude does not account for the difference in temperatures.

Both of the cities are at nearly the same latitude. Altitude is not the cause. Although Springfield is higher in altitude than San Francisco, its temperature is not lower but higher than San Francisco's.

Look at a map of the United States to see what accounts for this temperature difference. Notice that Springfield is surrounded by land. It is far from any large body of water. San Francisco, in contrast, is on the coast near the Pacific Ocean. Winds that blow over the water bring cool air to San Francisco. The air that circulates in Springfield remains warm as it passes over the warm continent.

Ocean Currents

The oceans contain large rivers of water called currents, or streams. Prevailing winds blowing over the oceans' surfaces tend to push the currents along in a certain direction.

Earth's rotation and the Coriolis effect influence ocean currents as well as winds. In the Northern Hemisphere, currents move in a clockwise direction. In the Southern Hemisphere, they move in a counterclockwise direction.

Water temperatures are affected by latitude, just as land temperatures are. Warm currents begin close to the equator, and cold currents begin near the poles. The map on page 131 shows some of the world's major ocean currents.

Find the Gulf Stream on the ocean currents map. Follow its course as it moves north and east. Notice that it moves along the east coast of North America, crosses the Atlantic Ocean, and flows toward Europe.

The name for this place in the Caribbean Sea, called Hurricane Hole, gives an indication of the winds that come here.

The warm current flows all year long. In winter, it makes the temperatures in northwestern Europe milder than they would otherwise be at such a high latitude. Prevailing winter winds blow northeast toward Europe. As the winds pass over the warm Gulf Stream, they pick up and carry some of its heat across the British Isles toward the continent of Europe.

Great Britain usually has mild winters. At the same latitude across the Atlantic, however, winters in Labrador are bitterly cold. The difference is that in Labrador, the prevailing winds blow from the land or from the cold waters of the Labrador Current.

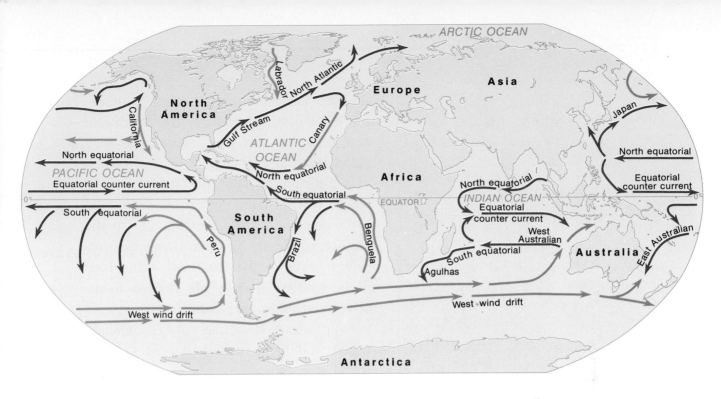

WORLD: OCEAN CURRENTS

→ Warm current

→ Cold current

MAP SKILLS: Find on the map three warm and three cold ocean currents. How can you tell whether they are warm or cold?

Continents

Just as the world's oceans influence climate, so, too, do the continents of the world. Movements of air are affected by the shape of the landmasses over which they pass. The altitudes of all oceans are almost the same—sea level. Land, however, varies in altitude. As a movement of air flows over the land, it may be blocked and redirected by mountains, by hills, by plateaus, and by other features.

The size of the landmass influences its effect on climate. The larger the landmass, the greater the effect. The vast continental landmasses of North America and Asia es-pecially affect the world's climates. In winter, for example, the large cold air mass over Canada dominates the climate across the whole interior of the North American continent. In which hemisphere do these land-controlled climates occur?

Areas near water, such as the northeastern coast of the United States, also feel continental influences. The climate of the Northeast is modified by air masses which form over the oceans. However, the climate is also controlled by the same continental air mass which forms over Canada. Prevailing winds sweep the cold air down and across the Northeast.

131

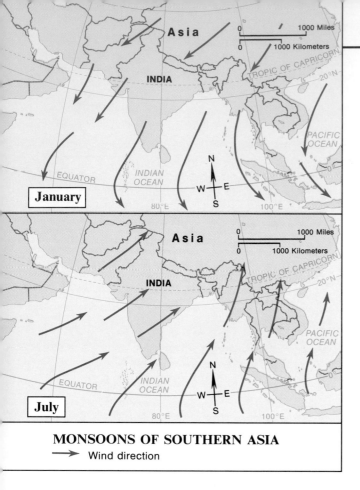

MONSOONS OF SOUTHERN ASIA
→ Wind direction

MAP SKILLS: What do the arrows show about wind directions over India in January and in July? When do monsoons begin?

Monsoons

The operation of seasonal winds called **monsoons** can help to show how a large landmass affects climate. *Monsoon* is an Arabic word meaning "season." In summer, the monsoon winds blow over India from the ocean to the southwest. They bring moist tropical air from the Indian Ocean to the land. As this moist air rises over the Ghat Mountains in southwestern India, it cools and releases heavy rains. The summer monsoon in India is so regular that most people can predict the dates on which the summer rains will begin in their areas.

The wet monsoon continues through the summer. Distance from the ocean, altitude, and other factors determine how much rain any particular area gets. Some areas may get as much as 250 inches (635 cm) of rain in a 5-month period. That amounts to 20 feet (6.1 m) of rain.

As autumn begins, Earth moves to the position where the Northern Hemisphere receives fewer of the sun's rays. The land cools quickly. The winds reverse themselves and blow over India from northeast to southwest. These are dry continental winds, and India remains dry through the winter monsoon.

Lesson 3 Review

Recalling Information

1. Why do land and water heat and cool at different rates?
2. How are water temperatures affected by latitude?

Interpreting Information

3. Suppose India were surrounded by ocean to the north as well as to the south. How might this affect its climate?
4. How can a warm current influence the climate of nearby land areas?

Applying Information

5. Is your climate influenced more by land or by water, or is it influenced by both?
6. In what direction do the prevailing winds blow in your area? How do these influence your climate in winter? In summer?

Special Feature
Citizenship: Storm Disaster Relief

During a 6-hour period in the spring of 1984, 24 tornadoes (violent storms) swept through the Carolinas. In their wake, more than 60 people were dead, more than 1,000 people were injured, and thousands were left homeless.

People across the nation offered help to victims of the storm. One of the most remarkable offers came from the people of Marion, Illinois.

Marion had almost been wiped out by a tornado in 1982. The people of Marion vowed to help others who suffered as they had.

The people of Marion sent food, clothing, and furniture for the tornado victims in Bennetsville, South Carolina. Some even went to Bennetsville. "They helped to clean houses, to cut trees, to remove debris—whatever needed to be done," said one grateful Bennetsville official about the Marion volunteers.

Skills for Thinking

READING FOR CAUSE AND EFFECT

Suppose that you live in a hot climate that is relieved from time to time by cooling thunderstorms. When you hear a rumbling sound in the distance, you think that it is caused by the thunder of an approaching storm. However, no rain falls. Instead, the rumbling gets louder and louder. "What's happening?" you wonder.

You realize that you don't have enough information to determine what's happening. You have only one fact. A loud rumbling is in the distance. That sound is an *effect* of something, but you don't know its *cause*.

Imagine that it is a few hours later, and you are reading the news report below. As you read, look for information that establishes cause and effect. Look for signal words or phrases that link causes and effects, such as *so*, *because of*, *as a result*, *caused by*, *for that reason*. In the news report, signal words and phrases have been marked to identify the facts that determine causes and effects.

A telegraph message from the coastal town of Anjer reports that a volcanic eruption has begun on the island of Krakatau, Indonesia. Because of the eruption, the skies have been blackened for miles. Here in this city, the rumbling that was caused by the volcano has been heard for hours.

How Are These Facts Related?

The more facts that you know about an event, the easier it is to determine cause and effect. You will also see that a cause can bring about a series of effects, one after another. Read the facts in the paragraph below. The main cause is the eruption on Krakatau. List all the effects of that eruption. Then, identify the series of effects.

The 1883 volcanic eruption on Krakatau caused many other disasters. Waves more than 120 feet (36.6 m) high swept away homes, tore up trees, and carried boats inland. Coastal towns such as Anjer were wiped away, and more than 36,000 lives were lost. Rumbling was heard about 3,000 miles (4,827.9 km) away. In addition, the volcano filled the atmosphere with enormous amounts of dust, causing dark skies and strange sunsets over Earth. As a result of this dust, Earth was cooler than normal for several years.

Chapter 6 Review

Summary of Key Facts

In this chapter, you learned that

- the angle of the sun's rays determines how much heat is received by Earth's surface.
- seasons are caused in part by the revolution of Earth around the sun.
- the latitude zone in which a place is located influences its climate.
- the path of the jet stream influences the weather and the climate below it.
- land and water heat and cool at different rates.
- both ocean currents and landmasses affect winds that blow over them.
- mountains affect the climate of the land around them.

Using Vocabulary

On a separate sheet of paper, write the number of the statement and then the term that correctly matches the statement.

jet stream   solstice
latitude zone   altitude
equinox

1. This marks the beginning of summer and winter.
2. This marks the beginning of spring and autumn.
3. There are three of these: low, middle, and high.
4. Usually, the higher this is, the lower the temperature.
5. This zigzags high in the troposphere.

Discussing the Chapter

1. Explain the two major ways in which Earth's rotation affects climate.
2. How does Earth's revolution around the sun cause seasons?
3. How does the jet stream affect the weather below it?
4. Why does water heat and cool slower than land?
5. How do the climates of cities near oceans differ from those of cities surrounded by land? Why do they differ?

Reviewing Skills

Rewrite the paragraph below. Put it in the correct order and add signal words to show three causes and three effects.

People in India can predict the date on which the monsoons will begin. Monsoon winds are very strong. Moist tropical air rises and cools. Monsoons occur at the same time each year. Heavy rains are released. Trees can be bent almost to the ground.

Climate Regions

Introduction

If you were a new farmer and were thinking about which crops to plant, what factors would you have to consider? You would need to know how hot it usually gets each year in your area and how much rainfall it usually receives. You would need to know whether frost occurs and how many months are good for growing crops. All these factors are related to the climate of a place and would affect what plants you would choose.

The most powerful influence on climate is *latitude*, or distance from the equator. As you know, geographers divide Earth into three major climate zones. The low-latitude, or tropical, zone is the area straddling the equator. The middle-latitude, or temperate, zones lie north and south of the tropics. The high-latitude, or frigid, zones lie north and south of the middle latitudes and extend to the North Pole and to the South Pole.

Climates in the same zone are often similar in some ways but are different in others. For this reason, each zone is divided into subzones, or regions. A fourth climate that is found on Earth is not directly connected with latitude. This is the highlands climate. In the highlands, altitude, not latitude, controls the climate. Highlands are cooler than the surrounding lowlands.

In this chapter, you will survey the world's climates. You will journey from the equator toward the poles. As you do, remember that highlands generally are cooler than the lowlands that surround them.

Why are humans more adaptable to different climates than any other form of life? What clues do you see here?

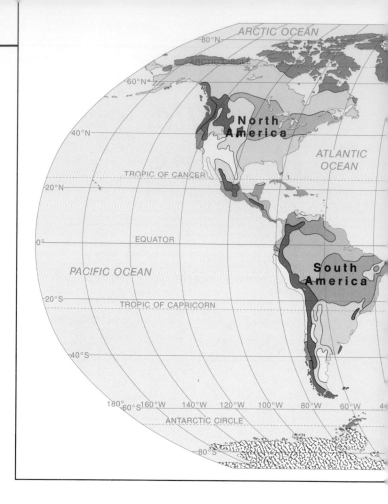

Lesson 1

THE LOW-LATITUDE CLIMATE REGIONS

Imagine that you are in a dense green forest. Foliage abounds. So thick is the growth that only a dim light reaches the forest floor. A heavy thunderstorm has just ended. The steamy, hot air carries the scent of all the vegetation that surrounds you. The thunderstorm has brought no relief from the heat.

Blink, and you're on a grassy plain. A few trees enhance the broad plain. Winter is a hot and dry season here. The grass is dry, and so is the ground. It will not rain until spring.

Blink again, and you're in a desert. The sun shines scorchingly, and the hot air is very dry. Small clumps of scraggly plants relieve the otherwise bare and rocky ground. You wonder when it last rained here. Was it months or years ago? There are only a few green spots in this environment.

The three regions in which you have just imagined yourself are located in the same climate zone. They are all found at or near the equator, in the tropics. The sun's rays shine directly overhead there at least once a year. Most places in the tropics are warm all year long. Can you think of a place in the tropics where you might feel cold?

Each of the three regions in this zone differs from the others according to how much precipitation it gets. Just north and south of the equator, two global wind systems, the **trade winds** and the monsoon winds, help to create climate patterns. Trade winds bring dry weather to land that is near the eastern edges of ocean, and wet weather to land that is near the western edges of oceans. Monsoon winds bring warm, wet summers, and dry, hot winters.

The Wet Tropics

Look at the climate map on these pages. In the zones 0° to 10° north and south of the equator are located the wet tropics. This climate region includes the Amazon Basin, the Congo Basin, and the islands of Southeast Asia. This region has only one season—summer, with high heat and high humidity.

As you read in Chapter 6, the sun's direct

138

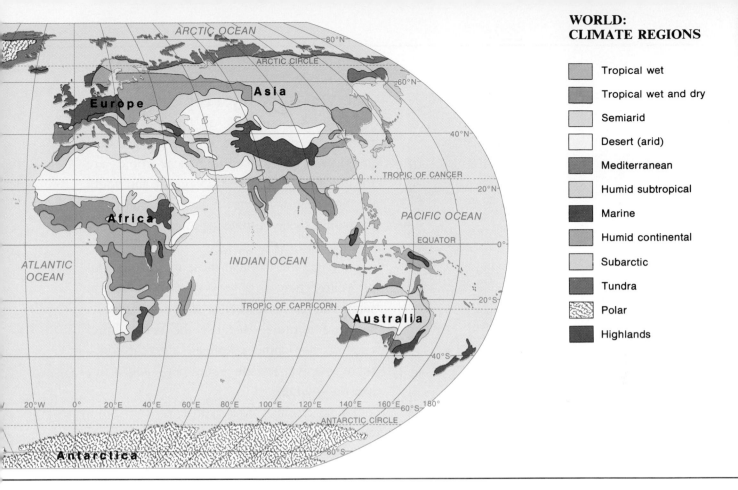

Tropical wet

Tropical wet and dry

Semiarid

Desert (arid)

Mediterranean

Humid subtropical

Marine

Humid continental

Subarctic

Tundra

Polar

Highlands

MAP SKILLS: The climate regions that are discussed in the chapter are shown on the map. Locate the wet tropics region. Which color represents it? On which continent is it found?

rays shine on or near the equator throughout the year. No wonder it is always hot in the wet tropics. The average temperature is 80°F (26.7°C).

Brief showers are a part of daily life in the wet tropics. Thunder is often heard. Parts of the wet tropics receive 75 to 150 thunderstorms a year. To a resident of Bogar, located on the Indonesian island of Java, that would seem like nothing. In one year, Bogar recorded 322 days of thunder and rain.

The **growing season** in the wet tropics lasts all year. A growing season is the part of the year when conditions are favorable

for plants to grow. Growing seasons vary widely from place to place around the world and also within countries. The growing seasons of the United States are shown on the map on page 142. Which parts of the United States have the longest growing seasons? Which areas have a growing season of less than three months?

In Chapter 9, you will read more about the dense forests of the wet tropics. These forests supply chemicals, spices, and lumber to the rest of the world. Farmers who live in this region are able to grow bananas, yams, cacao, palms, rubber trees, and manioc in the year-round warmth.

The Wet-and-Dry Tropics

Locate the regions of the wet-and-dry tropics on the climate map on pages 138 and 139. You can see that these tropics are located between 5° and 25° north and south of the equator. Parts of several continents lie within these climate regions. Which continents are they?

Like the wet tropics, these regions are hot all year. There is a very small variation in temperature. Nevertheless, there are seasons in these regions. Because the sun's direct rays do not shine overhead all year long, there is a wet season—summer—and a dry season—winter.

Thick clouds block some of the sun's heat during the summer rains. Therefore, summer is a relatively cool season in this region. The warm, sunny season is the dry winter.

In the tropics, climates are drier and the growing seasons are shorter the farther the area is located from the equator. Sugarcane, cotton, rice, wheat, peanuts, and sorghum (a kind of grass that is grown for its grain and syrup) are among the crops that are grown in the wet-and-dry tropics.

Farther away from the equator but still in the region of the wet-and-dry tropics, stunted trees grow at great distances from one another. The climate is becoming drier.

At the edge of these regions, only a tall, thick grass called **savanna** grows. The wet-and-dry tropics are often called savanna. You will read more in Chapter 9 about the plant and animal life of the savanna.

Ethiopian farms grow crops that are suited to the climate. What clues tell you that this is the wet-and-dry tropics?

This Egyptian village is located in the Sahara. How can you tell that it has not rained there in a long time?

The Dry Tropics

The savanna blends into the third tropical climate regions, which extend from 15° to 35° north and south of the equator. The climate map on pages 138 and 139 shows the vast continental areas of the dry tropics.

Water is precious in these regions. The climate is **arid**, which means that it is "dry" throughout the year.

The average yearly rainfall is under 10 inches (25.4 cm). Remember, however, that average yearly rainfall is calculated over a period of several years. In some years, it might not rain at all, and in other years, almost 20 inches of rain (50.8 cm) may fall.

Then, suddenly, a violent storm may pour several inches of rain in one day. At such times, dry riverbeds begin to resemble mighty rivers but almost immediately, the water evaporates, or sinks into the dry, sandy soil. The skies clear. Did it really happen at all?

In the daytime, it becomes very hot. These are the regions in which some of the world's great deserts, including the Kalihari Desert of southeast Africa and the Sahara of northern Africa are located. The highest temperatures in the world have been recorded in the dry tropics. The average yearly temperature is 95°F (35°C).

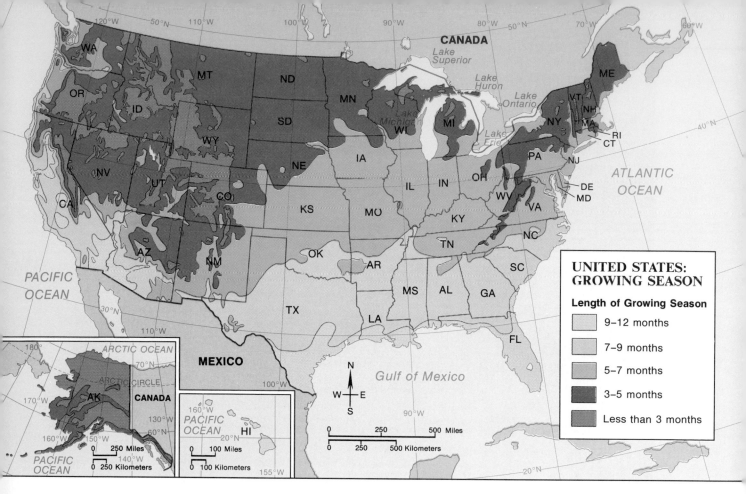

MAP SKILLS: Locate on the map the area in which you live. How many months long is the growing season there? How can you tell this?

Because rainfall is irregular in the dry tropics, the growing season is unreliable. Where a steady water supply—whether natural or based on irrigation—is available, farmers have been able to grow such different crops as cotton, dates, alfalfa, wheat, sesame, and barley.

Lesson 1 Review

Recalling Information

1. What are the three tropical climate regions? Describe them.

2. What is a growing season?

Interpreting Information

3. In the tropic regions, what happens to precipitation and the growing season in areas farther away from the equator?

4. How do the wet tropics and the wet-and-dry tropics differ?

Applying Information

5. Would you recommend major irrigation projects for the dry tropics? Explain.

6. Pick one of the three tropical regions, and discuss the opportunities for and the problems of living there from your point of view.

142

THE MIDLATITUDE CLIMATE REGIONS

Most of the world's people live in the climate zones known as the middle latitudes. Five major climate regions are located in these zones, which extend from 20° to 60° north and south of the equator.

The first region in the midlatitude climate zones is the humid subtropics. Beyond the subtropics lie the humid continental regions, the mediterranean regions, the semiarid regions, the marine west-coast regions, and arid regions.

The Subtropics

A part of each continent has a humid subtropical climate. Look at the climate map on pages 138 and 139. You will notice that the southeastern parts of the United States, China, and southern Japan fall within the subtropical climate region. *Subtropical* means "nearly tropical." Each of the subtropical regions differs from the others, but they all have features in common, too.

As in the wet tropics, summer in the subtropics is hot and humid. The heaviest rains fall during the hot summer months and in early autumn. In the subtropics of the United States, autumn brings large, dangerous storms called **hurricanes**. Many different crops, including tea, fruits, rice, and cotton, grow well in these regions, which have subtropical climates. In wintertime, when temperatures occasionally fall below freezing, citrus growers set up "smudge pots" that contain small fires to warm the air in the citrus groves.

Can You Imagine?

In Crowley, Louisiana, the growing season begins in March or April. By then, it is warm enough to plant rice. Farmers use irrigation systems to keep their fields flooded throughout the season. Then, in July, the harvest begins and by September, all the rice has finally been gathered.

Soon after, the town of Crowley holds a huge party to celebrate the harvest. People come from miles away to enjoy Crowley's annual Rice Festival. Some children plan all year for the big event.

Imagine what it is like. Planning starts months earlier. People choose a rice king and queen and participate in fiddling and rice-eating contests. There are amusement-park rides, exhibits, and parades. For three days, the people of Crowley celebrate the end of the rice-growing season and all their hard work.

The Mediterranean Regions

Around the Mediterranean Sea, in parts of southern California, central Chile, and South Africa, the summers are hot and dry and the winters are mild and wet. These regions, although they exist around the world, are known as mediterranean regions. They are known for their good weather and a long growing season. The high summer temperatures, the long hours of sunlight, and the mild winters are ideal for raising such fruits as olives, grapes, oranges, and grapefruit.

In Greece, the climate is mediterranean. What do you see in this scene that indicates a mediterranean climate?

Locate three signs of frequent rainfall in this photo of the Olympic Rain Forest in the state of Washington.

Where irrigation is used, even more kinds of fruits and vegetables grow.

The amount of precipitation in these regions ranges from 10 to 20 inches (25.4 to 50.8 cm) per year. Most of it falls during the cool months as rain. When rain falls in summer, the water quickly evaporates under hot, sunny skies. Drought occurs during the summers.

Marine West-Coast Climates

People learn to live with the cloudy weather that dominates the marine west-coast regions. These regions are located between 40° and 60° north and south of the equator. Much of Western Europe falls in

these climate regions. Parts of the west coasts of North America and South America, the entire country of New Zealand, and the southeastern tip of Australia are located in the marine west-coast climate regions.

These are regions of rich vegetation and good farms. The state of Washington's Olympic Forest, the rainiest place in North America and one of the most valuable lumber regions in the world, has a marine west-coast climate.

Orographic precipitation (see the diagram on page 108) is a factor in the marine west-coast regions of North America and South America. Annual rainfall can be more than 100 inches (254 cm) a year. Where there

144

are no mountains, for example, in Europe, the average annual rainfall is about 40 inches (101.6 cm). In summer, there is less rainfall than in winter, but no month passes without some rain.

Mild temperatures provide a long growing season. Wheat, potatoes, barley, feed grains, hay, fruits, and nuts grow in these regions, and the abundant greenery also supports a large dairy-farming industry.

The Humid Continental Regions

People in the humid continental climate regions know what all four seasons feel like—quite intensely, too. Continental summers can feel as hot as those in the rainy tropics. Continental winters are cold. The average winter temperatures of areas in the regions fall below freezing, sometimes with catastrophic results.

Look at the climate map on pages 138 and 139. You will notice that the continental regions are located both inland and along the eastern coasts of continents. Notice, too, that these climate regions exist only north of the equator. Air masses that form over large continents are partly responsible for the extreme weather in these regions. Within the midlatitudes of the Southern Hemisphere, there are no landmasses large

Three climate zones are shown on the chart. In which zone is the greatest variety of regions found?

THE WORLD'S CLIMATE

	Climate region	Latitude range	Crops
LOW LATITUDE	Tropical wet	0°–10° N and S	banana, plantain, coconut, manioc, yams, cacao, palms, rubber
	Tropical wet and dry	5°–25° N and S	rice, sorghum, wheat, peanuts, millet, beans, sesame, sugarcane, cotton
	Tropical dry (deserts and steppes)	15°–35° N and S	cotton, rice, sugarcane, dates, alfalfa, sorghum, fruits, corn, wheat, sesame
MIDLATITUDE	Subtropical	20°–35° N and S	wide variety of plants, including fruits, tea, fibers, vegetables, rice, cotton, mulberry trees (to feed silkworms)
	Continental	35°–60° N and S	corn, wheat, sorghum, fruits and vegetables, tobacco, hay
	Mediterranean	30°–45° N and S	wheat, barley, beans, olives, nuts, fruits and vegetables
	Midlatitude dry	30°–50° N and S	wheat, cotton, sorghum, corn, millet
	Marine west coast	40°–60° N and S	barley, feed grains, hay, fruits, nuts
HIGH LATITUDE	Subarctic	50°–70° N	potatoes, rye, oats, hay, cabbage, small fruits. Agriculture limited by short growing season.
	Tundra	60°–75° N	some grasses, mosses, scrub and flowering plants. No true crops.
	Polar	North of Arctic Circle South of Antarctic Circle	none

enough to result in humid continental climate regions.

During spring and summer, the meeting of polar and tropical air causes violent thunderstorms and tornadoes. During 1965, a total of 898 tornadoes were recorded in the United States alone.

Growing seasons vary in the continental regions. The heartland of the United States has a growing season of six and one-half months. The length of this growing season is ideal for raising grains, and corn and wheat are principal crops that are grown in these regions. Fruits, vegetables, sorghum, tobacco, and hay are also grown in continental climate regions.

The Semiarid Regions

You read that *arid* means "dry." *Semi* means "partly." What do this word and this prefix tell you about the semiarid climate regions?

The climate map on pages 138 and 139 shows that semiarid climate regions occur between 30° and 50° north and south of the equator. Notice, too, that these regions occur mostly in the interiors of continents and on the leeward side of mountains. The semiarid places in the middle latitudes receive little moisture from oceans. Average annual rainfall is between 8 and 20 inches (20.3 cm and 50.8 cm), with the maximum amount falling in the summer.

Low precipitation and recurring drought are major concerns of farmers in these regions. Grasses, though, do not need much water. They grow throughout these regions and are used for grazing sheep, goats, and cattle.

The Arid Regions

Deserts, too, are located in the midlatitudes, in central Asia, in parts of Nevada and Utah, and in southern Argentina. These deserts receive fewer than 8 inches (20.3 cm) of rain a year. They have cold winters and great temperature ranges.

Irrigation has allowed some farming of desert regions. **Oases,** too, make farming possible. An oasis is an area within an arid region that has a constant water supply. When water is available in arid regions, farmers are able to grow cotton and some grains, especially wheat and corn.

Lesson 2 Review

Recalling Information
1. What kind of climate does southern California have?
2. Which climate region has the widest temperature range within a year?

Interpreting Information
3. How do summers in the mediterranean climate regions differ from subtropical summers? How are they similar?
4. Why do so many people live in middle-latitude climate regions?

Applying Information
5. In which one of the climates in the middle-latitude region do you live? Describe your climate region.
6. How does your climate region affect what you do throughout the year?

Lesson 3

THE HIGH-LATITUDE CLIMATE REGIONS

In 1909, after numerous expeditions, Matthew Henson and Robert Peary became the first explorers to reach the North Pole. They survived the extreme cold because of the skills that they had learned from the Innuit, popularly known as Eskimo, who had lived in this region for centuries.

A year later, two groups began a race that captured the imaginations of people in Europe and all over the world. Roald Amundsen of Norway and Robert Scott of Great Britain led expeditions to the South Pole. On December 14, 1911, in midsummer, Amundsen and his party reached the pole. One month later, Scott and his party also arrived at the pole. There they found a sympathetic note left for them by the winning Amundsen party.

The lands that so fascinated these explorers are the coldest places on Earth. In contrast to the year-long summer of the tropics, the high-latitude regions are lands where winter weather dominates. In these latitudes, the sun's rays never shine directly overhead.

Three climate regions occur in the high latitudes. The first region poleward of the midlatitude zone is called the subarctic region. Forests grow there, and summer is short and cool. Winter is harsh. Beyond the subarctic is a region known as the **tundra**. It is too cold there for trees to grow. The polar regions, north and south, contain year-round ice and the most forbiddingly cold climates of all.

The Subarctic

The subarctic climate region is located between 50° and 70° north of the equator. Parts of Alaska, Canada, Scandinavia, and the Soviet Union fall within this climate region. Only the Northern Hemisphere has large landmasses within this zone of latitude. In its being limited only to areas north of the equator, the subarctic climate region resembles the humid continental climate region of the midlatitudes.

For at least six months a year, average temperatures in the subarctic region are below freezing. Alaska recorded a temperature of -80°F (-62.2°C). No wonder fish that are caught frozen from the sea are one of the main delicacies of this region.

The cold air does not hold much moisture. Average annual precipitation is about 15 inches (38.1 cm). Although the subarctic is sometimes classified as arid because of its low annual precipitation, there is water available. Snowfalls in winter remain on the ground for months. People can melt snow to drink.

Growing seasons in the subarctic vary from as much as 90 days to as little as 50 days. Summer days have as much as 18 1/2 hours of sunshine, which partly makes up for the shortness of the growing season. Most people would not want to be farmers in the subarctic, but people have been able to grow grains, hay, potatoes, and small fruits in order to feed their families.

Located in the subarctic region is one of the largest forests of pine, fir, and spruce in the world, the **taiga** (TEYE*guh*). You will read more about this very swampy, high-latitude forest in Chapter 9.

147

Though permafrost and short summers make the tundra region poor for human development, many kinds of birds and other animals spend the summer here.

The Tundra

The tundra gets its name from the Russian word that means "frozen plain," which describes the tundra throughout most of the year. The tundra region, as shown on the climate map, falls between 55°N and 85°N of the equator.

Neither winter nor summer is pleasant. Winters are long and cold. For 9 to 10 months of the year, the average temperature is below freezing. For two or three months in winter, the sun does not rise above the horizon because of the tilt of Earth as it orbits the sun. It is almost completely dark, except for starlight, moonlight, and the glimmering lights of the aurora borealis.

The lack of sunlight is compensated for in summer when the sun never sets. Nevertheless, only indirect sun rays ever reach the region. The sun may melt some snow and ice, but the area never becomes warm. Summer temperatures average below 50°F (10°C).

Yearly precipitation, which falls as rain or snow, averages only 10 inches (25.4 cm). Yet, the tundra contains moisture as low temperatures ensure that little evaporation occurs.

As seasons change, the top layer of tundra soil freezes and thaws. Below the top

Snowdrifts that look like sand dunes cover the poles. Both polar and desert regions receive little precipitation.

tica, may be the world's coldest spot. It has a record low of -127°F (-88.3°C). Even in the warmest months, temperatures in polar regions remain well below freezing. Snowfall is light, but it does not melt after it has fallen. Over long periods of time, the snow turns to ice.

Conditions in these regions are more hostile to plants than are the driest deserts. A few simple plants can gain a foothold, but as a rule, nothing can grow where temperatures each month remain below freezing.

soil is **permafrost**, or soil that remains permanently frozen.

During the short summer, the tundra springs to life. The soil above the permafrost thaws and short-rooted plants carpet the land. No crops, however, can be grown in this climate region.

The Polar Regions

The polar climate regions are located north of the Arctic Circle and south of the Antarctic Circle. Ice never melts there.

Interior Greenland, the arctic coasts of North America, Europe, and Asia, and Antarctica have polar climates. Vostok, a Soviet research station located in Antarc-

Lesson 3 Review

Recalling Information

1. What is the most hostile high-latitude climate region? Explain.
2. Which two high-latitude climate regions are located only north of the equator? Why?

Interpreting Information

3. Precipitation in the subarctic is higher than in the tundra. Why is the ground in the tundra wetter in the summer?
4. What do you think the worldwide effect would be if the high latitudes became warm enough for the glaciers to melt?

Applying Information

5. Why do you think people have wanted to explore the South Pole? Would you want to? Why or why not?
6. Compare the taiga and the tundra. Which, from your point of view, would be a better place to live? Why?

Special Feature

Celebrations: Spring Around the World

Spring comes to many parts of the world. Wherever it does, people celebrate.

In the Netherlands, people celebrate *whitsuntide*, or the return of good weather. They may spread hundreds of yellow daffodils, blue irises, and red geraniums all over the town courtyard.

In Greece, children join in the "Procession of the Swallow." They walk from house to house carrying baskets filled with ivy leaves. They trade leaves for fresh eggs. Which other places use eggs as symbols of spring?

If you lived in Egypt, you and your family would take a day off on March 21 to "sniff spring." You would visit the most beautiful spot you could find.

beautiful spot you could find. You might spend the day in a desert oasis or take a trip on the Nile River.

In America and parts of Europe, many children hang May baskets. In the basket, each child may put some candy, a handful of posies, a poem, and the name of the person who is to receive the basket. Children leave baskets outside friends' doors in the evening, hoping that no one sees who delivered them.

In Japan, May brings "kite battle days." Expert kite flyers meet. Their kites have small blades attached to the strings. The best kite flyer is the one who can cut down the other kites.

Whenever spring arrives, it brings feelings of hope and strength, and the exchange of the new for the old. How is spring welcomed in your part of the world?

Skills for Thinking

OBSERVING AND RECORDING DATA

Imagine that you are an ocean biologist. Your ship is anchored in a small bay. You see one fish with fins that look like seaweed. You almost miss seeing a crab whose shell is the same color as the sand. You take notes on what you see. Then, you think about the **data**, or information, that you have recorded.

Observing and recording are important skills. They help you to collect information.

Then, you can study the information and make conclusions. A conclusion is a decision that results from making judgments about specific data.

What Conclusions Can I Make?

If you were an ocean biologist, you might make this conclusion. "The colors of those animals match their surroundings. Such coloring protects them."

Now, imagine that you have just returned from a trip around the world. You have taken notes on many birds and animals that you have seen. Here are a few of your notes.

1. In the tropical forests, large numbers of animals are green. This color is not typical of animals in other climates.
2. The snowy owl is usually found only in the Arctic regions.
3. Tigers are found among the tall trees of tropical forests. They have stripes.
4. The caribou, a polar animal, is brown in summer and white in winter.

Write some of the conclusions that can be made from these observations.

Chapter 7 Review

Summary of Key Facts

In this chapter, you learned that

- the three major climate zones, which are determined by latitude, are divided into climate subzones, or regions.
- growing seasons differ in length by climate region.
- the low-latitude climates—wet tropics, dry tropics, and tropical wet-and-dry climate—vary in amount of precipitation.
- the midlatitude climates include the subtropics, the semiarid, the mediterranean, the marine west-coast, and the humid continental climates.
- the high-latitude climates are the subarctic, the tundra, and the polar climates.
- highlands have cooler climates than the regions in which they occur.

Using Vocabulary

On a separate sheet of paper, write whether each sentence is true or false. Correct it if necessary.

1. An arid region is very moist.
2. A savanna is a tropical grassland.
3. Permafrost is found in the marine west-coast region.
4. The tundra supports large forests of pine, spruce, and fir.

Discussing the Chapter

1. What climate changes would you find if you took a trip through the low-latitude region beginning at the equator and going north?
2. What climate changes would you find if you took a summer trip through the three high-latitude regions?
3. What is the difference between an arid and a semiarid climate?
4. How do highland climates differ from the lowlands around them? Why?
5. Which two midlatitude regions have greater seasonal changes in temperature? What causes these changes?

Reviewing Skills

What conclusions can you make about the climate region of each place, based on the data below?

1. Most of the nation of Surinam lies between the equator and 5°N latitude.
2. In Kristiansund, Norway, there is little vegetation most of the year since the soil is usually frozen.
3. Death Valley lies on the leeward side of a chain of mountains which are located at about 36°N latitude.

Unit 2 Review

Summary of Key Facts

In this unit, you learned that

- the atmosphere is made of various gases that are necessary for all forms of life.
- weather is the condition of the atmosphere over a brief period of time and is determined by moisture, wind, temperature, and air pressure.
- seasons are caused by the tilt of Earth on its axis and its revolution around the sun.
- the angle of the sun's rays determines the amount of heat that will fall on Earth's surface.
- climate is the condition of the atmosphere in a region over a period of years.
- climate is affected by latitude, landforms, winds, and ocean currents.
- jet streams are high-altitude winds that influence weather and climate.
- the low-latitude zone includes the wet, the wet-and-dry, and the dry tropics, each of which is warm but varies in amount of precipitation.
- the middle-latitude zone includes the subtropics, the semiarid, the arid, the humid continental, the mediterranean, and the marine west-coast climate regions.
- the high-latitude zone includes the subarctic, the tundra, and the polar regions.
- highlands have climates different from the regions in which they lie.

Discussing the Unit

1. In what ways is the weather layer of Earth's atmosphere similar to a greenhouse?
2. Weather is a combination of factors. Name and describe each one.
3. Describe jet streams and explain how they affect weather and climate.
4. How is weather affected by the cycle of day and night?
5. How are the climates of the middle latitudes different from those of the high and the low latitudes?

Activities

1. Prove that different surfaces absorb heat at different rates. Expose to sunlight a container each of water, sand, and dark soil. Take each one's temperature close to the surface both before placing the containers in the sunlight and after five hours of exposure to sunshine. Explain your results.
2. Choose a major city somewhere on Earth. Find out its exact latitude, altitude, and surrounding landforms. Then, write a description of the climate of the city, based on your information.

Test

Using Vocabulary

On a separate sheet of paper, write the number of the statement and then the term that most closely matches the statement.

prevailing winds   monsoons
growing season   weather
latitude zone   air pressure
troposphere   mediterranean
trade wind   climate

1. This part of the atmosphere is closest to Earth's surface.
2. This is the atmosphere's weight that pushes down on the surface of Earth.
3. Vegetation is dense in the wet tropics because this lasts all year.
4. These occur every year, bringing heavy rains.
5. With this climate, central Chile's winters are mild and its summers are dry.
6. These bring dry weather to eastern coastal areas in the tropics and wet weather to western coastal areas.
7. This can be described in terms of temperature, air pressure, wind, and humidity.
8. These are regions where climates are similar and are determined by latitude.
9. These are constantly moving around Earth, in similar patterns, due to the Coriolis force.

The Big Question

What determines the climate of an area?

Write your answer in complete sentences. Draw upon the information in this unit to write a good answer.

Using Map Skills

Use the map on page 116 to complete this exercise.
1. Look at the key. What is the symbol for a high-pressure area?
2. What weather does a low-pressure area usually bring?
3. What is the temperature of the air ahead of a cold front?

Identifying a Geographic Theme

Think about the geographic theme of **region** as you complete this exercise.

1. Look at the map on pages 138–139. What climate region do you live in?
2. What are the common characteristics of temperature and moisture in your climate region?

Unit 3

The Living Earth

Look around at our varied planet. Mountains, plains, hills, and plateaus are all parts of our physical Earth. So, too, are air and water. But Earth is composed of much more than these nonliving features. Earth is a "living" planet—one that is filled with many forms of living things. Life on Earth ranges from simple, single-cell plants in the ocean to your complicated human body.

On Earth, all things live together and affect one another. Soil, plants, and animals need one another and their nonliving environments in order to survive.

Concepts

biome   ecosystem
biosphere   interdependent

The Big Question

How do the living and the nonliving parts of Earth interact?

Focus on a Geographic Theme

In this unit you will study the geographic themes of **region** and **human-environment interactions**. As you know, a region is an area defined by certain human or physical characteristics. The theme of human-environment interactions refers to the way people interact with their surroundings.

Throngs of penguins often surround visitors
to the Antarctic.

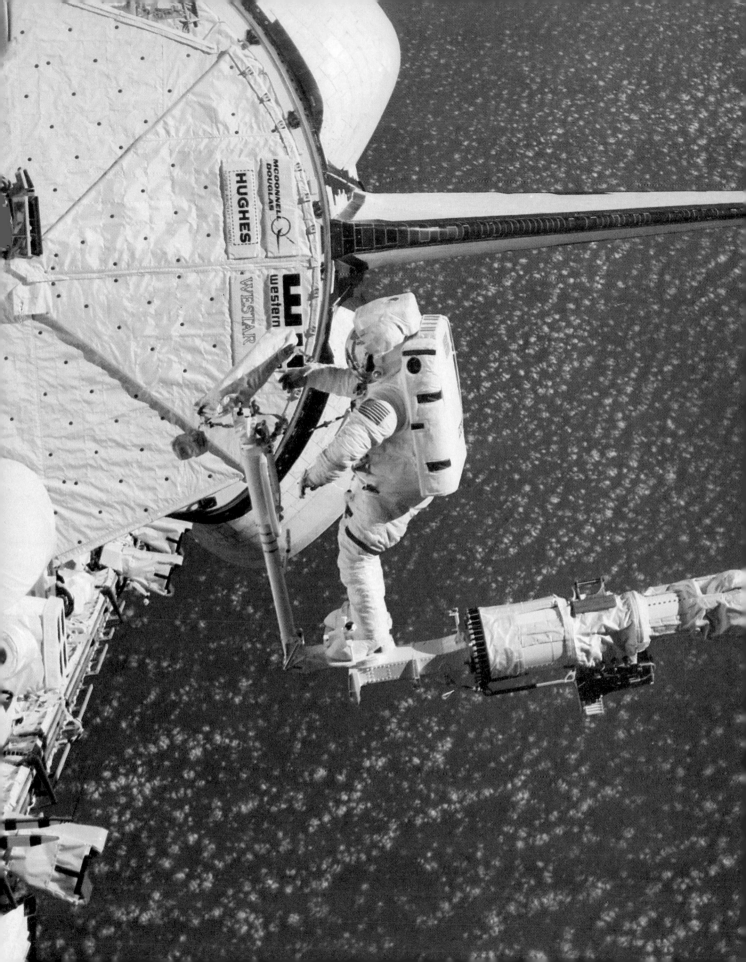

The Life-Support System

Introduction

On the first floor of the Air and Space Museum in Washington, D.C., is the *Apollo 11* space capsule, which in 1969 took astronauts on the first trip to the moon. When astronauts go into space, their spacecraft must be loaded with things that you do not need on an earthbound trip.

Because there is no atmosphere in space, tanks of oxygen had to be put aboard *Apollo 11*. When Neil Armstrong walked on the moon, he carried a backpack that held a small oxygen tank for breathing. The space-

craft also carried water, food, and fuel for the journey. Moreover, *Apollo 11* was outfitted with materials that shielded the astronauts from the sun's harmful rays.

Scientists and engineers have learned how to support life in space. Except for sunlight which helps to power some spacecraft operations, all other means of supporting life in space come from Earth. Earth is the only place that we know of that has a natural life-support system.

The life-support system aboard a spacecraft can support only a few people for a short period of time. The life-support system of Earth has supported billions of people and other living things for billions of years. In this chapter, you will find out about Earth's remarkable system for supporting life.

◀ **Everything needed to support life is found on Earth. Which of these things must people bring with them into outer space?**

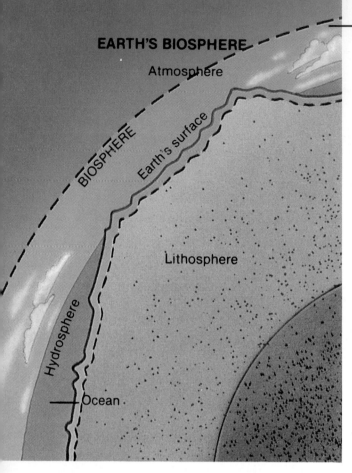

EARTH'S BIOSPHERE

Atmosphere

BIOSPHERE

Earth's surface

Lithosphere

Hydrosphere

Ocean

Which part of the biosphere is the thickest—the lithosphere or the atmosphere?

EARTH IS A SYSTEM

Scientists have used telescopes to gaze billions of miles into space. They have discovered stars and galaxies. They have studied other planets, moons, comets, and bands of asteroids. They have concluded that there is no body in space that is more impressive than Earth. As far as we know, Earth is the only place where the right conditions exist to support life.

The Biosphere

All of Earth's plants and animals—everything, from creatures so small that you need a microscope to see them, to huge whales—live in a thin zone called the **biosphere** (BY*oh*sfeer). The biosphere includes a thin layer of Earth's land, the oceans, and the lower part of the atmosphere, where life exists. It extends only a few miles above and below the surface of Earth.

All parts of the biosphere are interdependent. This means that the atmosphere (the air zone), the **hydrosphere** (the water zone), and the **lithosphere** (the land zone) interact with each other and are linked together as a system. What happens in one part of the system affects the system as a whole.

The entire biosphere is too complex a subject to study all at once. Scientists often study a small part of a specific environment, such as a pond, a forest, or even a city park. All living and nonliving things that exist together in such a specific environment form an **ecosystem**.

As in the biosphere as a whole, all parts of an ecosystem are interdependent. Every plant and animal in an ecosystem—and even a nonliving thing such as soil—influences and is influenced by the other parts of the system. Change or take away any one part of an ecosystem and you change the ecosystem as a whole.

The Nonliving Ecosystem's Parts

An ecosystem is made up of living and nonliving parts. The nonliving parts of an ecosystem include sunlight, water, air, soil, and rocks. You will read about the living parts of an ecosystem later in this chapter. As you will see, each part plays an important part in making the system work.

The sun is not only the source of energy for Earth's water cycle and weather systems, but it is also the energy source for every ecosystem. You will read later about how green plants use energy from the sun to make their own food. Other forms of life depend on these plants for their energy.

Another important nonliving part of an ecosystem is water. On a hot day, you know that water is necessary to your life. Water, the most common substance on Earth, has to be available in order for life to exist.

In Chapter 4, you read about the water cycle. You learned that water from Earth's surface enters the atmosphere and comes back to Earth again. Plants and animals, too, are a part of this system. All living things are made up mostly of water. For example, 65 percent of the human body is water. All living things use and release water into their environments.

Water provides a home for living things. Many insects lay their eggs in or on water. Fish spend their whole lives in water, as do such mammals as whales and porpoises. Some plants grow only in water.

Rocks and soil are also parts of an ecosystem. Soil is especially important because most plants need it to grow. You will learn more about soil in the next lesson.

The Living Parts of an Ecosystem

An ecosystem is composed of three kinds of living members. Each plays an important role in the system. One kind, producers, consists of living things that use the nonliving parts of the system to make food. Most producers are green plants. Using energy

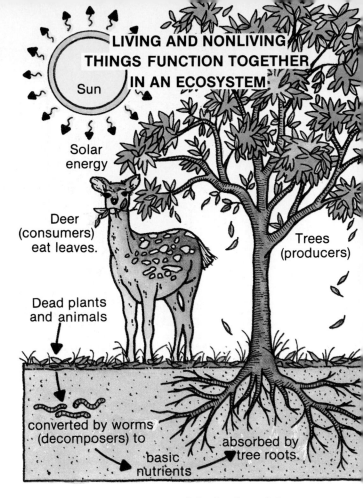

LIVING AND NONLIVING THINGS FUNCTION TOGETHER IN AN ECOSYSTEM

Sun

Solar energy

Deer (consumers) eat leaves.

Trees (producers)

Dead plants and animals

converted by worms (decomposers) to basic nutrients

absorbed by tree roots.

What other consumers might be found in this woodland ecosystem?

from the sun, they take water, carbon dioxide from the air, and minerals from the soil to make food. This chemical process of producing food is called **photosynthesis** (*foh＊toh＊*SIHN*＊thuh＊suhs*).

Another kind of living member of the ecosystem cannot use the sun's energy to make its own food. These living things get their food by eating. They are called consumers. They consume, or eat, other living things as food. Some consumers eat plants; some eat animals, which have eaten plants; and some eat both plants and animals. Therefore, the consumers depend on the producers for their food, either directly or indirectly.

An earthworm feeds on dead plant material beneath the soil. It turns over as much as 11 tons of soil per year.

Although the consumers are dependent on other members of the system, they contribute to the system, too. When consumers get rid of wastes or die, they make a contribution by returning vital elements, such as minerals, to the system. These elements enrich the soil, and thereby support the further growth of plants. In fact, without consumers to eat producers, Earth would be overgrown with plants. Rabbits, mice, and insects are some plant-eating consumers.

For the recycling to occur, however, the third kind of living member of an ecosystem, the decomposers, is needed. Decomposers live on the remains of living things that have died. They use these remains for their energy. In the process, they break the dead matter down into its essential minerals. These minerals are returned to the soil and can be used by the producers to make food. Thus, the decomposers complete a food cycle which begins with the producers. Among decomposers are found earthworms, molds, mushrooms, and bacte-

ria. Undoubtedly, you have seen examples of the important work that they do.

Lesson 1 Review

Recalling Information

1. What two categories of things make up an ecosystem?
2. What is the power source of the biosphere?

Interpreting Information

3. What would probably happen in an ecosystem that had lost all of its decomposers?
4. What is the importance of water to life on Earth?

Applying Information

5. Choose an ecosystem that you are familiar with, and describe it.
6. In what ways might you change the ecosystem that you have just described?

Lesson 2

SOIL

At some time when you were younger, you probably made mud pies. Perhaps you planted a garden. The material for your mud pies and the matter in which you planted seeds was soil.

Soil is the top layer of Earth's land, the part of the lithosphere that supports plant life. Soil is a mixture of tiny bits of rock and the remains of living things. Soil is one of the nonliving parts of most ecosystems.

Soil is home to most forms of plant life, as well as to worms, insects, small mammals, and many kinds of tiny living things called microorganisms. Soil provides the minerals that plants need to grow and to make food. It also stores the plants' supply of water.

Some soils are more **fertile**, or better for growing plants, than others. To understand why some soils are more fertile than others, we must first understand completely how soil is formed.

How Soil Forms

In Chapter 3, you learned that weathering is a process that contributes to the making of soil. Soil is composed largely of matter that had been rock. The weathering process through which rock becomes the primary ingredient of soil occurs in several ways. Ice plays a big part. So do wind and water.

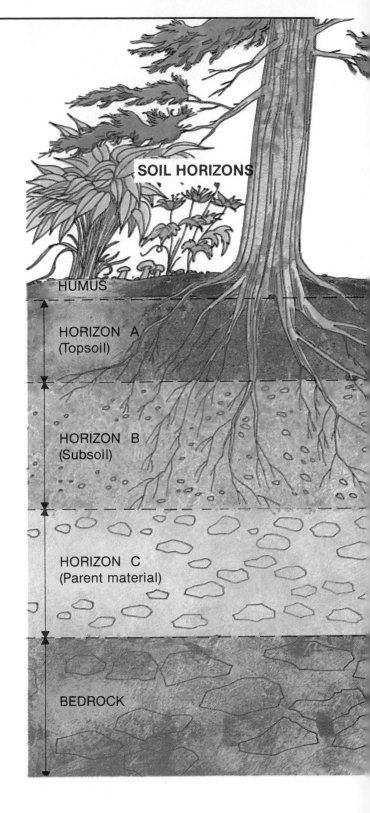

SOIL HORIZONS

HUMUS

HORIZON A
(Topsoil)

HORIZON B
(Subsoil)

HORIZON C
(Parent material)

BEDROCK

A tree's roots may penetrate both topsoil and subsoil. What benefits might it obtain by tapping two layers of soil?

Over many thousands of years, rocks are gradually worn down, fragment by fragment, into small particles of soil through the work of these agents.

Weathering is aided by both chemical and physical reactions. Some plants that attach themselves to bare rock give off an acid that slowly causes rock to dissolve and to crumble. Other plants take root in the small cracks in rocks. As they grow, they enlarge the cracks and help to split the rocks.

All of these weathering processes result in the small, grainy particles that we think of as soil. Before such particles can be classified as soil, however, one thing must be added—the dead plant and animal matter.

The remains of dead plants and animals are changed into a dark, rich substance called humus (HYOO*muhs*). This process of change is caused by the actions of such decomposers as earthworms and bacteria, which feed on dead plants and animals. The mixture of humus and the small, grainy particles that are produced by the weathering process of rock is what we call soil.

Humus increases the amount of water that topsoil can hold, and it contains most of the minerals that growing plants need. To a large extent, the amount of humus in the soil determines how fertile the soil is.

The kinds of minerals that are in the soil are also a factor. Decomposition supplies soil with some of these minerals. River flood plains and deltas, about which you read earlier, often possess very rich soil, especially when the river overflows its banks seasonally. The Nile, the Euphrates, and the Huang He are three rivers whose overflows enrich the soil around them.

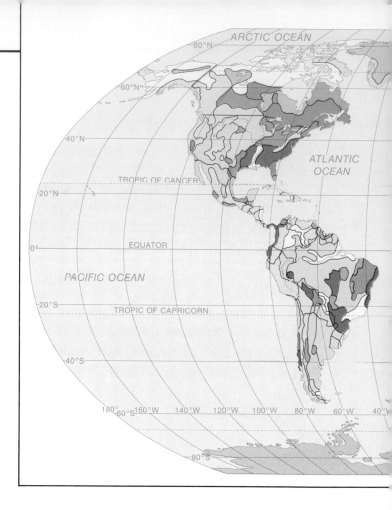

The Structure of Soil

A cross section of soil which shows layers that are distinct from one another is called a soil horizon. Look at the drawing on page 163 to see how these layers appear in a soil horizon.

The topsoil, or uppermost layer, is called the "A" horizon. This is where humus is found. Below it is another layer called the subsoil, or the "B" horizon. The subsoil contains rich nutrients and minerals that rainfall has washed out, or *leached*, from the topsoil. Beneath the subsoil is the "C" horizon. This layer contains hundreds of small pieces of broken-up rock like that from which the soil was originally made.

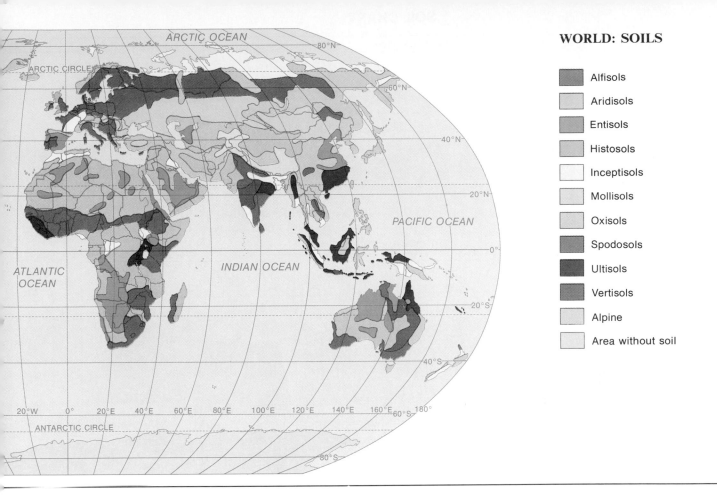

Alfisols

Aridisols

Entisols

Histosols

Inceptisols

Mollisols

Oxisols

Spodosols

Ultisols

Vertisols

Alpine

Area without soil

MAP SKILLS: Aridisols are desert soils. Where in Africa are they found? Where in North America? Are these regions alike?

The original rock, the climate, and the kinds and amounts of plant and animal waste matter combine in many ways to produce a great variety of soils in the world. Warm, humid climates are ideal for the growth of decomposers, which quickly consume large amounts of dead material. The soil in a tropical forest is composed mainly of humus, although heavy rains leach out many of its minerals. In a cold climate, on the other hand, the decomposers are fewer in number and work more slowly. The soil in arctic climates has little humus.

Soils can be classified in several ways. One system of classifying them, which was developed by soil scientists of the U.S.

Department of Agriculture, is shown in the chart on page 166.

As you can see, soils range from poor to rich and from thin to thick. Some are stony. Some are full of clay. Desert soils tend to be poor. So do certain forest soils.

Grasslands such as the Great Plains have rich fertile soils. As grass dies, it produces a rich humus. The soils of the Great Plains are some of the deepest and the richest in the world. This level of fertility is one of the major reasons that the area that is called the American "heartland" is able to produce such large crops.

The map above shows where the different kinds of soil are found. Examine the map.

SOIL CHART

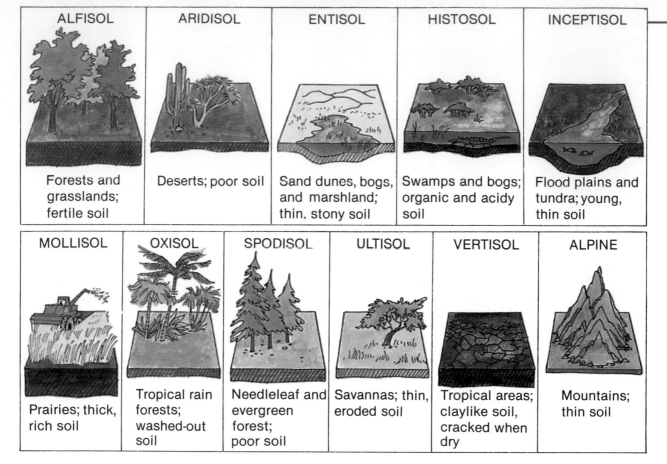

ALFISOL	ARIDISOL	ENTISOL	HISTOSOL	INCEPTISOL
Forests and grasslands; fertile soil	Deserts; poor soil	Sand dunes, bogs, and marshland; thin, stony soil	Swamps and bogs; organic and acidy soil	Flood plains and tundra; young, thin soil

MOLLISOL	OXISOL	SPODISOL	ULTISOL	VERTISOL	ALPINE
Prairies; thick, rich soil	Tropical rain forests; washed-out soil	Needleleaf and evergreen forest; poor soil	Savannas; thin, eroded soil	Tropical areas; claylike soil, cracked when dry	Mountains; thin soil

Why might areas of tropical rain forest be unsuited for agriculture? What types of soil might be suitable?

What other areas of the world have deep, rich soils? What is the scientific name for rich prairie soil?

Compare the soil chart and the map. What is the soil of swamps and bogs called? What is it like? Where in the world are there large areas of swamps and bogs? How can you tell?

Lesson 2 Review

Recalling Information

1. What elements form soil?
2. What is a soil horizon? What are its main layers?

Interpreting Information

3. Is soil still being made today? How?
4. Which climate regions have the most fertile soil? Which have the least fertile soil?

Applying Information

5. Is the soil where you live good for farming? How can you tell?
6. Although you water them carefully, the potted plants near your window are not growing well. What might be the reason? What can you do to help the plants to grow?

THE WORLD OF PLANTS

Wherever you live, there are plants. The kinds and the numbers of plants vary from place to place. The only places where there are no growing plants are the polar ice caps. Even they have pollen and seeds.

The almost 30 million species, or kinds, of plants that grow on Earth can be divided into three major groups. They are flowering plants, nonflowering plants, and simple plants. In this lesson, you will learn about the three major groups of plants.

Flowering Plants

Most plants that are familiar to us are flowering plants. Their scientific name, angiosperm (AN*jee*oh*spurm), means "covered seed." All flowering plants produce seeds. Fruits, vegetables, many kinds of trees, herbs, shrubs, and cacti are all angiosperms. Seeds can be scattered by wind, by birds, or by other animals, allowing new plants to grow miles away from the "parent" plant. Seeds develop in the flower.

Nonflowering Plants

The first plants to develop seeds did not have flowers or seed coverings. Their seeds developed on open leaves that were clustered into cones. As the seeds ripened, the cones opened up. This process caused the seeds to fall onto the soil. Pine trees are an example of this kind of plant, which is called a gymnosperm (JIHM*noh*spurm). Cypress, spruce, fir, cedar, and the giant redwood are all gymnosperms.

California's bristlecone pines are the world's oldest trees. Some are 4,000 years old.

Simple Plants

This category includes a large number of very different plant species that do not produce seeds. There are many more species of simple plants than there are seed-producing plants. Although some can grow fairly large, most are small. In fact, many of them are microscopic.

Moss is one example of a simple plant. "To know which way is north, look for the moss on a tree." This piece of folk wisdom is generally true in the Northern Hemisphere. Moss grows well in moist, shady places. North of the equator, the shadier side of a tree is its northern side.

TYPES OF PLANTS

TYPE	DESCRIPTION	EXAMPLES
Flowering plants (angiosperm)	Produce covered seeds that develop in the flower.	Corn, Elm, Rose
Nonflowering plants (gymnosperm)	Produce seeds that sit on an open leaf that is shaped like a cone.	Cypress, Spruce, Fir
Simple plants	Produce no seeds or food. Rely on living and dead plants and animals for food.	Mushrooms, Lichens, Moss, Seaweed
Broadleaf	Plants with broad-shaped leaves.	Maple, Oak
Needleleaf (coniferous)	Plants with needle-shaped or scaly leaves; cone-bearing trees.	Fir Pine
Deciduous	Trees or shrubs whose leaves fall off seasonally or in times of drought.	Oak Maple
Evergreen	Trees or shrubs whose leaves stay green throughout the year.	Pine, Fir, Rubber
Xerophyte	Plants that are adapted to life in dry environments.	Saguaro cactus Creosote bush

What is the difference between a shrub and a tree? From which do we get more resources?

Algae (AL*jee) are simple plants that grow in water, in soil, and on the bark of trees. An alga can have only one cell, or it can be composed of many cells.

Fungi are decomposers. Fungi range from simple molds, mildews, and yeast to large mushrooms. Fungi do not make their own food. They rely on living and dead plants and on animals for food.

Some of the algae that live on land form partnerships with fungi. Together, they form lichens (LY*kehnz), which live in cold and alpine climates. The two plants help each other to survive. Algae produce food, and fungi store water.

Other Categories of Plants

Botanists are scientists who study plants. Besides classifying plants as angiosperms, gymnosperms, or simple plants, they classify plants in other ways, too. They classify them by size and by the kinds of stems and leaves that plants have. They also classify plants by the different kinds of adaptations that plants make to their environments. *To adapt* means "to adjust to the circumstances of the environment." Look at the chart on this page. It shows some of the classifications that botanists use to distinguish and to describe plants.

Trees have one main trunk from which

branches grow. Trees are either angiosperms or gymnosperms. Because the leaves of angiosperm trees are broad, they are called **broadleaf** trees. Oak, maple, birch, and elm are examples of broadleaf trees.

If there are cold winters where you live, you see leaves drop from broadleaf trees every autumn. Trees that lose their leaves in certain seasons are called **deciduous** trees. There are also deciduous trees that lose their leaves in a dry season.

The leaves of most gymnosperm trees are needle shaped or scaly, and they belong to a group that is called **needleleaf** trees. Gymnosperms are also called conifers because they have cones.

Trees that stay green all year are called **evergreen** trees. Many people mistakenly think that *evergreen* means the same thing as *needleleaf*. While it is true that needleleaf trees retain their leaves throughout the year, so, too, do some broadleaf trees. In warm, wet climates, many broadleaf trees are evergreen.

Shrubs, like trees, have woody stems, but instead of one main trunk, they have several stems that branch near the ground. Many common garden bushes, such as forsythia and most roses, are shrubs. Shrubs can be deciduous or evergreen.

To a cook, an herb is a leaf that is used to flavor food. To a botanist, however, herbs include all green plants that have fleshy stems and that die off at least down to their roots during the cold or the dry season. Many common vegetable and flower plants, such as marigolds, zinnias, tomatoes, and beans, are herbs.

What do lawn grass, wheat, sugarcane, rice, corn, and bamboo have in common? They are all grasses. Grasses are angiosperms with leaves that are partly wrapped around the stem of the plant.

All plants need water to survive. Plants that grow in deserts have adapted to dryness. Some, like cactus plants, have very thick, fleshy stems that store water from the quick, heavy rains that fall from time to time in the desert. Some have stems and leaves with thick, waxy coatings to prevent water from evaporating. Plants that have adapted to life in dry environments are called xerophytes (ZEE*roh*feyets).

Lesson 3 Review

Recalling Information
1. Describe the seeds of an angiosperm and of a gymnosperm.
2. Describe four kinds of simple plants.

Interpreting Information
3. In what way are seeds an effective means of plant reproduction?
4. Describe how we use stored sun energy from plants.

Applying Information
5. Which kind of plant that you have read about grows best where you live?
6. Scientists grow plants without soil in buildings without windows. What do they have to provide in order for the plants to grow?

Special People

Gifford Pinchot

When Gifford Pinchot took over the forest service in the early 1900s, many Americans thought that there was an unlimited supply of trees. Paper mills and construction firms often used up entire forests.

Pinchot studied botany at college. Later, he explored the forests of Europe. The traditional method of forestry that was followed by many European countries permitted trees to be cut down only bit by bit. This method ensured that trees would continue to reproduce, to grow, and to be available for use in the future.

Pinchot tried to convince Americans to change the way in which they used forests. Instead of stripping the land of all trees, he suggested cropping it. *Cropping a forest* means "taking some trees and leaving others." Cropping preserves the natural features of the land and allows a forest to continue to grow.

President Theodore Roosevelt approved of Pinchot's views. He asked Pinchot to advise him on matters of conservation. The two men quickly became friends. With Roosevelt's help, Pinchot set up a program that made sure that American businesses used methods that preserved our nation's forests.

Skills for Thinking

CHOOSING APPROPRIATE LIBRARY SOURCES

Where do you look first for information for a research report? You probably begin with an encyclopedia, which is a good place to start. The volumes of a general encyclopedia are a treasury of facts about important people, places, and ideas. They also provide valuable background information on most topics.

Don't stop there. A library has a wealth of reference materials to choose from. If you choose sources carefully, you'll have a rich collection of facts and ideas to help you to write an informative report.

What Are the Best Sources?

- Use encyclopedias on special subjects that concentrate on the topic of your report. For example, suppose that your report is about *hydroponics*, the growing of plants in water instead of in soil. You might look in either a nature or a science encyclopedia. If you were writing about the work of Ansel Adams, who photographed the natural beauty of the American West, you might check the information in an encyclopedia of art.
- Refer to the subject cards in the card catalog to find titles of books that are related to your report topic. For example, if you were writing about how the delta of

the Nile River was formed, you might look under *Nile*, *delta*, or *rivers*.

- If your report were about a particular person, such as conservationist Gifford Pinchot, you might refer to the subject cards in the card catalog to find a book about the person. You might also go to references on people, such as the *Dictionary of American Biography* or *Who's Who*.

- Many libraries have special files that contain materials that are too small or too fragile to be put on the regular shelves. These may contain pamphlets, photographs, or articles that have been cut out of newspapers or magazines. In these files, you may find just the information that you want. If you were writing about a blight that was damaging local trees, you might find useful information in your local paper.
- Look for magazine articles on your report topic. Use the *Readers' Guide to Periodical Literature*. Find the general subject headings, such as *gardening* or *Ansel Adams*. Under the subject headings are listed the titles of the articles, the names of the magazines in which the

articles were published, the dates of the magazine issues that contain the articles, and the page numbers on which the articles appear.
- Refer to almanacs, atlases, and gazetteers for maps or for facts about place names, routes, and locations. If you were writing about the Nile Delta, for example, you would want to look at an atlas.

It is customary to look at more than one reference in preparing a report. Deciding which ones will be more helpful than others is a skill that takes time to acquire.

One way to start is to take a tour of your library. Note where the various reference materials are kept and how they are arranged. Look through them, and note the kinds of information that each contains. Practice looking for something that you want to know more about. Never be afraid to ask for help. Learning where and how to find information is one of the most valuable study skills that you will ever develop.

Now, put some of what you have learned into action. Suppose that two new students have asked you to help them to find library resources for their reports.

Janet's report is to tell about conservationist John Muir. Matthew is writing about organic gardening. Make a list of three suggestions for Janet and three for Matthew. Do not repeat the same reference sources. Try to be as specific as possible. Give the kind of help and advice that you would want from a friend.

You can base your suggestions on what you have learned from this selection. If you know of other references in your library, you may want to suggest them, too.

Chapter 8 Review

Summary of Key Facts

In this chapter, you learned that

- the biosphere is the thin layer of Earth in which life (plants and animals) exists.
- the three parts of Earth's biosphere—the atmosphere (air), the hydrosphere (water), and the lithosphere (land)—are interdependent.
- an ecosystem is made up of all living and nonliving things that exist together in an environment.
- different soils are created by different kinds of rocks and climate and by the remains of different kinds and numbers of plants and animals.
- the almost 30 million species of plants can be divided into three major groups— angiosperms, gymnosperms, and simple plants.

Using Vocabulary

On a separate sheet of paper, write the term that will correctly complete each sentence.

ecosystem   deciduous
biosphere   broadleaf
soil horizon   evergreen
photosynthesis   decomposers

1. ____ trees lose their leaves in certain seasons.
2. An ____ is the group of living and non-living things that exist together in a specific environment.
3. Green plants make food through ____ .
4. Angiosperm trees are ____ trees.
5. Distinct soil layers make a ____ .
6. Trees that do not lose their leaves in certain seasons are ____ trees.
7. The zone of life on Earth is the ____ .
8. Molds and mushrooms are examples of ____ .

Discussing the Chapter

1. What are the nonliving parts of an ecosystem?
2. How do the living parts of an ecosystem depend on sun, water, air, and soil in order to survive?
3. How are producers, consumers, and decomposers interdependent?
4. What determines how fertile soil is? How does leaching make soil less fertile?

Reviewing Skills

Make a list of sources that you would use if you were writing a report on the plants of the Gobi Desert.

Plant and Animal Communities

Introduction

"Why don't you review what you'll need?" Ms. Jackson suggested.

Ms. Jackson runs a pet store. She has just been telling Don how to put together an aquarium.

"Well," Don began, "I'll need a tank that is filled with water, and I'll need a small light bulb to keep the water heated. And the fish, of course, plus food for the fish." Don paused. "I'll need a few snails, too," he continued. "They'll feed on the slime that collects in the tank."

"Algae," Ms. Jackson said. "The snails feed on algae, the tiny plant life that grows in still water. But you're right. It can look slimy when it builds up. The snails will keep that from happening."

"Then, I'll want some plants that grow underwater," Don added.

"Do you remember what the plants do?" Ms. Jackson asked.

"Besides looking nice, they keep the water supplied with oxygen for the fish to breathe. But what do the plants feed on?"

"The waste products from the fish," Ms. Jackson replied. "So you see, everything in your tank works together to support life. Do you remember what I called an aquarium that works like that?"

"You said it was like a small ecosystem," said Don.

"Right," said Ms. Jackson.

A good aquarium closely recreates the natural environment of fish. What does each part of this aquarium contribute?

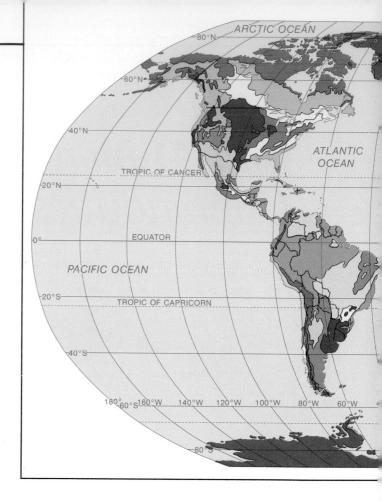

Lesson 1

PLANTS AND ANIMALS TOGETHER

An aquarium is a small world of its own. It is like an ocean or a lake that is enclosed in glass. Everything that lives and grows in an aquarium works together to support its community in the environment of water. An aquarium forms a small and simplified ecosystem.

Every plant and animal on Earth lives in its own special environment. Scientists call this close match between a living thing and its special environment a fit. If a plant or an animal is taken out of its natural environment, it may have trouble surviving.

Plants and animals have special ways of fitting within their special environments. For instance, a cactus plant stores water in its stem to sustain it through many months of dry weather.

Animals fit within their environments, too. Some have thick fur or feathers to keep them warm in cold climates. Others have ways of keeping cool in hot places. An elephant's big ears, for example, form a kind of natural air-conditioning system. They provide a large surface for the wind to blow over and to cool the animal's skin. Each animal fits within or is adapted to living in a special **habitat**, or environment.

In Chapter 7, you learned that the world can be divided into climate zones and regions. In this chapter, you will discover a way to divide the world into environmental regions—regions in which special kinds of plants and animals exist. These regions are called **biomes**.

What Is a Biome?

A biome is a community of plant and animal life that is held together by a common environment. As in any community, its members—individual plants and animals—depend on one another. In many ways, a biome is like an aquarium. However, it includes a whole region of Earth's surface, not just a tiny bit of it. As in an aquarium, however, everything in a biome is connected. As you may have guessed, a biome is an ecosystem. It is a particularly special kind of ecosystem that supports a special kind of plant and animal life. The kinds of plants in a biome are determined by the availability of sunlight, warmth, water, and types of soil, among other things.

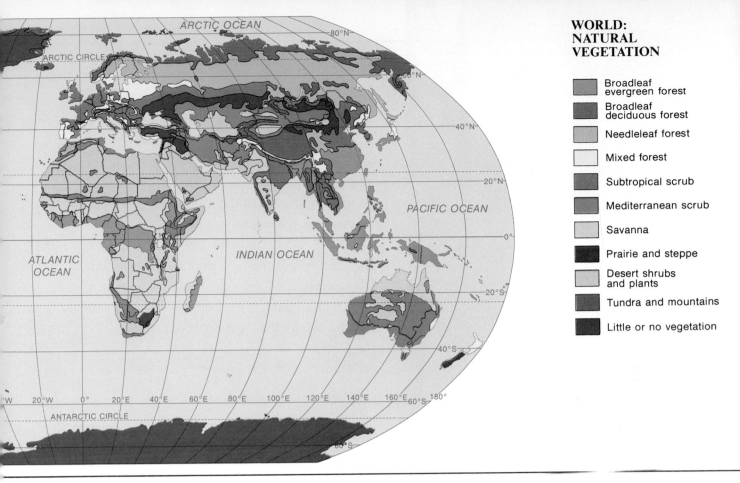

Broadleaf
evergreen forest

Broadleaf
deciduous forest

Needleleaf forest

Mixed forest

Subtropical scrub

Mediterranean scrub

Savanna

Prairie and steppe

Desert shrubs
and plants

Tundra and mountains

Little or no vegetation

MAP SKILLS: Needleleaf forests grow only in the Northern Hemisphere. Where are broadleaf evergreens found?

Animal life, too, is influenced by these same factors because many animals depend on plants for food. As you know, even animals that feed on other animals depend on plants. A lion, for instance, may feed on a zebra, but the zebra feeds on grass. Without the grass, there would be no zebra, and without the zebra (or some other grass eater), there would be no lion.

Just as animals depend on plants, plants depend on animals. For instance, bees feed on nectar, a sweet liquid from flowers. As they move from flower to flower, they pick up bits of pollen from each flower and spread them to other flowers. Pollen enables flowers to form seeds that will grow into new plants. Thus, within a biome, plants and animals interact with one another and are interdependent.

Kinds of Biomes

Earth can be divided into a number of major biomes, or types of land environments, because water, warmth, soil type, and sunlight are distributed differently from place to place. Water environments—ocean or lake regions—are also ecosystems, but they are not referred to as biomes. You will learn about these water regions in Lesson 5.

The major kinds of biomes are forests,

The giraffe eats leaves. What might prey on the giraffe?

grasslands, tundra, and deserts. The map on pages 176 and 177 shows the location of the major forests, grasslands, tundra, and desert regions. As you read about biomes, continue to refer to the map.

As you learned in Chapter 6, warmth varies with latitude and position of Earth in relation to the sun. Water varies with nearness to a body of water and with precipitation. In polar regions, availability of light is also seasonal. Therefore, if you know where a biome is on Earth, you can predict its main vegetation, or plant population.

Forests exist in climate regions with plentiful rainfall because trees need a lot of water. There are forests in the tropics, in the midlatitudes, and in the high latitudes.

Grasslands exist where rainfall is moderate—not enough for trees, but enough for grass and small shrubs. There are grasslands in the tropics and in the midlatitudes but not in the high latitudes.

Deserts occur in both the tropics and in the midlatitudes where rainfall is less than 10 inches (25.4 cm) per year. In areas of low rainfall and high latitude, tundra, not desert, occurs because it is cold, not hot.

Lesson 1 Review

Recalling Information

1. Define a *biome*.
2. What are the four main biomes?

Interpreting Information

3. Which climate element do you think is most responsible for differences among the four main kinds of biomes? Explain.
4. Maps generally show clear dividing lines between one region and another. On a vegetation map, for example, you can see where the forest ends and a grassland begins. What do you think the natural environment is like at the point where the two regions meet?

Applying Information

5. Biomes are natural environments. What is the natural environment where you live?
6. How is your life different from that of other living things in your environment?

Lesson 2

FORESTS—TREES AND MORE TREES

When you hear the word *forest*, do you think of trees? Trees grow in forests, but forests are more than trees. Forests include a wide variety of plant and animal life.

Plant growth in a forest can be divided into five (top-to-bottom) layers. The top layer is the **canopy**. It consists of the top branches of the tallest trees. The canopy stretches toward the sun to collect sunlight. Like an umbrella, this thick canopy of leaves keeps much of the sunlight from reaching the lower layers of plant life.

Below the canopy is the **understory**, which mostly consists of shorter trees that grow in shade and of saplings, or young trees. Some of these trees may grow to become part of the canopy.

Lower still is the shrub layer. As you know, shrubs are low, bushy plants with woody stems. Below this layer is the herb layer, which includes ferns, grasses, and wild flowers.

The lowest layer is the **forest floor**, which is usually covered by dead leaves and twigs, or litter. Mosses and fungi grow among the dead leaves and twigs on the forest floor.

The animals of a forest may occupy one or more of these five layers, or levels. Birds make their homes in the canopy and at lower levels. Some climbing animals, such as squirrels and monkeys, live and feed at the upper levels. Insects can be found at every level. Some prefer the forest floor. Others climb or fly to higher levels. Some of the animals never leave the canopy.

The plant life and the animal life in any ecosystem depend on two main sets of conditions: how warm or cold it is and how wet or dry it is. Generally speaking, warmth increases biological activity or growth; wetness increases it, and dryness decreases it. So, you will have the greatest biological activity where it is warmest and wettest, and the least where it is coldest and driest. A warm but dry place or a cool but wet place will be somewhere in between.

Tropical Rain Forests

As you probably know, tropical rain forests are located in the warm, humid areas of the tropics. Because they enjoy the warmest, wettest, and longest growing season (it continues all year), these lush forests support more species of plants and animals than any other land ecosystem. They are dominated by broadleaf trees, which remain green all year long. Along the Amazon River in Latin America is the biggest tropical rain forest in the world. Let us take a walk through a tropical rain forest.

It is early morning, but the air is already warm and heavy with moisture. The broad, green leaves of evergreen trees and shrubs are dripping the last few drops of water from an early morning rain.

The steamy climate seems to encourage growth. Everything is big—tall trees with large leaves form a dense canopy and understory over your head. Many of the vines that grow up the trees support bright flowers that are as big as baseballs. Few plants grow at the shrub and the herb levels. The thick, leafy canopy blocks the sunlight and

prevents plants at lower levels from growing tall.

You hear sounds from every direction. Birds of all kinds are tweeting, chirping, hooting, whistling, and making noises that you never expected to hear from a bird. From time to time, a howler monkey, high in the trees, adds its voice to the chorus.

Other sounds, you suspect, come from insects. They are everywhere. You see spiders that are the size of a fist, beetles as big as a mouse, and things that you cannot even name. You know that there are huge snakes nearby that can swallow a monkey whole. Maybe you had better move on.

Broadleaf Deciduous Forests

Now, you have moved north and are in a middle-latitude forest. Much of the eastern United States is situated in this broadleaf deciduous forest biome. It is colder here than in the rain forest. The growing season becomes shorter as you move north. The trees are all deciduous. They lose their leaves in fall and put out new ones in spring. Life here must fit within or "be adapted to" the changing seasons.

It is summer, and the trees—oak, elm, hickory, ash, and many more—are in full leaf. As in the tropical rain forest, a canopy covers the highest level, but the leaves are thinner and smaller. More sunlight filters through the leaves to lower levels. This forest has a heavy understory and plenty of growth at the shrub and herb levels.

How is the rain forest biome at the top similar to the deciduous forest biome shown below? How are they different?

Still, there are paths through the growth. You suspect that deer and other animals have created the paths in their daily search for food and water. You look for other animal life. A few squirrels are climbing the trees, which also contain many birds.

You know that if you come across a pond or a stream, you will find more animals—frogs, turtles, maybe even a beaver. Slapping at an insect that has just bitten you, you note that these creatures are plentiful, too.

The seasons change in this forest. Squirrels and chipmunks are already stocking up on food to last them through the winter. It would be fun to observe this forest during a full year, but you have other forests to see in parts of the world with a milder climate.

Mediterranean Scrub Forest

Scrub is a good name for it, you think. Those thick, woody bushes look like shrubs. They are really trees that have been dwarfed by the lack of rain. The plants put out very long roots in order to obtain moisture from deep below the ground's surface. The mediterranean climate is slightly cooler and more seasonal than the tropics and has both wet and dry seasons. Plants here have to survive for many months without rain.

The animals, too, must be able to live through a long dry season. Though there are goats, deer, and a few other large animals, they are not as numerous as they are in wetter forests. Snakes and lizards seem to do well here, though, and the insects help to keep alive an abundance of birds.

It is not all scrub. There are clumps of fruit trees, among other types of vegetation.

Will this northern needleleaf forest be green when winter comes? Explain.

Still, it is not your idea of a forest. You move on.

Northern Needleleaf Forests

Your map shows that you are now traveling in the subarctic region, the climate region that stretches across the northern parts of North America, Europe, and Asia. This is more like it. There are plenty of tall trees here in the taiga, or northern needleleaf forest. They are all evergreen needleleaf trees—pine, fir, and spruce, all of which make fine Christmas trees.

The thick upper growth of the evergreens blocks out nearly all the sunlight. Except for a few mosses and some seedlings that might or might not grow taller, there is little growth at the herb and the shrub levels. Plant-eating animals, such as deer, moose, and caribou, prevent most seedlings from reaching their full growth. In the summer, the grazing animals will move farther north to feed in the tundra region. Many birds also migrate between the northern forest and the tundra.

Smaller animals, such as mice, hares, and beavers, seem to find enough to eat here, and they provide food for foxes and wolves. Many of the animals here, you note, are similar to those of the middle-latitude forests.

Other Forests

Your journey has taken you through four major forest biomes. There are other kinds. Some of them are similar in many ways to the kinds that you have visited.

Tropical deciduous forests grow in parts of the tropics and the subtropics that have both wet and dry seasons. The deciduous trees lose their leaves during the dry season. A few broadleaf evergreens also grow here. There are fewer climbing plants here than in the tropical rain forests. Other than that, the plant and animal life is similar to that of the rain forest, although far less varied.

Tropical scrub forests, too, grow in regions of seasonal wet and dry weather. Much of the growth resembles that of the mediterranean scrub region. In some places where the dry season is very long, trees and bushes are so scattered that the area hardly looks like a forest at all.

In the middle latitudes, there are also re-gions of mixed forests and needleleaf forests. The middle-latitude mixed forests include both deciduous and coniferous trees. You might find a clump of oaks standing next to a few pines or spruce. The middle-latitude needleleaf forests contain only coniferous trees. In parts of the southern United States, these forests are predominantly pine trees. The animal life in both forests is similar to that of other forests in the middle latitudes.

Lesson 2 Review

Recalling Information

1. Name three kinds of forests that are found in the middle latitudes. Name three kinds that are found in the low latitudes. Which kind of forest is found in the high latitudes?
2. Which kind of forest is most likely to have all five of the top-to-bottom layers of plant life? Why?

Interpreting Information

3. How do precipitation and temperature influence forest types?
4. Name some ways in which forest plants and animals adapt to their environments.

Applying Information

5. What kind of forest are you most likely to find near where you live? How do people use this forest?
6. Which kinds of forests would you find in the 48 connected states of the United States? In Alaska? In Hawaii?

Grazing in large herds helps protect animals of the savanna, such as these zebras, against predators.

GRASSLANDS—AS FAR AS THE EYE CAN SEE

Forests grow where there is plenty of water. Even the scrub forests depend on plentiful rainfall during at least one season of the year. Where precipitation is lighter, smaller plants dominate the landscape. In some places, grasses are likely to be the main form of vegetation. Grasslands are found on all the continents except Antarctica, which is too cold.

Some grasslands may support a few scattered trees or perhaps clumps of trees along a river or a stream. Wild flowers and shrubs also grow in the grasslands.

When you think of grass, you may picture a neatly mowed lawn or a lush, green park. Grasses, however, are quite varied. They can be no longer than your little finger or tall enough to hide a tall person. The grains and cereals that you eat—corn, wheat, oats, barley, and rice—are specially grown forms of grasses that once grew wild.

Grasses are the most important plants in their biomes. They provide food for grass-eating animals which, in turn, provide dinner for such meat-eating animals as lions, wolves, and coyotes. A great variety of birds also feed on grassland vegetation or on the insects that live there.

Grasslands, like forests, vary according to climate. Each kind of grassland is suited to a special climate. The three main kinds of grasslands are savannas, **prairies,** and **steppes**.

Savannas

The savanna is a tropical grassland. It occurs in the wet and the dry tropics. Savanna grasses are tall and rough. They tend to grow in patches that are bordered by bare

183

ground. A few widely scattered trees may grow in some parts of a savanna.

Large areas of savanna are found in Africa, South America, and Australia. Find these areas on the map on pages 176 and 177. Where else do savannas occur?

The wet and the dry seasons bring startling changes to the savanna. During the wet season, temperatures are warm, which encourages a lush plant growth. When the rains end, cooler, dry winds blow over the savanna and parch the land. In the dry season, streams and water holes dry up. Then, the savanna grazers—such as kangaroos in Australia, deer in South America, elephants and zebras in Africa—move out of the dri-est areas of the savanna. They return only when the wet season comes again.

Prairies and Steppes

Prairies and steppes are middle-latitude grasslands. The main difference between the two grasslands is the result of rainfall patterns. Prairies occur where climates are slightly warmer and wetter than steppes. Steppes occur in semiarid areas.

Although few prairie regions remain today, their natural location is in central North America and southeastern South America. Prairie grasses are tall, usually growing to at least 2 feet to 6 feet (61 cm to 183 cm).

Past and Present

Picture it as it was 500 years ago: a vast expanse of long grasses waving in the wind. The American prairie stretched over North America from southern Canada to Texas. Grass covered most of what became the states of Nebraska and Kansas and large parts of many other states.

The prairie, then in its natural state, could not support large populations of humans because the sod could not be easily tilled. American Indians lived there in small groups, living off what the land had to offer and changing the environment very little.

Grazing animals abounded and were a main supply of food and other useful materials. Bison (American buffaloes) roamed the prairies by the millions. Deer, jackrabbits, chipmunks, foxes, coyotes, and other animals were numerous.

The big change began after the development of the railroad, in around 1865. People moved there to raise cattle and to farm. As for crops, what would grow better in a grassland than grass? The farmers planted wheat and corn, and these grasses thrived.

Now, picture the prairie today—thousands of square miles of farmland and ranches, great cities and many smaller towns. The North American prairie is gone, for the most part. Only a few small patches remain, protected as state or national parks to preserve the species that once grew in abundance and to remind us of what had been one of the world's largest prairies.

How are these caribou like the zebras shown on page 183?

Plant-eating animals, of course, thrive in natural prairies. In North America, these animals include deer, bison, rabbits, and prairie dogs, as well as such meat eaters as coyotes and foxes. Birds and insects are also plentiful, though in less variety than in the wetter ecosystems.

The grasses of the steppe are shorter than prairie grasses because it is colder and drier in the steppe and the growing season is shorter. Grasses usually range from 4 inches to 8 inches (10.2 cm to 20.3 cm).

The world's largest steppe region extends from Eastern Europe across the Soviet Union through Mongolia and into China. Prairies can contain occasional clumps of trees, but the dryness of the steppes inhibits the growth of trees.

Because plant life is more scarce in the steppes than in the prairies, animal life is more sparse and less varied. Many of the animals that inhabit the prairies also live in the steppes, but their numbers are smaller because each one needs more land to support itself. Steppe regions, as you can see from the vegetation map, often border desert regions.

Lesson 3 Review

Recalling Information

1. What are the three kinds of grasslands?
2. How do precipitation and temperature influence life in each of the three kinds of grasslands?

Interpreting Information

3. What factors do you think favor farming in a grassland?
4. Which two grassland biomes are most similar? Could the same animals survive in both of these biomes? Why or why not?

Applying Information

5. Do you live in a grassland region? If so, what climatic factors favor the growth of grasses? If not, what climatic factors prevent your area from becoming a grassland?
6. What is most appealing about a grassland? Why might people want to save grasslands?

Special Feature

Environment:
Saving the Whooping Crane

Throughout history, many kinds of animals have suffered from contact with humans. Since about 1600, several species have become extinct because hunters killed them off or because people destroyed their habitats.

In North America, one animal that almost became extinct is the whooping crane. This beautiful bird has become a symbol for wildlife conservation. Whooping cranes live in the lake areas of Canada and migrate to the marshy areas of the Texas coast during the winter. They began to die out in the 1800s when their summer areas and the land over which they flew south became increasingly *developed*, or built up. The grasslands where the birds rest along the way have shrunk as

WHOOPING CRANE

development continues. The activities of hunters also contributed to their demise.

When it was discovered, in 1941, that only 21 whooping cranes remained, concerned scientists decided to try to save this bird. Today, hunting of the birds is prohibited. Their breeding grounds and migratory routes are closely guarded. Scientists have used an interesting method to increase the number of whooping cranes. They have taken eggs from nests in the wild and placed them in the nests of another kind of crane, the sandhill crane. Sandhill cranes then hatch and raise the young whoopers as their own.

By providing the means for whooping cranes to be raised in two different kinds of flocks, scientists have increased the cranes' chances for survival. By 1984, there were more than 80 whooping cranes in the wild and 26 in captivity. Thanks to efforts that were made to preserve rare wildlife such as the whooping crane, scientists have learned a lot about saving other endangered species and are putting this information to use.

Sheep graze on the alpine tundra in the Soviet Union's Caucasus Mountains region.

Lesson 4

WHERE WATER IS SCANT

As you have seen, regions that have a lot of rainfall can produce forests. Those that have light to moderate precipitation can only produce grasslands. The driest areas of the world support the smallest variety of species: these areas are deserts and tundra regions.

Tundra

A tundra is a cold northern plain where, even in summer, the temperature is never high. Although the ground is icy most of the year and is often soggy in the summer, the tundra is considered to be a very dry place. It rarely rains in the tundra, and moisture is locked in the frozen soil for most of the year.

A short growing season, low precipitation, frozen soil, and strong, cold northern winds prevent large plants—trees—from growing in the tundra. Vegetation mainly consists of low-growing, shallow-rooted mosses, shrubs, grasses, a few flowering herbs, and lichens. There is, surprisingly, a varied animal life. A few animals live in the tundra all year long. Others stay only for the short summer season.

Some ducks, geese, and other birds fly north to mate, to lay their eggs, and to raise their young in the short summer. At summer's end, the flocks fly south. Shaggy musk oxen, northern foxes, and wolves stay all year, eating as much as they can in summer. They put on a thick layer of fat that helps them to survive the winter.

Some high-mountain regions are similar to the tundra. Such regions are often called alpine tundra. In these dry highlands, altitude, not latitude, makes temperatures low and growing seasons short. Much of the Tibetan plateau, which is to the north of India, consists of tundra, although the area is in the middle latitudes.

Around the snow-covered peaks of the highest mountains, there is little or no vegetation. At lower levels, plant life is similar to that of the northern tundra. Goats, sheep, yaks, and vicuna graze on mountain vegetation. As seasons change, the grazers migrate—not north or south but to higher or lower levels in their search for food. Mountain grazers are good climbers.

In the spring, the Sonoran Desert is ablaze with wildflowers. It covers 120,000 square miles (310,000 square km) in Arizona, California, and Mexico. What other plants do you see?

Deserts

When someone mentions a desert, many people think of an immense region of hot, burning sand, with hardly a plant in sight. Some desert areas are like this, but most are more varied. Many, such as the North American desert, support a variety of plants and animals. Desert life-forms have various ways of coping successfully with heat, cold, and dryness.

As you know, xerophytic plants such as cacti survive droughts by living off the water that they have stored in their stems or leaves during the infrequent rainfalls. Some have thick, waxy leaves that keep them from losing moisture to the dry desert winds. Some also have deep or wide-spreading roots that collect whatever rainwater falls. Many desert plants simply shed their leaves during dry periods and go into a kind of hibernation. After rain, they quickly grow new leaves.

Animal life has also adapted to the desert climate. Camels and some tortoises are two kinds of animals that store water in their bodies. This allows them to go for weeks without drinking. Many desert animals sleep through the heat of the day and search for food in the cool of the night. Many, such as desert mice, squirrels, snakes, and

lizards, either burrow under the ground or sleep in the shade of rocks or plants.

Lesson 4 Review

Recalling Information

1. Describe at least two ways in which plants have adapted to the tundra. Do the same for the desert.
2. Describe two ways in which animals have adapted to the tundra. Do the same for the desert.

Interpreting Information

3. Describe two ways in which altitude affects climate and gives mountains an environment like that of the tundra.
4. Which other biome is most similar to that of the desert? Give reasons for your answer.

Applying Information

5. What can you learn from desert animals that might help you to survive in a desert?
6. Are there zoos in your area? How do they manage to keep animals from many different biomes alive?

The camel is warm-blooded and can stand the full heat of the desert sun. The desert tortoise is cold-blooded and must take shelter to avoid over-heating.

Lesson 5

WATER ECOSYSTEMS

Life in water is as varied as life on land, depending on the warmth and sunlight available. **Aquatic**, or water, regions are ecosystems, although they are not referred to as biomes.

Ocean Regions

Ocean life ranges all the way from floating plants and animals that are so tiny that you need a microscope to see them, to whales, which are the largest of Earth's animals. The very tiny plants provide food for the equally tiny animals. These small plants and animals are called **plankton**.

Plankton floats near the surface of the ocean, where the plants can absorb sunlight. Small as plankton is, it provides food for millions of other ocean creatures.

The ocean can be divided into four general regions—the open ocean, the deep ocean, the coastal region, and, last, the shoreline. Large and small fish live in the coastal region as well as in the open ocean. Plankton is also plentiful in these regions.

In some places, the ocean is more than 30,000 feet (9,144 m) deep. At such depths, the weight of the water would crush a person. Only a few species of fish live in the deep ocean. Those species have tough bodies that can take the pressure.

The continental shelves supply most of the fish caught and eaten by human beings.

OCEAN REGIONS

COASTAL WATERS

OPEN OCEAN

SHORELINE

High tide

Low tide

Continental shelf

Continental slope

DEEP OCEAN

Ocean floor

191

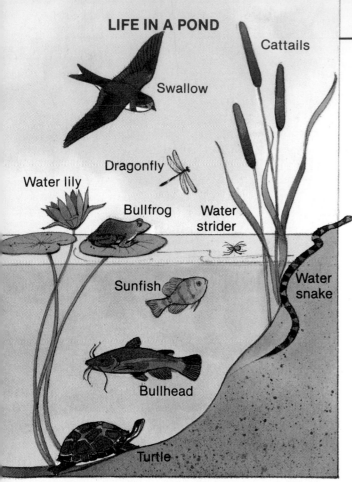

LIFE IN A POND

Cattails

Swallow

Dragonfly

Water lily

Bullfrog

Water strider

Sunfish

Water snake

Bullhead

Turtle

Ponds and their shores are a natural habitat for turtles, snakes, and frogs.

Plants cannot grow in the ocean deep. No sunlight filters down to such levels. Many of the fish are blind. Others produce their own light and glow in the ocean darkness.

The coastal region is the shallow-water region near the continents. Coastal waters are seldom more than about 650 feet (198.1 m) deep. Sunlight penetrates such depths, and plant life is plentiful. Kelp, a long, stringy alga, can grow to lengths of over 100 feet (30.5 m). Plankton are numerous and supply food for many fish. Shellfish also live in coastal waters.

Very close to shore, life is influenced by the action of waves and tides. Where the

water is shallow, a low tide removes all water from a large area. Waves wash back and forth along the shores. Plants and animals in shoreline regions must be able to survive in places where they are covered with water at some times and exposed to air at other times.

There, too, plankton provides food for many animals, including mussels and other shellfish. Algae often grow on rocks in such areas, providing food and sometimes shelter for other living things.

Animals that can live on land as well as in water, such as sea turtles and some crabs, are found in shoreline regions. Many birds inhabit these areas, too.

Freshwater Regions

Fresh water includes lakes, ponds, rivers, and streams. Fresh water refers to nonocean water. Ocean water is called salt water. A very small part of the world's aquatic regions—only about 1 percent—consists of fresh water.

Generally, plants and animals from one kind of water region cannot survive in the other water region. There are, however, some fish that can live in both regions. Salmon, for example, are born in freshwater rivers. Then, they move into the ocean where they grow to maturity. Finally, they return to the rivers where they were hatched to lay their eggs.

Each freshwater environment has its own characteristics that help to determine the kind of life that will survive there. A large lake, such as Lake Michigan, has tides, waves, and even currents. A river or a stream is always in motion as water flows,

How do caribou use the ponds and the lakes in their tundra environment?

sometimes very quickly, along its length. Ponds are relatively still waters, and if they are not fed by underwater springs, they can dry up in a dry season.

Insects, which usually are not found in great numbers in ocean waters, are abundant in fresh waters. They provide food for many freshwater fish and for birds that make their homes near fresh water.

Plant life is limited in swiftly flowing rivers and streams, where the movement of the water prevents many plants from taking root. More kinds of plants grow in ponds, however, and at the edges of lakes. They root in the muddy shallows and send stems and leaves upward to the surface of the

water. Cattails and other reedy plants rise high above the surface. Certain kinds of algae also inhabit ponds and lakes.

Freshwater life in the high and the middle latitudes must adapt to the changing seasons. The water of small lakes and ponds can freeze in winter. Much of the plant life dies and then grows again the following spring. Animals may die or move to warmer areas. As every ice fisher knows, however, many fish survive in the cold water under a heavy layer of surface ice. Frogs and turtles hibernate in mud beneath the water.

Lesson 5 Review

Recalling Information

1. Name the four main regions of ocean life.
2. What are some differences between ocean environments and freshwater environments?

Interpreting Information

3. How might ocean currents influence an aquatic environment?
4. In what ways might humans influence or change aquatic environments?

Applying Information

5. Which aquatic environment is the nearest to where you live? Describe it.
6. If all the plankton in the ocean died, what would be the effect on you?

Skills for Thinking

USING AN OUTLINE

Any list—even a shopping list—is a way of recording information. An outline is also a list. This type of list records information in a way that shows main ideas, supporting ideas, and details.

What Are the Key Ideas?

Study the outline that begins below. The Roman numeral I precedes the main topic. What comes before each subtopic, or supporting idea? What comes before each detail under the subtopic? What Roman numeral will come before the next major topic?

Outlining sharpens your ability to focus on key ideas and their importance. As you study, you can put your notes in outline form. As you prepare a report, you can make an outline to show how you will present your ideas and support information.

1. Rewrite the material below so that it shows the next part of the outline of *The Ocean Ecosystem*. As a guide, use the words in parentheses. Refer to the first part of the outline to see how numerals, capital letters, periods, and indentations are used in an outline.

2. Special Challenge: Choose a section of this chapter and outline it. Show at least two main topics, two subtopics under each main topic, and two details under each subtopic.

The Ocean Ecosystem

I. The food chain
   A. Decaying matter as food for bacteria
   B. Bacteria as food for plants
   C. Animals as food and feeders
      1. Small fish feed on plankton.
      2. Other fish and squid feed on small fish.
      3. Ocean mammals feed on a wide variety of ocean life.

(main topic)	ocean plants
(subtopic)	the algae
(detail)	floating algae
(detail)	seaweed
(subtopic)	the vanishing eelgrass
(detail)	differences between algae and eelgrass
(detail)	animals that depend on eelgrass
(detail)	results of eelgrass disappearing

Chapter 9 Review

Summary of Key Facts

In this chapter, you learned that

- Earth is divided into biomes, or environmental regions, according to availability of light, heat and water, and type of soil.
- four kinds of biomes are forests, grasslands, tundras, and deserts.
- plant growth in a forest is divided into five top-to-bottom layers called the canopy, the understory, the shrub level, the herb level, and the forest floor.
- four kinds of forests are tropical rain forests, broadleaf deciduous forests, mediterranean scrub forests, and northern needleleaf forests.
- three kinds of grasslands are savannas, prairies, and steppes.
- both the cool tundras and the warm deserts receive scant rainfall.
- examples of freshwater regions are lakes, ponds, rivers, and streams.

Using Vocabulary

On a separate sheet of paper, write the term that will correctly complete each sentence.

biome   habitat
steppes   forest
plankton   prairies

1. Each animal has adapted to living in its own particular ____ .

2. A ____ is a community of plant and animal life with a common environment.
3. A ____ is a biome where trees grow.
4. ____ and ____ are middle-latitude grasslands.
5. Tiny animals and plants that float freely in water are called ____ .

Discussing the Chapter

1. How are plants and animals in an ecosystem interdependent? Use examples to explain.
2. Describe two kinds of forest biomes.
3. How do grasslands differ?
4. Compare tundras and deserts.
5. Describe the four ocean regions.

Reviewing Skills

Choose another chapter section to outline. Show at least two main topics, two subtopics under each main topic, and at least two details under each subtopic.

Unit 3 Review

Summary of Key Facts

In this unit, you learned that

- the biosphere is the thin layer of Earth where life exists.
- all parts of Earth's biosphere are interdependent.
- an ecosystem is made up of all living and nonliving things that exist together in an environment.
- five nonliving parts of an ecosystem are sunlight, water, air, soil, and rocks.
- the three living parts of an ecosystem consist of the producers, the consumers, and the decomposers.
- a biome is a community of plant and animal life that is held together by a common environment.
- the major categories of biomes are forests, grasslands, tundras, and deserts.

Discussing the Unit

1. How is plant life dependent on the position of Earth in relation to the sun?
2. In what way is climate an important factor in an ecosystem? Use examples to explain your answer.
3. How is soil influenced by plants and animals? How are plants and animals dependent on soil?
4. How do ocean regions differ from land biomes? How are they similar?
5. Why is Earth considered an ecosystem?

Activities

1. Read a newspaper article about a changing ecosystem. Do research to find out what is happening to the living parts of the ecosystem. Report your findings to the class.
2. Choose one kind of forest to research. Find out what kinds of plants and animals live at each layer of this kind of forest. Draw a diagram or a picture that shows the living parts of the forest ecosystem and label each part.

Test

Using Vocabulary

On a separate sheet of paper, write the word that will correctly complete each sentence in the paragraph.

biosphere   scrub
interdependent   coniferous
ecosystem   desert
biomes   steppes

The thin zone of Earth where plants and animals exist is called the _____. Special kinds of plant and animal communities are called _____. One kind, where xerophytic plants and animals live is called a _____. Together with the nonliving parts of their environment, animals and plants form an _____. When living things depend on each other for their survival, we say that they are _____. Savannas and _____ are two kinds of grasslands. The mediterranean _____ forest is a biome of low, stunted trees. The needleleaf forest is a place where _____ trees grow.

The Big Question

How do the living and the nonliving parts of Earth interact?

Write your answer in complete sentences. Draw upon the information in this unit to write a good answer.

Using Map Skills

Use the map on pages 176 and 177 to complete this exercise.

1. What is the name of the parallel at 0°?
2. What is the interval between labeled lines of longitude on this map?
3. Where do the lines of longitude intersect?
4. What vegetation can be found south of 60°S?

Identifying a Geographic Theme

Think about the geographic themes of **human-environment interactions** and **region** as you complete this exercise.

1. What are some differences between the life-support system of Earth and that of a spaceship?
2. Look at the map on pages 176–177. What region of natural vegetation lies along the Arctic Ocean?

Unit 4 — People on Earth

The biosphere, that thin shell of Earth that supports all the life of which we know in the universe, contains perhaps 30 million species of plants and animals. Humans are only one of these species, but we are the most powerful. While most other species live in limited environments where conditions are right for them, we inhabit nearly all of Earth.

In some places, we live very simply, taking very little from the world around us. In other places, we make broad and far-reaching demands on the environment.

Concepts

natural resource   technology
civilization   Industrial Revolution

The Big Question

How do a people's technology and culture affect how they live on Earth?

Focus on a Geographic Theme

In this unit you will study the geographic theme of **human-environment interactions**. People interact with their environment and try to change it to make life easier or better. Geographers study the consequences of such changes.

**A crowd near London's Stock Exchange
reflects Earth's varied peoples.**

People, Resources, and Environment

Vocabulary

calories	inexhaustable
natural	resources
resources	nonrenewable
biological	resources
resources	renewable
human resources	resources
fossil fuels	reserves

Lesson Preview

Lesson 1: People and Environment
Lesson 2: People Use Resources
Lesson 3: Where Resources Are

Introduction

People have looked at Earth in different ways. A Kagaba (Indian) song describes Earth as our mother.

She is the Mother of Songs, the mother of our whole seed, who bore us in the beginning. She is the mother of all races of men and the mother of all tribes. She is the mother of thunder, the mother of rivers, the mother of trees, and of all kinds of things. She is the mother of songs and dances. She is the mother of the older brother stones. She is the mother of the grain and the mother of all things....She is the mother of the rain, the only one we have.

Here is what Adlai Stevenson, once the United States ambassador to the United Nations, said about Earth.

We travel together, passengers on a little spaceship, dependent on its vulnerable resources of air and soil; all committed for our safety to its security and peace; preserved from annihilation [death] only by the care, the work, and I will say the love we give our fragile little craft.

Each description of Earth is correct. Each recognizes that Earth sustains living things, that it provides them with what they need to live. In this chapter, you will learn what people need and use from Earth.

◀ **A gigantic digging machine in the Athabasca Tar Sands. What machinery brings minerals to you each day?**

PEOPLE AND ENVIRONMENT

You know some of the things that plants and animals need to stay alive. Think for a moment about what things *you* must have to live. Think in general terms such as food rather than in specific terms such as hamburgers. Distinguish between absolute necessities—things that you need every day to stay alive—and wants such as television. Also, distinguish between things that you need but that are always available—such as air and sunlight—and things that people need to provide for daily, or to work for.

All living things need food. Food provides energy for our bodies, just as gas does for cars. This energy is measured in **calories** (KAL*uh*reez). When we say that an apple has 100 calories, we mean that it provides that much energy for the body's use. The number of calories that a person needs each day varies according to age, size, and activity, but the average number that is needed daily by Americans is about 2,350 calories.

All living things need water. Without water, our bodies could not digest food, our blood could not carry oxygen, and our cells could not use energy to make our bodies work.

Besides water and food for energy, our bodies need to be kept at the same temperature, 98.6°F (37°C). We must wear clothing to keep warm in cold weather. Some people must also use clothing to protect their bodies from the effects of very hot weather.

Shelter, our final basic need, also helps us to keep our bodies warm in cold weather and, in some places, safe from animals and insects. We also use shelter to provide wants—to keep cool in hot weather or to stay dry when it rains.

Our Environments

As you learned in Unit 3, plants and animals can live only in places where the environment supplies their needs. Humans, however, live just about everywhere on Earth. We have mastered ways of protecting ourselves in different environments.

In cold places and in hot places, in places with a lot of rain and in places with almost none, people have made their homes. Wherever people live, they must obtain their basic needs. How they do this depends to a large extent on the environment in which they live.

As you would expect, it is more difficult to obtain basic needs in some environments than in others. It is hard to live in dry or in polar environments. Dry regions lack fresh water that is needed for drinking and for raising both plants and animals for food. In polar regions, there is not enough warm weather for more than a few kinds of plants to grow. Few people live in such places. Nobody except scientists who are doing research lives permanently in Antarctica, the coldest place of all, and the scientists' needs are brought to them from outside.

Very high, steep mountains are also difficult places in which to live. There is little flatland for raising crops. The steep slopes make transportation difficult.

Most people live in environments where

What equipment do the members of this Louisiana family use to make the best use of their environment?

the climate is favorable to satisfying their basic needs. Such environments have enough water, farming and grazing land, and materials for building shelter. Most of the densely populated areas are near rivers, lakes, and seas or oceans.

Adapting to the Environment

Whatever their environment, people live by using its supplies. People adapt their way of life to fit their environment. Adaptation is the act of people's adapting to the environment.

Think about how the environment affects your life and the kinds of adaptations that you make to it. If you live in a place where

winters are cold and snowy, you probably own a heavy winter coat, a warm hat and a scarf, warm gloves, and heavy boots. If winters are relatively warm and rainy where you live, your raincoat, umbrella, and galoshes are very useful to you. What other environments would require you to make adaptations?

People Change Environments

Besides adapting to the environment, people also make changes in the environment. We bring water to dry land, we remove natural vegetation, and we even change landforms.

When we build shelters, we create small

Explain how people adapted to this environment. Also, explain the ways in which people adapted this environment to their needs.

spaces of a more suitable environment. We heat or cool our shelters to a comfortable temperature, and the buildings keep out rain, snow, strong winds, insects, and wild animals.

We can create climates only in small spaces—indoors. However, out of doors, we can correct for what a climate lacks. For example, irrigation helps to correct a lack of sufficient rainfall. *Irrigation* means "the bringing of water to dry land."

Water for irrigation may come from a nearby river that flows from an area that has enough precipitation. The Imperial Valley in southern California is irrigated by the Colorado River. Water that comes from wells is used to irrigate wheat fields in the Great Plains. In places such as India, where there is a very rainy season followed by a very dry season, water for irrigation is collected and stored in ponds. Dams have been built across rivers in many parts of the world to store water for irrigation. When people change the environment, they try to solve problems that are caused by natural conditions.

Wherever farmers have planted new fields, they almost always have had to change the natural environment by clearing the land—removing whatever had been growing there. All over the world, fields have replaced former grasslands and forests. If a farmer were to stop using the land for farming, the grass or the trees would gradually grow back.

As you know, plains are better for farmland than mountains with steep slopes. In many parts of the world, however, there is not enough flat land on which to grow food for all the people. Farmers have obtained more farmland by changing the slopes into a series of terraces.

People also change landforms for other purposes. Before a new highway is built, huge machines may level small hills and fill small valleys to make the road flatter than it would otherwise have been. Land may also be leveled to provide a site for a building, a housing development, or a swimming pool.

Some of the changes that people have brought about to solve problems have made other, and sometimes worse, problems.

People have cut down all the trees in rain forests to clear land for farming, for example, only to find that the rain washed away all the topsoil so that they could not farm there. You will learn more about the problems of clearing rain-forest lands in later chapters.

Lesson 1 Review

Recalling Information
1. Name people's four basic needs.
2. What are the two major ways that people can deal with the environment?

Interpreting Information
3. Americans have made many big changes in their environment. What changes have created worse problems? How?
4. Do you think that, someday, people will settle in Antarctica? Why?

Appying Information
5. If you were to move to an environment that is very different from your present one, how would your life change?
6. Suppose that you could take only one of the following on a lifeboat. Would you take fresh water, a compass, a hat, an umbrella, or a flare? Why?

The rice farmers of Sri Lanka have used terraced fields for centuries.

The raw materials for this Bolivian village were easy to find. Why would villagers build along the Amazon River?

Lesson 2

PEOPLE USE RESOURCES

The eerie silence is broken only by the whistle of the wind. Everywhere you look in this arctic scene, it is white. Snow and ice cover the ground 12 months a year. An Innuit on a hunting trip is building an igloo. He cuts blocks of ice and carefully fits them together to form his ice shelter.

Thousands of miles away, a Zuni (Indian) family is building its house in the desert of New Mexico. They mix clay and straw together and shape the mixture called adobe (*ah*∗DOH∗*bee*) in the form of bricks. They bake these bricks in an oven and use them to make a house.

Still farther south, near the equator, the air is full of the sounds of the Amazon rain forest. There, an Indian family is also building a house. They build it by weaving grass around a framework of branches.

These house builders are separated from each other by thousands of miles. They live in very different environments. Yet, two enterprises link these people: first, they are all building houses, and, second, they are also solving the problem of shelter by using materials that are readily available in their local environments. These materials are the **natural resources** of their areas.

RESOURCES

RESOURCE	COMMON USES
Aluminum	Light building materials, medicine, dyes
Chromium	Iron and steel plating
Coal	Fuel, dyes, perfumes, fibers
Cobalt	Medicine, cutting tools, magnets
Copper	Electrical wire, jewelry, coins
Gold	Medium of exchange, jewelry, dentistry
Iron	Building materials, cars, machinery
Lead	Batteries, gasoline, solder
Limestone	Cement, fertilizer, chalk
Manganese	Hardening steel, computer parts
Natural gas	Heating, industrial fuels, cooling
Nickel	Hardening metals for machine parts, coins
Nitrate	Fertilizers, explosives
Petroleum	Fuels, polyesters, plastics
Potash	Glass, fertilizer, soap
Silicon	Computer parts, waterproofing, lubricants
Silver	Photographic film, medicine, coins
Tin	Metal plating, containers, pewter
Tungsten	Cutting tools, light-bulb filaments
Uranium	Nuclear power, nuclear weapons

Which mineral is used to make film? Which mineral is used to make chalk?

Kinds of Resources

Natural resources are the raw materials of Earth that people use to live. There are several kinds of natural resources.

The first group is necessary for life itself. These are our most basic resources—sunlight, air, water, and soil.

A second group is made up of **biological resources**—the plants and the animals of Earth. Our food comes from plants and from animals. We also use these resources in other ways. We make clothing from such plants as flax (linen) and cotton, and from parts of, or products from, such animals as sheep and silkworms. We use wood from trees to build shelter and to make furniture

and paper. Many people heat their shelters and cook their food by burning wood.

Resources that we mine from Earth form a third group, mineral resources. The chart on this page lists some of these important resources and how people use them.

You can understand the importance of this group of resources by imagining their absence. No minerals would mean no iron, no steel, no glass, and no gasoline. Therefore, there would be no concrete, no asphalt and no paved roads, no nails or screws, no plastics, and no television. We could not use electricity, for there would be no wiring, no batteries, no light bulbs, and no light switches. Resources from mines may not seem to be necessary to life, but they are basic to human life as we know it today.

People are also resources. They can use their intelligence and their talents to make use of other resources. **Human resources**—the abilities that people have to draw on—will be discussed in later chapters.

Recognizing Resources

Resources such as air and sunlight are everywhere on Earth. Sunlight strikes Earth at differing intensities, as you have read. Water can be found in some places but not in others. Some materials lie buried far beneath Earth's surface.

Wherever they are found, materials are not resources unless people have discovered uses for them. At different times, people have considered different things to be resources, depending on their immediate needs.

Let us look at some examples. For centuries, most people did not find much use

Rubber automobile tires on an ox-drawn cart show a meeting of old and new.

for oil. It was regarded as nothing more than some black, gooey stuff that oozed out of the ground. It was messy and it could ruin perfectly good farmland. When it was observed that oil burns with a hot flame, people wondered whether it could be used in lamps.

In 1859, Edwin Drake drilled the first oil well in Titusville, Pennsylvania. Now it was possible to obtain oil in large quantities, and many uses were found for it. Oil was soon called black gold because of its value.

Most of the minerals listed on the chart on page 207 have similar histories. For

centuries, no one found uses for them. When people did, these minerals became valuable resources.

A resource may be valued at one time and then lose its special value because something cheaper or better is found to replace it. Many years ago, the American Indians of northern California valued acorns as a food. Today, they eat other things, and acorns have lost their value.

A resource may have to be replaced if the supply disappears. The Plains Indians of North America supported themselves by hunting buffaloes. They used buffalo meat for food and buffalo skins for tepees and for clothing. They used the sinew of buffalo muscle to make their bowstrings and to tie their moccasins. Almost every part of the buffalo was used by American Indians.

When white hunters moved west, they killed millions of buffaloes. Without this important resource, the Indians had to find substitutes, which made their lives change dramatically.

Other people also have depended heavily on animals. Most people today use animals for both food and clothing. Until about 1800, most people also depended on animal power for many energy needs. Horses, oxen, donkeys, mules, camels, llamas, and dogs carried people and goods or pulled wagons, plows, and sleds. They turned grist mills and the waterwheels of pumps.

In countries such as the United States, animals are rarely used for their power anymore. In many parts of the world, however, it is still common to see animals being used for transportation and for work.

What new resources might be available in

the future? New plants and new insects are being discovered all the time, especially in rain forests and in oceans. Drug and chemical companies are trying hard to discover uses for them. Who knows? New uses may be found for common objects—for stones, tree bark, and sand.

Limited and Unlimited Resources

We can look at Earth's resources in another way. Some are **inexhaustible resources**. Like sunlight, tides, and wind, they cannot be used up. **Nonrenewable resources** are those that exist in limited amounts. Once a nonrenewable resource is used up, it is gone forever. **Renewable resources** are those whose supply can be replenished or sustained by human effort.

Most biological resources are renewable if they are cared for and harvested properly. Some, such as most crops, can be grown within the few months of a growing season, harvested, and planted again. Others take longer to replace. If you cut down a forest, you cannot replace it right away. It will take at least 20 to 30 years to replace.

You read earlier about how soil is formed. Although soil is continuously forming, this process takes place over many centuries. Soil can last forever if it is replenished with minerals and organic animal and plant materials, and if it is not allowed to erode. If too many plants are grown in the soil or if the same crop is grown year after year, plants may use up all the food in the soil. Once soil is eroded or destroyed, it may take a thousand years to form 1 inch (2.5 cm) of new topsoil.

Nonrenewable resources take so long to

Miners adapt to the underground environment. They bring lights and special tools.

form that they are considered irreplaceable. They include minerals, **fossil fuels**, and nonminerals. Fossil fuels are fuels that have formed on Earth from plants and animals that lived millions of years ago. Coal, oil, and natural gas are fossil fuels.

As you know, minerals are natural substances in the earth that have specific chemical and physical properties. Many of our most important mineral resources are ores—the rocks that contain such metals as iron, copper, bauxite (the ore of aluminum), silver, and gold.

We also mine clay and rocks from the earth. Clay is used for many products, from

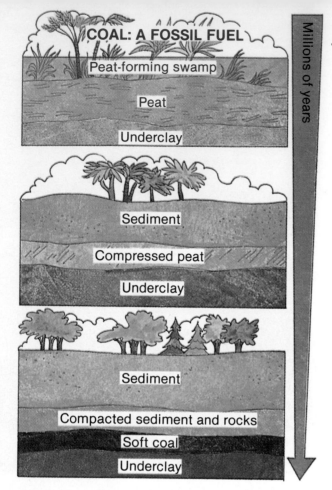

COAL: A FOSSIL FUEL

Peat-forming swamp

Peat

Underclay

Sediment

Compressed peat

Underclay

Sediment

Compacted sediment and rocks

Soft coal

Underclay

Millions of years

Pressure and heat turn buried organic material into coal, oil, and natural gas.

pottery to bricks. Limestone, marble, and granite are rocks that are used in buildings and in monuments. Crushed stone and gravel are used for building roads, among others things.

All these nonrenewable resources have been formed over millions of years by the same forces that made the landforms discussed in Unit 1. Though it may seem that we have enough to last forever, our tools have vastly increased our use of natural resources. Scientists are beginning to keep track of the relations between supply and demand so that resource depletions—running out of them—can be predicted and alternatives can be found in time.

Because some resources can only be replaced by natural processes over a long time and others cannot be replaced at all, people need to conserve them. As you know, *to conserve* means "to use carefully and to save for future use." In later chapters, you will read about some of the conservation measures that people are taking to control our use of resources.

Lesson 2 Review

Recalling Information

1. What is a renewable resource? Give three examples.
2. What is a nonrenewable resource? Give three examples.

Interpreting Information

3. Trees are a renewable resource. How can we use trees for building and, at the same time, have trees for the future?
4. How might new studies change our ideas about what can be used as a resource?

Applying Information

5. Make a list of ways in which you can conserve electricity in your daily life.
6. Suppose that the United States could not buy any oil from other countries. The only oil that we would have is oil that is produced in the United States. You are a conservation expert. The Department of Energy has asked you to recommend a list of habits that Americans should change in order to conserve oil. What would you recommend?

Lesson 3

WHERE RESOURCES ARE

The frozen wastelands of the Arctic have sounds and sights all their own: the crunching sound of boots on the hard snow; the lonely music of the wind, now whispering, then howling across the vast, snow-covered landscape; and the whiteness of it all—everything covered with snow and ice.

It is just about the last place in which you would expect to find machines and people working around the clock, 365 days a year. Yet, along the North Slope of Alaska, that is what has been happening since oil was discovered there in 1968. The story of the North Slope shows that valuable resources sometimes have been found in the most remote places.

Oil is just one kind of resource that is found in some places and not in others. Forests, metal ores, other minerals, and even good soil provide other examples.

The map on pages 212 and 213 shows the distribution of some mineral resources. A glance at the map shows you that minerals are not evenly distributed around the world. As you have read, the same processes that made the rocks and the landforms that you read about in Unit 1 also formed minerals. Because these forces were different in different places, the different minerals are unevenly distributed throughout the world.

Oil was present under the sands of Saudi Arabia long before it was discovered. Drilling has changed the look of the land.

You can see that such countries in the Middle East as Saudi Arabia, Iran, Iraq, and Kuwait have large deposits of oil. So do the Soviet Union, the United States, and Canada. Can you locate on the map three other countries that have large **reserves** of oil? Reserves are known deposits that can be obtained with our present technology at a reasonable cost.

As you know, different things are resources at different times. Things can be resources only when people find uses for them, just as deposits can become reserves only when people can get at them.

From the example of the North Slope in Alaska, we know that resources can be found in remote places. The ocean floor is also such a place. Drilling rigs have been erected off the California and the Louisiana coasts because valuable oil fields have been discovered there. Another valuable oil field in the stormy North Sea between Great Britain and Norway is yielding oil. Oil is so important to our way of life that people are willing to pay the higher cost of getting it from such remote sites.

Other nonrenewable resources are also unevenly distributed. The map shows large reserves of coal in the United States. Coal is an important energy resource. When burned, however, it pollutes the air. Scientists are developing ways to purify the coal-burning process. If they succeed, we can use much more of this resource.

Resources and Wealth

In Chapter 13, you will see how the distribution of resources affects where people choose to live on Earth. This distribution

can also affect the wealth of nations. One reason that the United States has become such a wealthy country is the richness of its land and its resources. Besides its reserves of coal, oil, and natural gas, the United States has rich deposits of copper, zinc, lead, iron, nickel, uranium, and other minerals. In addition, it contains the fertile soil of the Great Plains, one of the richest agricultural areas in the world, and the vast timber reserves of the Pacific Northwest and of Alaska.

At the opposite extreme, some countries with resources are still poor. Zaire (*zah*∗IHR) is an African country that is rich in resources. Nevertheless, many of the people in Zaire are poor. You will read more about the wealth of nations in Units 6 and 7.

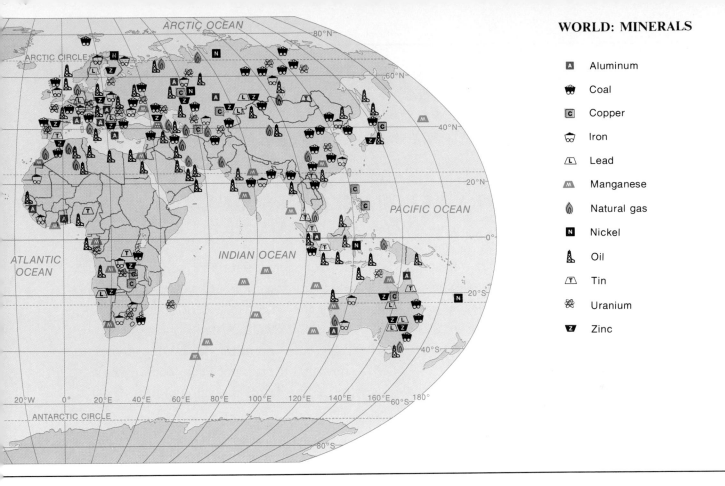

A	Aluminum
(coal)	Coal
C	Copper
(iron)	Iron
L	Lead
M	Manganese
(gas)	Natural gas
N	Nickel
(oil)	Oil
T	Tin
(uranium)	Uranium
Z	Zinc

MAP SKILLS: Maps such as this one give a general idea of world resource distribution. Where would exact information be found?

Lesson 3 Review

Recalling Information

1. Which resource is primarily found in the world's oceans?
2. What important resources have helped to make the United States wealthy?

Interpreting Information

3. What was the North Slope in Alaska like before the discovery of oil? How do you suppose the discovery affected the area? Explain.
4. If a deposit of copper ore were found in your community, how would the discovery change your community's way of life?

Applying Information

5. Which jobs in your community depend on nonrenewable resources?
6. As the secretary of the interior, you are expected to recommend to the president whether unused land in the United States should be mined, built upon, farmed, or preserved in its natural state for later use, or even forever. List the questions that you and members of your department will have to answer about these four land uses.

Skills for Thinking

WRITING A REPORT TO PERSUADE

Suppose that you have an idea, an opinion, or a belief that you want to express. You want to persuade an audience or a reader to agree with you. Perhaps you also want them to do something. How do you go about all this?

Learning how to persuade a person or a group is a valuable skill for expressing and sharing ideas and for encouraging action.

Can I Persuade My Audience?

Here are some guidelines to follow when you are writing a report to persuade.

- State your opinion or belief clearly.
- Support your opinion with both evidence and logic. Do not be vague or use incorrect information.
- If you want people to take action, be specific about what you want them to do.

Now, read the following report by a member of a bicycle club. Then, answer the questions about it.

1. What is the writer's belief?
2. What does the writer want the audience to do?
3. Which facts support the writer's argument?

4. Do you agree with the writer? If not, what arguments would you use to persuade the writer to accept your point of view? Construct an opposing argument. Take each point made by the writer; show that it does not make a strong case for getting rid of the automobile.

It is time to scrap the idea of the automobile. The automobile, which once opened up our country by making it easier for people to travel, is now a drain on our resources.

Consider how much energy automobiles waste. The average internal-combustion engine is only 10 percent efficient. Automobiles thus waste oil and gasoline.

In addition to wasting energy, automobiles are dangerous. Each year, almost 30,000 lives are lost in automobile accidents.

Finally, most old cars end up in junkyards where they are added to rusty, ugly piles of wrecks. Automobile parts are difficult to recycle because of the mixture of different materials that are used in their manufacture.

So let us stop wasting resources and marring the landscape. Stop buying cars. Use bicycles instead.

Chapter **10** *Review*

Summary of Key Facts

In this chapter, you learned that

- food, water, shelter, and clothing are basic needs of all humans.
- people adapt to and change their environments.
- our most basic resources are sunlight, air, water, and soil.
- natural resources are the raw materials of Earth that people use to live.
- some resources are inexhaustible; others are renewable or nonrenewable.
- resources are not distributed evenly over Earth's surface.

Using Vocabulary

On a separate sheet of paper, write the number of the statement and then the term that most closely matches the statement.

calories   fossil fuels
natural resources   biological resources

1. ____ are resources that have formed from plants and animals that lived millions of years ago.
2. ____ are raw materials of Earth that people use to live.
3. Energy is measured in ____ .
4. Plants and animals are ____ .

Discussing the Chapter

1. Discuss ways in which people make their lives fit the environment.
2. Why is energy important for life?
3. Explain the difference between renewable, nonrenewable, and inexhaustible resources. Give examples of each.
4. Why is it not always true that countries with the most resources are the richest ?
5. Why are things considered resources in one culture not considered resources in other cultures? Use examples in your explanation.

Reviewing Skills

Read the following paragraph. Then, answer the questions below.

It is a shame that we do not make better use of sunlight as a resource. There is enough sunlight to power every car on Earth. Using gasoline, a nonrenewable resource, instead of sunlight to power our cars is a great waste of energy.

1. What is the writer's belief?
2. Can you infer from the paragraph what the writer wants the audience to do?

People and Culture

Introduction

The American Indians who used to live in eastern Massachusetts satisfied their basic needs for water, food, clothing, and shelter from their environment. They got their water from streams and ponds. They hunted animals and grew corn, squash, and beans for food. They also gathered wild berries and fruits. They made their clothing from animal skins, and they made their dome-shaped dwellings of bark from the trees in the forest.

When the Pilgrims went to Massachusetts, they met their basic needs in a variety of ways. Besides getting water from streams, they dug wells and collected rainwater in barrels. They not only hunted and learned to grow corn, but they also grew wheat, apples, and other plants that they had used in England. They raised animals. They used wool and linen to make their clothes. They sawed trees into boards and built the kinds of houses in which they had lived in England.

The American Indians and the Pilgrims both lived in the same environment at the same time. Although each group used the resources of the environment to meet basic needs, the American Indians and the Pilgrims did so in different ways. Any environment contains resources that people can use in different ways to meet their needs. In this chapter, you will learn why.

Which skills does your society teach for use in your daily environment? Many young Mongolians learn hunting methods.

In Japan, modern and ancient cultures exist side by side. What modern and ancient influences do you see?

Lesson 1

WHAT IS CULTURE?

The way in which a group of people meets its needs depends a great deal on its culture. When some people think of culture, they think of such things as great books and fine art and music. Social scientists, however, include many other things in their definition of *culture*. Culture is the total way of life of a group of people. This includes a people's beliefs, language, ways of behaving, ways of making a living, their foods, and their style of housing, as well as art, music, and writing.

A group of people with the same culture is called a **society**. We learn and develop our culture as members of our society. Even though individuals in our society may do things a little differently, we share many aspects of our culture. In many ways, our lives and our behavior follow patterns that come from our culture.

Customs

In our American society, we greet each other by saying "Hi," "Hello," "Howdy," "What's happenin'?" or "How y'all?" When we leave, we say "Good-bye," "Adios," "See you later," or "So long." In our society, men wear trousers, while women can wear either skirts or slacks. There are also groups who dress to make a statement about society. Behaviors that are part of our culture are called **customs**.

Following the customs of our society helps us to know what kinds of behavior to expect from others. Our culture provides us with a kind of plan for living. Cultural patterns are ways that people have developed to meet their basic needs on a day-to-day basis. Many customs are associated with celebrations. Birthday cakes with candles, Christmas trees, parades on the Fourth of July, and turkey dinners at Thanksgiving are examples of customs.

Cultures Change

Cultures are always changing, although some cultures change faster than others, and some parts of a culture change faster than other parts. American culture has changed rapidly. Other cultures have been relatively stable for thousands of years. You will be reading about **traditional cultures** in Unit 5. A traditional culture is one that developed a long time ago and has remained much the same over a long period.

One way cultures change is through the process of diffusion (*dihf*∗YOO∗*zhuhn*), or the spread of new ideas, new inventions, and new ways of doing things. The use of

Japanese teenagers dance to rock music in the parks. This style of music and clothing originally came from America.

Can You Imagine?

Imagine landing on a tropical island after a terrible storm in which you and some friends have been shipwrecked. After you recover from the shock for a while, you set out to find food and shelter. As you wander inland, you excitedly notice signs of human inhabitants—cleared paths and gardens. Stones that are arranged in a circle, and charred wood that is in the center of the circle show you that people use fire here. You soon come upon the people who live on the island.

The islanders show you how they use the island's natural resources. You learn what fish they catch and eat, where they gather fruits, and how they weave the long grass into baskets. You observe their ways of greeting one another, their form of government, and other expressions of their culture. Eventually, you adopt some of the ways of the islanders, and they adopt some of yours. How do you feel?

an invention becomes widespread if it meets needs or solves problems. Bicycles spread worldwide because they proved to be a most economical means of local transportation.

New ideas and the use of new things usually spread first in the society where these were conceived and produced. Then, since societies have contacts with one another, these spread to other societies. Records and tapes that are played by radio stations and concerts that are broadcast by television networks and satellites have spread rock music around the world.

Although cultural diffusion is a two-way street, one culture may adopt much more

Quilting is a part of American culture that dates back to colonial times. How is the skill being passed on here? Might the girl pass on the tradition, too? How?

than it gives. Such a culture is an example of a culture that has become assimilated, or has absorbed or adapted most of the customs of another culture.

How Culture Is Learned

We are not born with culture. We learn it. We learn most of our culture when we are so young that we have forgotten when and how we learned it. For example, do you remember when you first learned to say "Hello"? To shake hands?

We go on learning about our culture for the rest of our lives. We learn, for example, to care for ourselves and for our children, and how our society uses our environment.

Some parts, or elements, of culture are things that we can feel and see. These things make up **material culture**. Baseball games and barbecues are all part of our material culture. Culture also includes many things that we cannot see or touch. These things are called **nonmaterial culture**. Beliefs, ideas, and feelings are examples of nonmaterial culture. In Lesson 2, you will read about material culture. In Lesson 3, you will read about nonmaterial culture.

Lesson 1 Review

Recalling Information
1. What is culture?
2. Why do cultural ideas spread? How are they spread?

Interpreting Information
3. Material cultures are similar to one another in many countries today. What effect do you think that this has had on the way in which people in different societies feel about one another?
4. What is the difference between a people's culture and their customs?

Applying Information
5. Choose your favorite holiday. Make a list of your family's customs for celebrating the holiday.
6. Do any people in your community have customs that are different from yours? Are there any that you admire and would like to adopt? Why?

Lesson 2

MATERIAL CULTURE

The things that we use every day are part of our material culture. By examining these parts of our culture, we can learn a lot about it. From mirrors to stereos to high-rise apartment buildings, the values and the necessities of our life are evident.

Our Tools

The first things that humans invented thousands of years ago were tools for getting food—spears, arrowheads, and the like. Since those early days, people have invented millions of tools for solving all kinds of problems. Just think of all the tools that you use each day. What problems do they help you to solve? You keep your orange juice in a refrigerator. You put your cereal in a bowl and eat it with a spoon. The farmer who grew the grain for your cereal used a tractor, a planter, a sprayer, chemicals to kill weeds and insects, and a harvester.

The tools of a society, together with the skills and the resources that people apply in using them, make up its **technology**. Because of technology, people can exercise far more control over their environment than animals can. They can adapt to it, and they can adapt it to serve their needs.

Our Buildings

As you have read, all people have to solve the problem of shelter. However, people do not all build the same kind of shelter, even in the same environment. The kinds of

Our Capitol was built for the United States Congress. As part of our material culture, it expresses important American values.

houses that people build show what kinds of environmental problems they needed to solve for themselves by their design.

The style of buildings, or the way that they look and function, is called architecture. The architecture of some American houses was copied from that of houses built before the Revolutionary War. Others are quite modern. Architects, or people who design buildings, such as Frank Lloyd Wright, tried to blend the need for shelter with a design which fit into the environment.

We build many kinds of buildings other than shelters. In your community, you will

see buildings that are designed for a variety of purposes. Some are for business, some are for education, and some are for government or for religion. Each is designed to fulfill a certain purpose.

Our national Capitol in Washington, D.C., was built in the style of the ancient Romans. This style expresses our respect for the system of laws that was established by Rome. Many state capitols were also built in this style.

Beauty to Look At

We want our buildings to serve a purpose and to look beautiful at the same time. We also want other things that we use to be attractive to the eye.

Since ancient times, people have decorated their tools. These decorative designs were important features of ancient culture.

Since ancient times, people have made paintings of things that have been important to them. Paintings have been made on many different kinds of materials: stone, wood, bark, metal, paper, and canvas. Styles of painting and their subjects change over time and vary among cultures.

Sculpture is another old art form. Sculpture is a three-dimensional composition. It can be made of wood, bone, stone, clay, metal, or of treasures that were gathered from a junk yard, or found around the home. Like styles of painting, styles of sculpture are different in different cultures.

The style and the material that a culture uses for its art may provide as much information about the culture as the art itself. What style differences do you see?

The Way We Dress

The kinds of clothes that people wear vary from one culture to another.

Most people use clothes that make them comfortable in the climates in which they live. Climate alone, however, does not determine what clothes people wear. Culture affects the style of clothing.

Lesson 2 Review

Recalling Information

1. What is technology?
2. What are three elements of material culture?

Interpreting Information

3. List five different tools that are commonly used at school or at home. What problem does each help to solve?
4. Two common types of housing in our culture are high-rise apartment buildings and ranch-style houses. What problem is each helping to solve? Explain.

Applying Information

5. If you were to move to a tropical island, which items of your material culture would you take? Which items would you leave behind?
6. List some of the important tools that form part of your material culture.

This traditional Indian costume is the product of climate and culture. Which parts seem climate related? Which parts seem culture related?

Special People
Margaret Mead

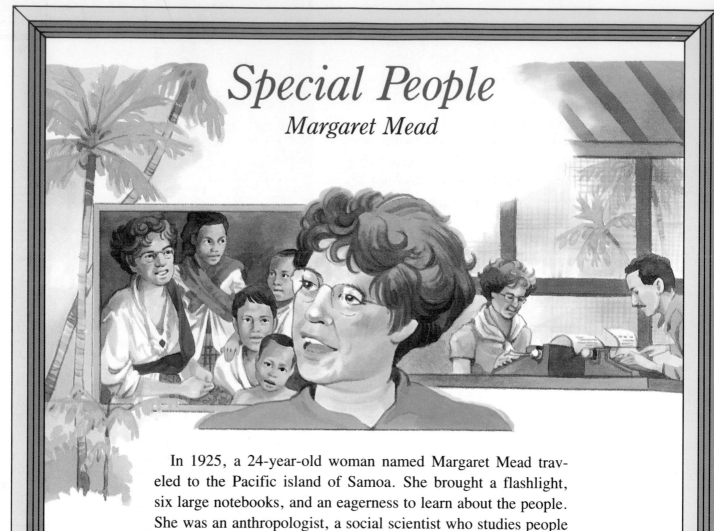

In 1925, a 24-year-old woman named Margaret Mead traveled to the Pacific island of Samoa. She brought a flashlight, six large notebooks, and an eagerness to learn about the people. She was an anthropologist, a social scientist who studies people and their culture.

She did not know the language of the Samoans, but she learned. In fact, she lived in a Samoan community to find out for herself how the people lived. She ate dried fish, learned Samoan songs, and took care of Samoan children. She watched for hours and wrote down what she saw. Films of her in Samoa years after her study show her still familiar with the language and the customs of the Samoans.

From her studies, Margaret Mead came to believe that people are different because of their environment, their history, and their culture and not because of their skin color. At the time of Margaret Mead's death in 1978, the people she had studied in Samoa mourned her passing as they would mourn a revered ancestor's death. Margaret Mead's ideas about the world have helped people to understand one another.

Lesson 3

NONMATERIAL CULTURE

Why do some societies build highly decorated buildings and others build very plain ones? Why do some peoples wear a lot of jewelry while others wear none at all? The material elements of a society are influenced by its nonmaterial culture. Those parts of culture that we cannot see or touch are as real as material things. For example, although a birthday cake is an item of material culture, it expresses a custom that is part of nonmaterial culture. Our customs, our family structures, our ways of educating the young, and our governments are parts of our nonmaterial culture, as are our beliefs, our ideas, and our feelings.

Societies Pass On Culture

Children require constant care in their early years when they learn about their culture. The first teachers of children are their families. When we are very young, our parents teach us how to talk and how to behave in order to get along in society. Even as we grow older and begin to learn from others outside the family, we still learn many things from our families. This process of cultural learning is called **socialization.**

Most societies provide additional kinds of education for young people. In traditional societies, this kind of education has been given by the adult members of the group. Modern societies such as ours have formal school systems. Young people are required by law to attend school for a certain number of years. Many obtain higher education, for most jobs in our society require advanced training.

Some societies give special instruction to young people who are about to become adults. Young people attend special ceremonies and listen to stories about the society. They may also have to prove that they can do the work of adults.

Kinds of Families

In most modern societies, the basic family unit is the **nuclear family**. A modern nuclear family consists of parents and their children.

In traditional societies, it is **extended families** that form the basic family unit. An extended family may include a married couple and their children, plus their children's husbands and wives and their grandchildren. In countries where farming is the principal means of earning a living, extended families serve the purpose of providing needed workers around the farm.

Some societies have been organized into clans. A clan is a group of families who believe that they are all descended from a common ancestor. Clan members are expected to help one another as they would help family members. Several clans that live together form a **tribe**. A tribal society, then, is one whose members are closely related. Generally, such a society has a leader or a council of leaders whose decisions on all tribal matters are sought, respected, and followed.

Societies Need Rules

When people live together, they need rules for preventing or solving problems.

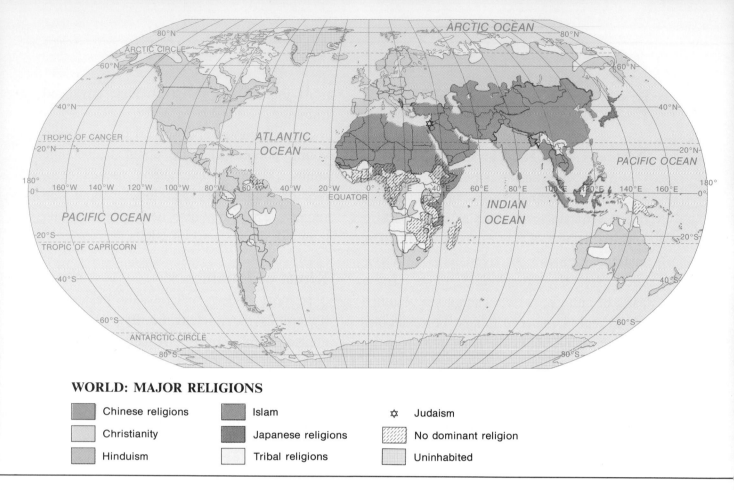

WORLD: MAJOR RELIGIONS

- Chinese religions
- Christianity
- Hinduism
- Islam
- Japanese religions
- Tribal religions
- ✡ Judaism
- No dominant religion
- Uninhabited

MAP SKILLS: Which color is used to represent the most common religion? In which continents does it appear?

Even if we try to get along and to be considerate of one another, we still need rules.

Customs have become rules in most societies. Many such rules are concerned with what we call good manners. From our parents, we learn such customs as not chewing with our mouths open and not interrupting people who are talking.

Societies must also make regulations and laws. Governments have been established to serve these purposes. A government is a group of people who have been given final authority to solve problems that affect the common welfare of people and to make laws for a society. Governments vary greatly from culture to culture.

Religions

All cultures have religions. A religion is a system of beliefs about how the world and people came into existence. A religion is based on the belief in one or more gods— the powers that order the universe. Religions include ceremonies of worship and prayer. The members of a religious group hold beliefs about how the world works and about how people should treat one another in order to live in the greatest possible harmony. Most religious groups believe that there is some kind of life after death. Religions usually have sacred writings that explain the origin of the world, the society, and the religion. Most religions

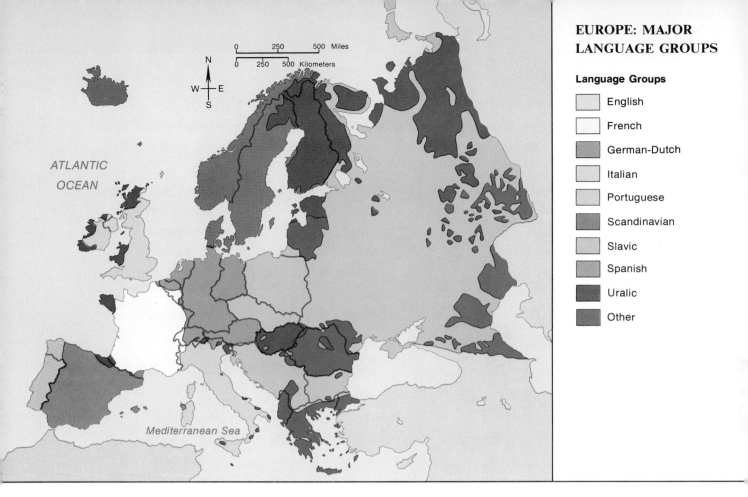

MAP SKILLS: Find the boundaries of the Soviet Union on the map. How many language groups are found in this area? Which languages are spoken elsewhere in Europe?

have places that they consider special for their group. The place may be a building where worship goes on. In other cases, it may be an area of open land.

There are many religions in the world today. The map on page 226 shows the largest ones. What is the predominant religion of the United States?

Religious beliefs affect material culture. In many cultures, paintings and sculpture have been made for religious purposes. They express religious beliefs and tell religious stories.

Many religions use special buildings for worship. This helps to instill feelings of awe or piety. The architecture of these buildings expresses the faith of the builders.

Ways to Communicate

In order for a society to function, people must be able to communicate with one another. All societies have languages, which are systems of words and ways of putting them together to express facts, thoughts, beliefs, feelings, needs, and questions. Without language, each person might operate in isolation. In fact, the phrase *not speaking the same language* means "poor communication."

All societies do not speak the same

227

Three distant cultures—ancient Roman, modern Italian, and Asian—are brought together on this street corner in Rome.

language, so we know that language is part of our nonmaterial culture. We are born with the ability to learn and to speak language, but the actual language that we speak has been learned from our culture.

Look at the map of Europe on page 227. Although there is one main language—English—in the United States, various languages are spoken in Europe. Spanish, Portuguese, French, and Italian developed from the language of the Romans, who once ruled Europe. Other languages developed from the speech of groups who lived outside the Roman Empire. Because all these persons had little contact with one another, they developed languages of their own.

Technology and Culture

The part of our culture that is most likely to influence how we use the environment is our technology. Technology gives us the power to use the resources of our environment. Our level of technology, however, is greatly influenced by our nonmaterial culture—our beliefs, our customs, our governments, and our relations with other societies. In the next chapter, you will learn about the history of human technology.

Lesson 3 Review

Recalling Information

1. In what ways do societies pass on culture? What is the process of cultural learning called?
2. What are three elements of nonmaterial culture?

Interpreting Information

3. Using the map on page 226, name the religion that is the most widespread.
4. In what ways does the kind of family structure that a culture develops affect the type of housing that the culture builds?

Applying Information

5. What ways of expressing yourself can you think of besides language?
6. List and explain as many reasons as you can for studying languages other than your own. Which language do you think would be most useful to learn? Why?

Skills for Thinking

RECOGNIZING PRIMARY AND SECONDARY SOURCES

In the early 1960s, Bradford and Marion Smith went to live and to work in India for almost two years. While they were there, they wrote letters to their friends and relatives telling about things that they did and things that they observed about life in India. Here is part of one letter.

> We went to the first part of a... wedding on Saturday, at the bride's house when the bridegroom came riding on a white horse. He got off, the men of the families greeted each other and gave small symbolic gifts (money, for instance, which then is given to the poor), and then everyone chatted and was fed a good Indian dinner in a large [bright-colored] tent out of doors. All this time the groom was greeting the people and the bride sat inside the house in a red sari and gold ornaments with a few girl friends .... She had one chance to speak to her future husband over a cup of tea.... The presents were on view and were all together a pretty complete simple household from underwear to beds and kitchen utensils.

Marion Smith's letter is an example of a primary source of information. Primary information comes from someone who actually witnesses or takes part in an event. Autobiographies are primary sources. So are journals and diaries. Other primary sources include documents, firsthand newspaper reports, paintings, photographs, and objects.

Secondary sources of information come from people who were not actually there but have studied and analyzed primary sources. Secondary sources are written after the event has happened. Encyclopedia articles are secondary sources. So are most research reports, textbooks, and nonfiction books.

How Should I Weigh the Facts?

As you study, read, and prepare reports, you will come across both primary and secondary sources of information. Both kinds can be important to you in different ways.

A primary source often provides everyday details that can help you to see and to feel the experiences of another person in another place or time. Secondary sources usually summarize events and help you to focus on major ideas and developments.

There is only one reliable way to think about events, and that is on the basis of evidence. Primary sources often are the most reliable. When you use all other sources, you must always ask: What is the evidence? As you continue to study the social sciences, you will develop your skills in using and weighing evidence.

Sometimes, primary and secondary sources contradict each other on the same subject. For example, there are many books about Stonehenge in England. Some say that it was built as a place of worship. Others state that Stonehenge was a scientific laboratory that was used to observe and to record regularities in sunrise, sunset, and changes of the seasons.

Parts of history are a mystery. Other parts are clear. Use your thinking skills to search for facts in primary and secondary sources of information. Then, if your research does not tell you what happened, say, "There isn't enough evidence. Therefore, I don't know."

Identify each of the following as either a primary source or as a secondary source:

- a spear from Africa.
- photographs from your vacation.
- letters from your cousin who is studying in France.
- an article by an anthropologist about Indian customs.

In three different secondary sources, find information about the giant statues on Easter Island. Who built them? How were they used? What did they stand for? Make notes to show how your three sources helped you to answer these questions.

Chapter **11** Review

Summary of Key Facts

In this chapter, you learned that

- culture is the total way of life of a group of people or of a society.
- a group of people with the same culture is called a society.
- customs are behaviors that are shared by a society or by a group within a society.
- cultures often change in response to contact with other cultures.
- a culture that has remained the same over a long period of time is called a traditional culture.
- we are not born with culture, we learn it.
- material culture includes all the physical objects of a culture.
- nonmaterial culture includes all the non-physical objects of a culture.

Using Vocabulary

On a separate sheet of paper, write the number of the statement and then the term that most closely matches the statement.

traditional culture	nuclear family
custom	extended family
technology	tribe

1. Several clans living together form a _____ .

2. Celebrating Thanksgiving or celebrating birthdays is an American _____ .
3. A married couple and their children make up a(n) _____ .
4. _____ increases control over our environment.
5. In traditional societies, needed workers are often provided by the _____ .
6. A _____ is one that has remained much the same throughout its history.

Discussing the Chapter

1. Explain how both diffusion and assimilation of culture take place.
2. What main concerns do most religions share?
3. How do language and religion spread?

Reviewing Skills

Write whether each of the following sources is a primary source or a secondary source of information.

1. a theater review by a critic who attended the opening-night performance.
2. a newspaper article based on information from an overseas news agency.
3. a book on Samoa written by Margaret Mead after her study of that culture.

The Growth of Technology

Introduction

Wearily, the sailor waded ashore. When he stood on the beach, he turned to look back. His ship was grounded on a sandbar, and the wreckage of his small lifeboat floated in the water. Now, he stood alone on a tropical island.

For food, the sailor ate waterfowl and turtle eggs. He lived in a cave and built a stockade of wooden posts around it. He even constructed an umbrella from leaves to shield himself from the sun and rain.

The sailor was Robinson Crusoe, the hero of an eighteenth-century book. Although the author made up many things in the book, he based the story on a true adventure.

The story of Robinson Crusoe has fascinated readers since it was published. People enjoy imagining what they would do if they had to survive by using only their intelligence and the natural resources at hand.

How people use tools to solve the problems of everyday life—technology—is one of the most important parts of the story of humankind. Alone or in groups, people take the resources of their surroundings and adapt them in ways that solve their problems. They create technologies that help them to make the best use of their resources. They refine old technologies, and they develop new ones. This process began with the first people on Earth, and the process still continues today.

A state-of-the-art robot plays for its creator. Do you think that machines will ever *compose* good music? Explain.

Lesson 1

EARLY PEOPLE

The woman who walked through the woods carrying her baby on her hip was short. Perhaps that's why she failed to notice the nuts that were ripening on the tree at her left. Then, one of them fell almost at her feet, and she looked up. What a find! But how could she harvest them? She couldn't climb the tree because it was too slim to bear her weight. Then, she had an idea. Carefully, she laid her baby down, removing the gazelle skin in which she had

Making and using tools took skill. People worked together and taught each other.

carried her infant. She spread the skin under the tree and struck at the branches with a stick. She was rewarded with a shower of golden nuts. Taking care to gather each one, she wrapped them in the skin, picked up the baby, and turned for home. Her family would feast today.

This scene might have taken place in Africa thousands of years ago. Like other early people, this clever woman spent much of her time looking for things to eat. Each day, finding food enough to survive was a challenge. Although life was hard, things like her skin-and-stick invention helped.

A Life of Hunting and Gathering

The warm lands of Africa and Asia were the home of the first people on Earth. There, humans lived as **hunter-gatherers.** Hunter-gatherers are people who depend for their food on what they can find and catch. The earliest people gathered berries, seeds, nuts, and roots from trees, shrubs, and grasses. They ate birds' eggs and insects. They also hunted animals. The first hunters probably killed only the animals that had been caught alive in natural traps.

Over thousands of years, the hunter-gatherers of prehistoric times were capable of improving their technology and thus increasing their food supply. Their first improvement was a tool that was made of stone. As you know, a tool is an implement, usually held in the hand, that people use to perform a task. Because so much of the evidence that scholars have found for this distant time is in the form of stone tools, the period has been called the Stone Age.

Some of the first tools that Stone Age people made were sharp chips knocked off larger rocks. As time went on, prehistoric people made axes, scrapers, and spear points from rocks by knocking off chips. They chipped blades with fine edges for cutting. With such tools, they were able to kill large animals. Stone tools also helped them to use animal skins, bones, tusks, and antlers to make other useful items, such as clothes, or containers for storing and carrying food.

Another improvement in Stone Age technology was the control of fire. At first, prehistoric people probably got fire from the flames that were started by volcanic eruptions or from lightning that had struck a tree or dry grass. By taking burning sticks from such "natural" fires, they built campfires. They protected their precious fire from wind and rain. Eventually, prehistoric people learned how to make their own fires by striking stones together and catching the sparks in bits of twigs or grass that would burn easily. Then, they could start fires wherever and whenever they wanted. Fire warmed campsites and cooked food. Along with stone weapons, it also provided defense against dangerous animals.

Stone Age people lived in small bands because they could not feed large numbers by hunting and gathering. Within each band, there was a simple **division of labor**, which meant that groups of people in the band were responsible for certain tasks. Men did the hunting, often working together in groups to attack wild herds. They were helped by such Stone Age inventions as spears and then bows and arrows.

Now that they had fire, people could work after nightfall or inside dark caves.

Women and children did the gathering. They were aided by another Stone Age tool, the digging stick. With its point hardened by fire, it helped food gatherers to pry plants loose at the roots.

Everyone wore clothing that was made from animal fur or skin. Women learned to make fitted garments by sewing skins together. A sharp bit of bone or antler made a needle, and animal sinews served as thread.

These hunter-gatherers of the Stone Age were **nomads**, or people who move from place to place in search of food. When plant and animal resources become scarce in one area, nomads move on to another location in search of more fertile areas.

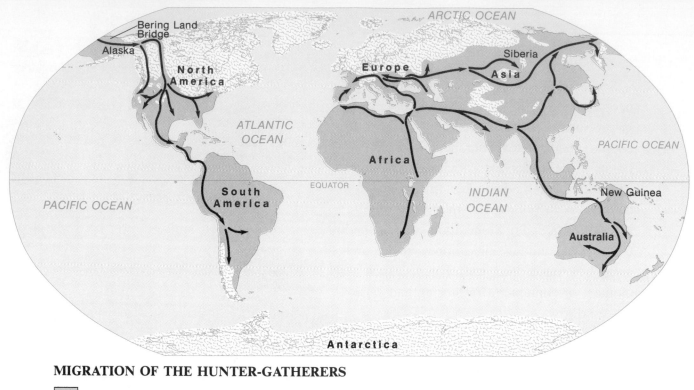

MIGRATION OF THE HUNTER-GATHERERS

Ice Age land area

Ice-covered land

→ Route of the hunter-gatherers

<u>MAP SKILLS</u>: Some hunter-gatherers of the Stone Age migrated to Australia. From where did they come?

Peopling Earth

As you have read, ice sheets that are called glaciers covered much of the Northern Hemisphere from time to time during the Ice Age. Although the regions near the glaciers were cold, they teemed with big game, such as mammoths and bison. As Stone Age technology—the control of fire and the ability to capture and skin large animals—improved, hunter-gatherers developed the ability to survive in cold climates. In time, therefore, Stone Age people spread out in large-scale **migrations** from Africa and Asia to colder parts of the world. Migration means "a movement of people from one place to another."

The Americas were one of the last regions to be occupied. When glaciers still covered much of Earth's northern regions, a land bridge connected northeastern Asia with North America. Nomadic hunter-gatherers tracking big game moved from Asia to America across this bridge. They were the ancestors of the American Indians.

Scientists believe that the migrations to the Americas may have begun more than 20,000 years ago. As time went by, bands spread out across the continent. By the time the Ice Age ended and ocean water covered the land route between Asia and North America, the Indians had peopled both North America and South America.

Can You Imagine?

Imagine that you live during the Stone Age. The only people you know are those in your own band of 20 persons—your mother and father, brothers and sisters, aunts, uncles, cousins, and grandparents.

Every day, you wear the same goatskin garment that your mother sewed for you. Every night, you sleep wrapped up in animal fur, in a hut that your father built with branches and leaves.

You have learned many important things. One is that you must always be on the lookout for food—nuts, berries, birds' eggs, seeds, and animals. Another is that you must always be ready to protect yourself from dangerous animals, using the spear that you made.

The most important thing that you have learned is that whatever food you find must be shared with everyone. By obeying this rule, your band has been able to support itself and survive for a long time.

People discovered that if they looked around carefully, the environment was full of resources that they could use in their daily lives.

Lesson 1 Review

Recalling Information

1. How did the first tools give people more power over their environment?
2. How did control over fire change life in the Stone Age?

Interpreting Information

3. Name at least three ways in which Stone Age people used the resources of their physical environment.

4. Where did the first people live? Where did early migrations lead their descendants during the Stone Age? Why?

Applying Information

5. Think about one of the tools that you use in your everyday life. (Remember that a tool can be something that is as simple as a toothbrush or as complicated as a computer.) How does the tool help you to influence your environment?
6. Is there a kind of tool as yet uninvented that you think could be useful? Explain.

THE DEVELOPMENT OF AGRICULTURE

Suppose that people could travel back and forth through time. Imagine that a group of "time travelers" visited a band of hunter-gatherers about 12,000 years ago. The location was a hilly area of the Middle East where present-day Turkey, Iran, and Iraq meet. Then, suppose that the travelers visited the same location about 2,000 years later. They would have been very much surprised on their return visit.

Instead of nomadic hunters, the travelers would have found people who were settled in small villages, with houses that were built of mud and stone. The villagers would be eating barley and wheat, peas and lentils that had been harvested from fields nearby. They would be tilling their fields with stone hoes, blades, and digging sticks.

What happened between the first and the second visits of the "time travelers"? A dramatic turning point in human existence had taken place—the agricultural revolution. The agricultural revolution was the change from hunting and gathering to farming and herding, from finding food to producing food. Agricultural revolutions have occurred at different times in different places. Scientists believe that the first one took place in the Middle East about 10,000 years ago.

The agricultural revolution depended on two main developments: the domestication of plants and the domestication of animals. **Domesticated plants and animals** are those that are raised by humans. No one knows how people were able to domesticate wild plants and animals. We do know, however, that the process probably took at least 1,000 years.

The light soils and the abundance of wild grains in the Middle East may have encouraged people there to observe that some plants seed themselves and to learn how to plant seeds for predictable growth and harvest. Women probably did much of the experimenting since they were the main food gatherers. Animals such as wild sheep and wild goats also roamed in this area. The first domesticated animals may have been lambs or kids that had been captured by hunters.

The agricultural revolution was not simply a matter of raising plants and animals instead of hunting and gathering. It meant that people could settle in one place. In fact, they had to. Crops must be cultivated. Domesticated animals must be fed. Thus, the first farmers were the first villagers—the first humans to live in settled communities.

Farming villagers exploited the resources of their environment in a number of new ways. They used reeds to weave baskets and other household items. They used clay to shape pottery. They also developed the potter's wheel, a horizontal disk that was used both to speed up the production and to improve the quality of pottery. (Not long afterward, the principle of the wheel—this time in a vertical position—was used to create carts and wagons.) Grain crops gave villagers the first food surpluses that could be stored for future use. Villagers stored these surpluses in baskets and pottery jars.

Farmers made flour by grinding grain between stones. They built stone ovens for cooking. From straw and mud, they made sunbaked bricks. They set the bricks in stone foundations to build houses.

Better Farming Methods

The early farmers soon learned that harvests would improve with better land. Larger tracts of flatter land, richer soils, and more water attracted them to some of the most fertile land in the Middle East: the plains of Mesopotamia (*mehs∗uh∗puh∗*TAY*∗mee∗uh*).

Look at the map that is on page 240. Mesopotamia is a flood plain bounded by the Tigris and the Euphrates rivers. There, the newcomers found an abundance of reeds and water birds, as well as level land and light fertile soil. Rainfall, however, was very low in summer. Summer heat baked the soil until it was hard and dry. A new technology was needed for farming the new area. Irrigation solved the problem.

The earliest settlers in Mesopotamia may have carried water from the rivers and streams to their fields. Eventually, though, they built a system of canals and ditches that connected the waterways to their fields. These irrigation channels carried water to thirsty crops throughout the year.

Another farming improvement was the wooden plow, a means of cultivating the soil that was more efficient than the digging stick or the stone hoe. A third improvement was the use of oxen as draft animals to pull plows. Irrigation, plows, and draft animals enabled farmers to work large fields and to harvest bigger crops.

Building methods that were developed long ago in Mesopotamia are still used there today.

Cities and Civilization

As farming methods improved, production continued to increase. As a direct consequence of increased production, the health of the people also improved. Better health meant an increase in population. With healthier people and more food available, fewer babies died and more people lived to adulthood. Thus, more children were born to each couple, and more children grew to adulthood, and parenthood.

Not all these people had to be farmers. Some people spent their time doing other things, such as making tools and weaving cloth. They traded what they made for food

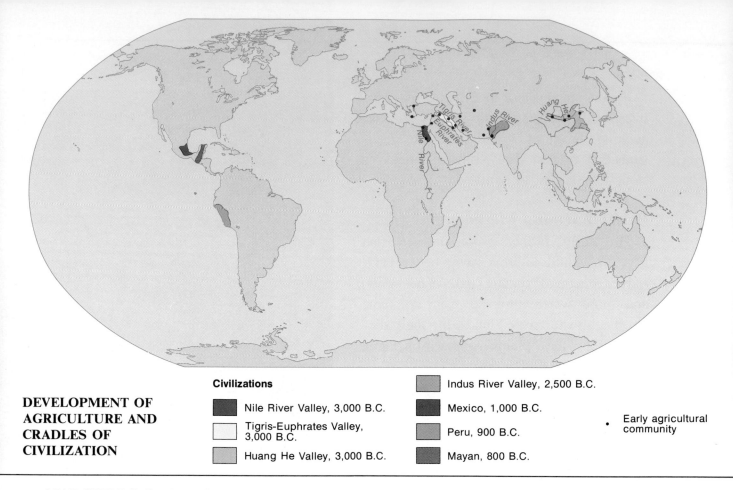

DEVELOPMENT OF AGRICULTURE AND CRADLES OF CIVILIZATION

Civilizations

Nile River Valley, 3,000 B.C.

Tigris-Euphrates Valley, 3,000 B.C.

Huang He Valley, 3,000 B.C.

Indus River Valley, 2,500 B.C.

Mexico, 1,000 B.C.

Peru, 900 B.C.

Mayan, 800 B.C.

• Early agricultural community

MAP SKILLS: Look at the patterns that exist between early civilization and farming centers. What is the connection?

and for other necessities. When the division of labor increases so that jobs formerly done by one individual are divided among two or more, it is called **specialization**. Specialization usually increases productivity because each person becomes an expert at his or her part of the job.

As populations continued to grow, towns grew into cities. City life encouraged even more specialization. Cities then, as now, depended on rural farmers for food. Trade flourished between farms and cities and between cities, too. For instance, tin was scarce in Mesopotamia, and so merchants brought it in by ships from other regions.

Ships with sails first came into use about 5,000 years ago.

City life brought new problems that called for new solutions. Since urban centers had more people than villages did, government became more complex. In Mesopotamia, a number of independent cities—called city-states—developed. These were ruled by small groups of men who held most of the power over city life.

Urban living led to important advances in learning. One was the calendar, an instrument which made planning easier for farming and business. Mesopotamian priests, after close observation of the stars

240

and the planets, worked out a year of 354 days. Another advance was a mathematical system. The one developed in Mesopotamia, based on the number 60, is still used for measuring time and circles.

The most important advance in learning was writing. The people of Mesopotamia pressed wedge-shaped symbols into wet clay. This kind of writing is called cuneiform writing. It comes from *cuneus*, the Latin word for *wedge*. Scholars date the beginning of recorded history from the invention of writing about 5,000 years ago.

As you can see, cities grew out of special circumstances, including population growth and specialization. They led to further milestones in human progress. When a culture has all these characteristics—a large population, specialization, cities, and advanced technology and learning—we call it a **civilization**. The world's first civilization developed in Mesopotamia about 5,000 years ago, or in around 3000 B.C.

The writing symbols that appear on this statue are the ancestors of our alphabet.

Changes Around the World

You learned that people had migrated to all continents except Antarctica by the end of the Ice Age. In regions, such as in Europe, people continued to live as hunter-gatherers. Another way of life developed in the dry climates of central Asia and Africa. There, nomads herded flocks of sheep and goats on the brush and grasses and camped at scattered watering places. Later, these nomadic herders domesticated horses and camels, mainly to carry trade goods.

One group of herders who lived in Asia near the Caspian Sea Northeast of Mesopotamia were the first people to make iron. About 3,500 years ago, they developed a process for removing large quantities of metal from iron ore. With iron they could make better weapons, which helped them to conquer other people. Knowledge of iron-working spread and led to the production of iron pots, tools, and plow blades.

Agricultural revolutions took place in many different parts of the world. Like the first one in the Middle East, they eventually led to the development of civilizations. Three others grew up along irrigated river valleys, too.

In North Africa, the Nile River provided water for farming villages as early as 5000

This ancient Andean toy makes use of a major technological breakthrough—the wheel.

B.C. It was the basis for Egyptian civilization, which dominated the Mediterranean Sea for centuries. In what is now Pakistan, the Indus River valley was the home of farmers who grew wheat, barley, and fruits in irrigated fields. The region's oldest cities date from about 2300 B.C.

In China, farmers first began to cultivate grains and to raise cattle and sheep in the Huang He (Yellow River) Valley. The first urban centers of Chinese civilization developed there about 1500 B.C.

In the Americas, civilizations developed in two highland regions rather than in river valleys. In Mexico and Central America, Indian farmers were growing corn, beans, and squash by about 7000 B.C. The first settled villages were established about 3500 B.C. In the Andes region of South America, farming villages date back to about 4000 B.C. The urban centers that were built by the Inca of Peru came thousands of years later, sometime in the century that began in A.D. 1400.

Lesson 2 Review

Recalling Information

1. Where and when did the first agricultural revolution take place?
2. Name at least three changes in technology that were developed by early farmers.

Interpreting Information

3. What was the connection between agriculture and the first civilization?
4. What discovery most changed life for humankind? What makes you think so?

Applying Information

5. Writing marked the beginning of human history. When and how did you learn to write? How would your life change if you did not know how to write—and to read?
6. How did life in early cities and villages differ from yours?

Lesson 3

WESTERN CIVILIZATION AND INDUSTRIALIZATION

With an oil lamp sputtering beside him, the old man scribbled into the night. His name was Vitruvius, and he lived about 2,000 years ago, around the time of Jesus Christ. A Roman architect and engineer, he wanted to record in a series of 10 books everything that he knew about building. Called *On Architecture*, it instructed generations of builders, inspired a renaissance (new birth or revival) of architecture 500 years ago, and is still read today. It is one of the bridges that connects the ancient civilizations of Greece and Rome to our own modern Western civilization.

Greece and Rome

You have read how the first civilizations developed in four river valleys in the Middle East and Asia. Those of Mesopotamia and Egypt had a lasting influence on other people who lived near the Mediterranean Sea. Because this great inland waterway was usually calm when compared to the open oceans, ships from surrounding lands used it for travel and trade. Contacts among many different cultures produced an exciting exchange of goods and ideas.

The civilization of the Mediterranean region that influenced the West most was that of the Greeks. The Greeks lived at the eastern end of the Mediterranean on a peninsula and several islands. Their rocky, hilly land was divided into many communities that became independent city-states.

Ancient ruins remind us of Greek achievements in architecture.

Each city ruled itself and refused to be ruled by others. Greeks were proud of their freedom and were the first people in the world to develop democracy.

The glory of Greece was its culture. Competition promoted human development of body, mind, and spirit. The Greeks were the first civilization on Earth to idealize human development to the extent that *all* activities were intended to be educational. Lawyers were thought to teach justice, and athletes to teach grace, courage, and strength. These ideals influenced Western educational traditions into modern times. Greek philosophy, literature, art and architecture, and science still influence the West.

While the city-states of Greece were

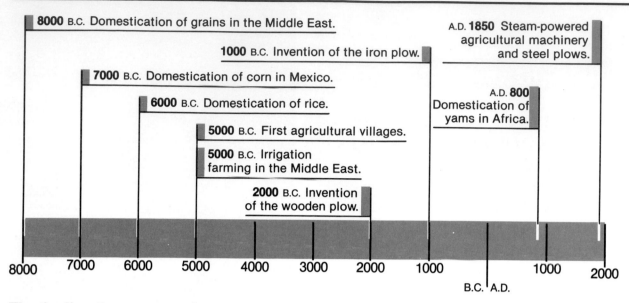

8000 B.C. Domestication of grains in the Middle East.

A.D. **1850** Steam-powered agricultural machinery and steel plows.

1000 B.C. Invention of the iron plow.

7000 B.C. Domestication of corn in Mexico.

6000 B.C. Domestication of rice.

A.D. **800** Domestication of yams in Africa.

5000 B.C. First agricultural villages.

5000 B.C. Irrigation farming in the Middle East.

2000 B.C. Invention of the wooden plow.

| 8000 | 7000 | 6000 | 5000 | 4000 | 3000 | 2000 | 1000 | | 1000 | 2000 |

B.C. A.D.

The timeline shows some major events in the development of agriculture.

flourishing, a small village located at the western end of the Mediterranean began its rise to power. This was Rome, which is located on the Italian peninsula. Gradually, the Romans extended their conquests, first over the Italian peninsula and then over the entire Mediterranean world. At the height of their power, beginning in A.D. 100, they ruled all the lands from Spain to Mesopotamia.

The most notable achievements of Roman rule involved the protection and the government of its empire. The Romans laid out a magnificent system of roads, over which they traded and moved their armies. They constructed aqueducts that carried water over long distances to supply Rome and other cities. They built impressive temples, government buildings, and triumphal arches, using concrete for the first time.

Latin (whose alphabet we use) was the language used throughout the Mediterranean region. The Roman calendar—revised

to contain 365 days—is the basis of our modern calendar. Most important, the application of Roman law enabled Roman administrators to solve problems in an orderly way.

Eventually, the Roman Empire collapsed. The empire could not feed all its people. The people lost confidence in the government. Roads fell into decay. Frontier forts were abandoned. Nomadic migrations of Northern European peoples swept into Roman territories. Finally, the city of Rome fell to invaders in the A.D. 400s.

The Rise of Western Civilization

After the decline of the Roman Empire, Europe endured centuries of violence and confusion. Trade almost died out. The population of cities dwindled. Food was scarce and serious illness was common. People lived in self-sufficient farming communities called manors. They grew their own food and made their own clothes. While bands of violent people roamed the countryside, a force for peace was the Roman Catholic church. This religious institution was based on the teachings of Christ. In its monasteries and convents, monks and nuns ran schools, maintained hospitals, and fed the hungry. They also kept learning alive. They valued the works of Greek and Roman scholars—not only philosophers but also practical writers such as Vitruvius.

The period from around A.D. 500 to 1500 is known as the Middle Ages, that is between the civilization of the Greeks and Romans and "modern" Western civilization. (It is also called the medieval period.) Western civilization arose in the early centuries of this era. It sought to combine the achievements of Greece and Rome with the teachings of Christianity.

The culture of the United States is sometimes referred to as American civilization. A branch of Western civilization, it includes not only the heritage of Europe but also elements from American Indian, African, and Asian cultures which were transmitted by immigrants (newcomers) to the United States.

Improvements in Farming

The early Middle Ages were grim but not without progress. Since almost everyone lived by farming, most advances in technology involved agriculture. There were several major improvements between A.D. 500 and 1000.

One of the most important advances was a new kind of plow. The light plow that was used in the thin soils of the Mediterranean could not cut through the denser soils of northern Europe. A heavier plow was invented. This plow required a team of as many as eight oxen to pull it.

The horse, a fast and versatile animal, was used as a draft animal to pull heavy loads. Ancient methods of harnessing draft animals were extremely inefficient. The solution to this problem was the horse collar, a padded ring that fit loosely over the animal's shoulders. Horses that were wearing such collars could freely pull more than their own weight. Horsepower was also made more efficient with the invention of horseshoes to protect the animal's hooves.

Another innovation was a new system of crop rotation. Previously, land was left fallow (unplanted) every other year so that it would regain some fertility. Half the land was always out of production. Medieval farmers learned that land would stay fertile if it was planted in a winter crop, then a spring crop, and then left fallow. This three-field system meant that only every third field was idle at one time.

One important technological change of the Middle Ages was a great increase in the use of waterpower. Water mills had served to grind grain in Roman times. (Vitruvius described them.) Nevertheless, they were not widely used because the Mediterranean region does not have many streams. Those that it has tend to be shallow in dry spells. Northern Europe has more streams.

Monasteries probably took the lead in the construction of mills. Soon, farming communities were using water mills to power many activities.

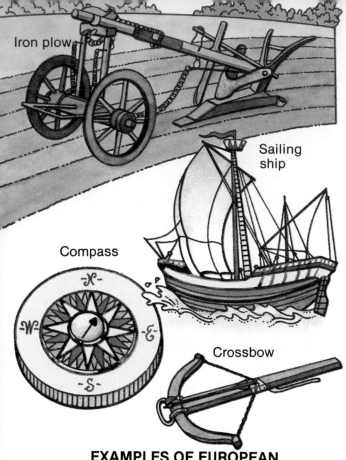

EXAMPLES OF EUROPEAN TECHNOLOGY IN THE MIDDLE AGES

Technology had already become very advanced by the time of the Middle Ages.

Another power source used in the Middle Ages was wind. Windmills were used in the grinding of grain and, later, to pump water for drainage and irrigation.

The Expansion of the West

The many advances in early medieval technology enabled Europe to grow more food and thus to support more people. (You will remember that the same thing happened in the Middle East during prehistoric times.) Cities began to thrive again, and trade revived. In the later Middle Ages, Europeans borrowed and developed new products, new ideas, and new technologies. Do you remember what such borrowing is called?

One series of inventions made water travel, especially ocean transportation, safer and more efficient. The addition of new types of sails made ships faster. A rudder at the stern (back) instead of an oar at the side made the ships easier to steer. The compass, with its metallic needle that points north, helped sailors to find their way. So did the astrolabe. This instrument helped sailors to tell time and to determine latitude. Improved maps and charts showed coastlines, islands, and harbors more precisely.

Metalworking advanced, too. Craftsworkers learned better ways to shape iron. Earlier, they had been able to make only wrought iron, or iron that was heated in fire and then hammered into shape. An invention, the blast furnace, made it possible to melt metal and to pour it into molds to form cast iron.

Advances in ironwork were combined with another innovation, gunpowder, to make new weapons. The Chinese had invented this explosive powder but used it mainly for making fireworks. Europeans applied the invention to weapons of war, and made the first cannon and muskets.

Undoubtedly, the greatest invention of the later Middle Ages was movable type, which was invented in Germany in the 1400s. A metal cast was made of each letter of the alphabet. These could be combined into words and then pages. After a page was printed, the metal casts could be carefully taken apart, enabling the printer to use the letters again. Earlier, the Chinese had discovered the idea, but in Chinese, individual letters are not used. Consequently, the Chinese had no practical use for movable type.

This English home and all the land surrounding it for miles belonged to one wealthy family.

Before the invention of printing with movable type, every book in the West had to be copied by hand (usually by monks). With the invention of movable type, books could be produced in quantity.

The energy and inventiveness of Western civilization seemed to increase with every achievement. Confidence inspired Europeans of the early modern period. They felt that they could go anywhere on Earth and do whatever they wanted to do.

Beginning in the late 1400s, Europeans embarked on a great age of exploration and discovery. Vasco da Gama of Portugal traveled around Africa to reach India. Christopher Columbus, sailing for Spain, opened up the New World when he voyaged across the Atlantic to America. Other daring seafarers ventured into many other lands that were previously unknown to Europe.

As Europeans moved out into the world, the resources of their new environments changed Europe. One important change was an increase in wealth. Gold and silver from America flooded into Europe.

Some people spent money on palaces and pomp. Others, called capitalists, invested it to make more money. They often financed voyages overseas to find new lands for goods to buy and sell. They set up colonies, or settlements in distant lands, such as those that eventually became the United States.

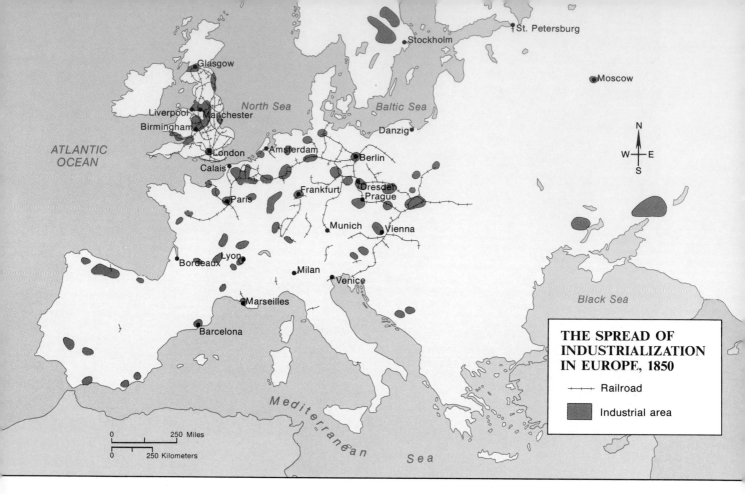

THE SPREAD OF INDUSTRIALIZATION IN EUROPE, 1850

†—†—† Railroad

▨ Industrial area

MAP SKILLS: Railroads connected areas that could not be reached by water. Locate these areas on the map.

The Industrial Revolution

By the 1700s, Europeans had opened up markets all over the world. Trading companies dealt in sugar and tobacco from America, cotton from Egypt, tea from the East Indies, and silk from China.

In spite of its progress, the world of the 1700s was very different from our own. Farming was the basic way of earning a living. Muscles, water, and wind provided power. Transportation depended mainly on horses and boats.

The reason that the world of the 1700s changed can be summed up in one phrase: the **Industrial Revolution**. It consisted of a transformation of industry by new sources

of power—steam, petroleum, and electricity—that affected production and trade. Machines that were powered by human-made energy sources replaced hand tools. Steamships and railroads speeded up transportation, and increased trade.

The Industrial Revolution began in Great Britain in the mid-1700s. The first industry to rely on machines was the cotton manufacturing industry. For a long time, cotton cloth had been made in people's homes on hand-operated spinning wheels and looms. A series of inventions produced big machines that could do the work of many people in less time. These were installed in factories and, at first, were operated by water power. Later, they were operated by steam power, the greatest innovation of the Industrial Revolution.

Steam engines had been in existence for years, but they were ineffecient. Only when James Watt improved the engine in the 1760s did steam become an efficient source of power. Factories no longer had to be located near water. Soon, people also discovered that because a steam engine could be movable, it could also power movement. This discovery led to railroads and steamships that could move people, as well as raw materials and finished products, to the places where they were needed.

Mechanization is the use of machinery. The factory system placed machines and workers in one place for long hours which improved production. Mechanization and the factory system were soon applied to all kinds of manufacturing. Cities grew rapidly to accommodate the workers needed to mass-produce goods. In countries where industrialization first took hold—Great Britain, the United States, and Germany—the basic economy, or way of making a living and using wealth, changed from farming to manufacturing.

The Industrial Revolution led to new technology in almost every field. Steel—iron processed into a harder and more useful alloy for machinery—became the chief metal. Petroleum soon provided a new source of power. Its by-product, gasoline, was used in a new kind of engine, the internal combustion engine. This engine fueled machinery and automobiles. Electricity was adapted to industrial use as another new source of power.

There was also a revolution in communications. New technology enabled people to send messages by telegraph, telephone, cable, and radio.

All these solutions to problems were developed in the West. Western civilization came to dominate the world economically. As you will learn in later chapters, the Western economy was the first truly global economy. The environment of Western civilization had become the entire Earth.

Lesson 3 Review

Recalling Information
1. How did European agriculture improve after A.D. 500?
2. In what industry and in what country did the Industrial Revolution begin?

Interpreting Information
3. Why were Europeans of the 1500s and the 1600s able to establish control over trade and colonies in new lands?
4. What are some important resources for industrialization?

Applying Information
5. Industrialization is so familiar that, often, we are unaware of it. Look around a kitchen. Make a list of the machines that it contains. How was the work that was performed by these machines done before they existed?
6. Make a list of the different kinds of energy used in your home. How would your life be different without these energy sources?

Skills for Thinking

WRITING A SUMMARY

Have you ever been asked to give an oral report? You often have to read a lot of information to prepare for an oral report. Then, you might write a summary, a short version of what you have read.

A summary helps you to remember important facts or ideas. The following rules are helpful in writing a summary.

1. Read each paragraph more than once.
2. Look for the main idea.
3. Include the important details, and leave out the unimportant ones.

Which Facts Are Important?

Read the paragraph that follows. Think about what the main idea is. Then, read the sentence that summarizes the paragraph.

> People have been cultivating plants for thousands of years, but not only for food. Some foods, such as corn, olives, and peanuts, are also good sources of vegetable oils. Industrial oils, such as castor oil and linseed oil, come from plants, too, and are used in such products as paint and soap.

Summary: People grow plants not only for food but also for the vegetable and industrial oils that they produce.

Compare the paragraph and the one-sentence summary. Then, read each of the following paragraphs. Think about the main idea in each one and which facts are most important. Finally, write a one-sentence summary of each paragraph.

> 1. Plant leaves, seeds, and stems are superb sources of fiber. Hemp has a flexible fiber that can be made into ropes or nets. Flax, also known for its blue flowers, is the source of linen. Cotton, which has been grown for more than 8,000 years, is made into a variety of fabrics and other popular products.
> 2. It is easy to see why cotton is such a valuable plant, for cotton fibers are used to make such products as lace, sheets, blankets, and carpets. Cotton is also used in film, plastics, and paper. Cottonseed oil is used in cooking, margarine, and even in cosmetics.
> 3. For thousands of years, the cotton industry grew slowly. Cotton fibers and seeds had to be separated by hand. Then, in 1793, everything changed with Eli Whitney's invention of the cotton gin. One of these machines could clean 50 pounds (22.7 kg) of cotton per day.

Chapter *12* Review

Summary of Key Facts

In this chapter, you learned that

- the first tools that were used by Stone Age people were chips of rocks to help in hunting animals, in digging, and in chopping.
- stone tools enabled people to make fire for cooking and for defense.
- the change from hunting and gathering to farming had occurred by 8000 B.C.
- the technology of irrigation was developed in Mesopotamia.
- specialized workers in the first civilization used metals to make objects.
- Western civilization developed new technology in farming and other areas.
- improved sailing technology led to European exploration and colonization.
- the Industrial Revolution began in Great Britain around 1760.
- technology continues to advance today.

Using Vocabulary

On a sheet of paper, write the terms that will correctly complete each sentence.

agricultural revolution
civilization
Industrial Revolution
nomads
division of labor

hunter-gatherers
domesticated
   plants
domesticated
   animals

1. The Stone Age people were ____ who got food by being ____ and had a ____ that was based on age and sex.
2. The ____ brought about a change from hunting and gathering to farming ____ and herding ____ .
3. The first ____ developed in Mesopotamia in about 3000 B.C.
4. The ____ brought about a change from manufacture by hand to manufacture by machine.

Discussing the Chapter

1. How did the Stone Age people make and use tools to help them to meet needs?
2. What changes in culture were brought about by the agricultural revolution?
3. How did Western civilization develop and spread through new technology?
4. How did the Industrial Revolution affect life in England and other places?
5. Pick any two important advances in technology. Explain their importance.

Reviewing Skills

Write a sentence that summarizes the first paragraph on page 244.

Population Today

Vocabulary

"baby boom"	infant-mortality rate
demographer	metropolitan area
birthrate	megalopolis
death rate	subsistence farmer
average life	cash crop
expectancy	

Lesson Preview

Lesson 1: Population Growth and Change
Lesson 2: Where People Live
Lesson 3: How Do People Make Their Living?

Introduction

Through the 1950s, the junior and senior high school building in Moorestown, New Jersey, became more and more crowded. More desks were jammed into each room until there were 35 or more students in each class. Smaller classes could not be formed because there was no more room.

Finally, in 1960, a building was begun that would make it possible for the junior high school and the senior high school to be located in separate buildings. Experts said that an additional junior high school might be needed in the future.

Earth's nations gather at the Olympics. How does population affect the way of life in your state? In your city or town?

Why was there so much crowding in the Moorestown schools?

A "**baby boom**" was responsible. From 1946 to 1964, American families had record numbers of children—77 million of them. This baby boom had far-reaching effects. New schools had to be built to accommodate all of the children.

After about 1964, families began to have fewer children. Five years later, the numbers of schoolchildren declined, and so did the need for new classrooms. Today, the baby boomers are starting to have children of their own. Perhaps some schools will have problems of overcrowding.

Population, as you can see, involves more than numbers of people. We are living at a time when population has become an issue—a subject of concern.

POPULATION GROWTH AND CHANGE

What is the largest crowd that you have ever been in? If the gathering was a major league baseball game or a professional football game, the number of people could have ranged from 20,000 to 80,000. If you were at a sold-out rock concert, there might have been even larger numbers of people in the audience.

In terms of population statistics, these numbers are very small. For example, some scientists have estimated that since the beginning of time, 95 billion people have lived on Earth. It would be impossible to count that many people if you counted day and night, every day of your life.

Look at the graph of world population on page 255. It shows how the population of the world has grown over time. How many people were there in 1650?

The graph shows that of the estimated 95 billion people who have ever lived, most did so in the last 3 centuries. For thousands of years, the population of the world grew very little. Then, it began to grow very rapidly. This growth was so rapid that it has been called a "population explosion." Today, it is growing at an extremely rapid rate. (The world population grew by about 85 million people in 1984.)

Today, the world's population is approximately 4.8 billion people. **Demographers** (*dih∗MAHG∗ruh∗ferz*), or the people who study populations, expect the population of the world to reach 10.5 billion by 2050.

This rapid growth will have great effects on the world's people. All those people will have to be fed; thus, food production will have to increase. All those people will have to be clothed; thus, the production of clothing will have to increase. All those people will have to be sheltered; thus, houses will have to be built. All those people will have to be cared for when they are ill. Thus, medical facilities will have to be built.

Earth, however, cannot grow. Meeting the needs of all these people will be one of the great challenges of the future. These challenges will not be the same everywhere because population growth will not be the same everywhere.

How Population Grows

Population grows when the number of births is greater than the number of deaths. Demographers measure births in terms of the annual **birthrate**, or the average number of births per 1,000 people in the population in 1 year. For example, if there were 20 births for every 1,000 people, the birthrate would be 20.

To figure out the birthrate in a given year, divide the population by 1,000. Then, divide the number of births by that number. Your answer is the average number of births per 1,000 people in the population.

Let's try it.

If the population of country X is 20,000,000, and the number of births is 400,000, what is the birthrate?

$$20,000,000 \div 1,000 = 20,000$$
$$400,000 \div 20,000 = 20$$

Thus, the birthrate of country X is 20; that is, for every 1,000 people in the country, 20 babies were born.

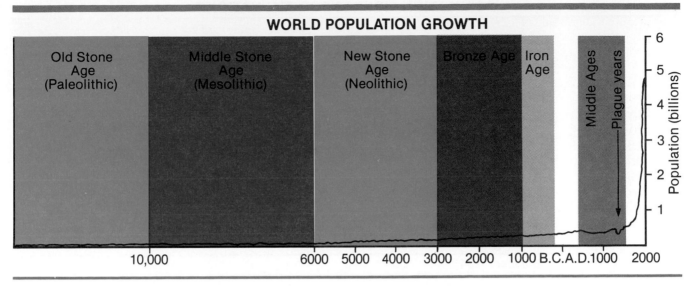

WORLD POPULATION GROWTH

Old Stone Age (Paleolithic) | Middle Stone Age (Mesolithic) | New Stone Age (Neolithic) | Bronze Age | Iron Age | Middle Ages | Plague years

Population (billions)

10,000   6000 5000 4000 3000 2000 1000 B.C. A.D. 1000 2000

Trace the course of world population growth with your finger. Where does it become steep?

The **death rate** works the same way—mathematically, that is.

Take the same country of 20 million people. Let us say that 200,000 died. What was the death rate?

$$20,000,000 \div 1,000 = 20,000$$
$$200,000 \div 20,000 = 10$$

Now, if you subtract the death rate from the birthrate, you will have the growth rate. In this case:

$$20 - 10 = 10$$

That is, the growth rate is 10 per 1,000 people, 1 per 100 people, or 1 percent.

What influences growth rate? One answer is **average life expectancy**, or the average age of the people who died in a particular country in a given year.

For the world as a whole, the average life expectancy is 56 years for men and 59 years for women. Look at the chart on page 256. What is the average life expectancy for men and for women in the United States? Mexico? Japan? Ethiopia?

If the average life expectancy is increas-ing, the rate of population growth will in-crease, also.

Another factor influencing population growth is the **infant-mortality rate**. The infant-mortality rate is the number of deaths of babies in their first year.

If the infant-mortality rate is going down, the growth rate will increase.

You can now understand the sharp rise in population and population-growth rates. Infant mortality has declined, and life expectancy has increased, owing primarily to the progress in health care, in medicine, and in nutrition that attended the moderniza-tion of the West and the spread of this progress into the rest of the world.

Consider these estimates: In the last minute, while you have been reading, 250 babies were born and 99 people died. This was a net gain of 151 people on Earth.

Comparing Population Growth

Some populations grow faster than oth-ers. The world population is growing at

POPULATION FIGURES FOR TEN NATIONS

Nation	Population	Birth rate per 1,000 people	Death rate per 1,000 people	Percentage rate of increase	Infant mortality per 1,000 births	Average life expectancy	
						male	female
Brazil	127,000,000	23.3	6.8	2.3	92	61.3	65.5
Egypt	44,000,000	37.6	10.1	2.7	110-120	53.6	56.1
Ethiopia	30,500,000	48.0	23.0	2.4	155	37.0	40.1
Iceland	232,000	18.6	6.5	1.2	9.6	73.4	79.3
Japan	118,600,000	13.0	6.1	1.0	7.1	73.4	78.9
Mexico	71,300,000	34.0	6.0	3.3	77	62.7	66.5
Pakistan	93,000,000	45.0	17.0	2.9	142	51.9	51.7
Sri Lanka	15,200,000	27.6	6.1	1.7	43	64.8	66.9
Sweden	8,310,000	11.7	11.0	0.4	6.7	72.8	78.8
United States	232,000,000	15.9	8.6	0.7	11.2	70.3	77.9

Source: *The World Almanac,* 1984

Compare the data for Egypt with the data for Sweden. What factors would account for the differences?

a rate of 1.67 percent per year. If that rate continues, the population will *double* in 42 years. We speak of such a span of time as the doubling time of a population.

Many of the poorer nations of the world grow at the rate of 2.02 percent per year. Their doubling time, then, is 35 years. The population of Africa, the continent of "lowest economic productivity," is growing at a rate of 2.9 percent—the highest of any region. At that rate, its population will double in 24 years.

In contrast, population growth in the United States is about 1 percent annually. Twelve European countries in 1983 had no growth—the number of people born equaled the number that died. In the next lesson and in later chapters, you will learn more about how the world's population is distributed, or spread out, around the world and why populations tend to grow fastest in poorer nations. An understanding of how these numbers work is necessary for good problem-solving.

Lesson 1 Review

Recalling Information

1. What is doubling time? What is the growth rate?
2. How is population growth calculated?

Interpreting Information

3. How has modern medicine affected population growth?
4. How is agriculture important to a growing population?

Applying Information

5. If the population of your town were to double overnight, what changes would have to be made?
6. What do you think the estimated increase in world population growth will mean in your life?

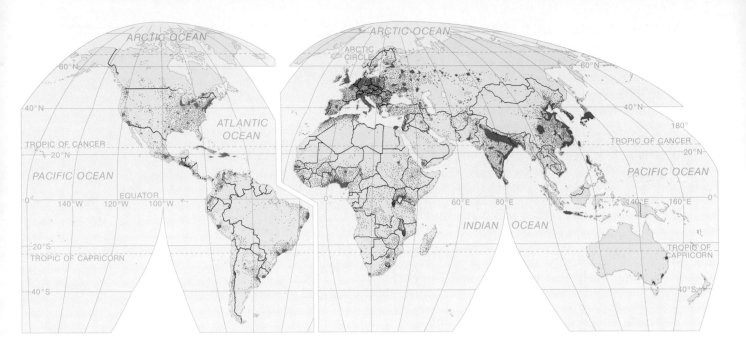

WORLD: POPULATION DISTRIBUTION

1 dot equals 100,000 people

MAP SKILLS: Locate two population centers. Use the text on pages 258 and 259 to find possible reasons for their development.

Lesson 2

WHERE PEOPLE LIVE

Who are the 4.8 billion people in the world today? Where do they live? What do they do? Demographers can tell us. By taking surveys and studying census reports, they can answer many questions about populations. A census is an official count of the people of a place.

Population Distribution

Look at the population-distribution map at the top of the page. It shows where people live in the world. Each dot stands for 1 million people. The circles stand for cities whose populations are many times the number represented by one dot.

You can see that the population of the world is not distributed evenly. Here arc some figures that will help to explain the uneven distribution of people.

More than one out of every five of the world's 4.8 billion people live in a single country—China.

Six out of ten people live in Asia. One out of nine lives in Africa.

One out of seven persons lives in Europe.

One out of twelve persons lives in North America.

One out of nineteen persons lives in South America.

The map on page 257 shows where on these continents the people live. Most live in the population centers of South Asia, East Asia, Europe, the northeastern part of the United States, and Southeast Asia. In fact, about 70 percent of the world's population live in places that make up only 8 percent of the world's land surface.

Why have people clustered in certain parts of the world and not in others? Imagine this.

You are attending a large party. Under a colorful tent are many tables. Some are covered with plates of delicious meat, vegetables, rolls, and salads. Some tables have only crusts of stale bread. Others are entirely empty.

It would not surprise you to find people crowded around the tables with food but no one around the empty tables or those with crusts of bread. Before the population explosion, the population distribution was something like the distribution of guests at this party.

As you know, early people tended to settle in areas where the climate and the landforms supported population growth. In general, population centers had environments that supported higher numbers. The climate was not too cold, too hot, or too dry. The land was flat enough so that transportation and communication networks could operate readily. Population centers were not marked by rugged mountains, harsh climates, or swamps, which would make people's lives more difficult.

Good soil has always been another attraction. Less than one-third of Earth's land is arable, or suitable for farming. Some of the

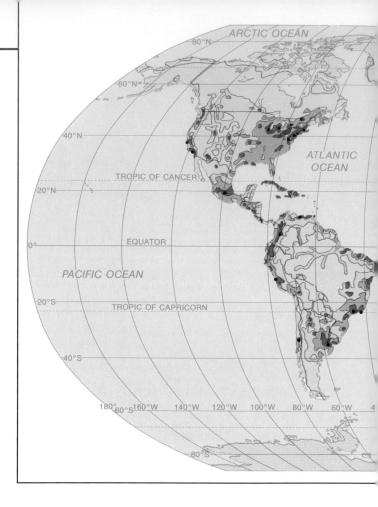

good farming areas were in or near the most crowded places on Earth.

Other resources have also encouraged settlement, such as gold, silver, coal, and oil. San Francisco in 1848 was a sleepy town of 800 people; within a few months after gold was discovered nearby, San Francisco grew into a major population center.

For the most part, climate, landforms, soil, and resources tell why people lived in some places and not in others. For example, history explains why more people live in cold, rocky lands in Europe than in Canada. Europe has been a settled area for more than 2,000 years. During that time, people spread out over the continent and adapted to the environment. Canada has been a settled

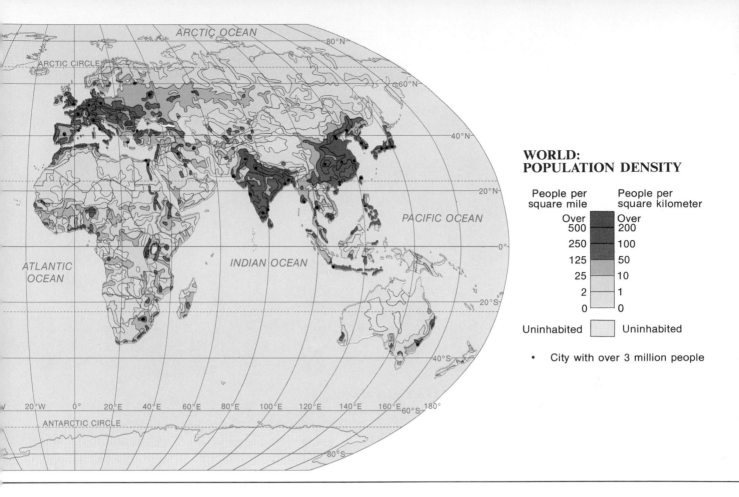

**WORLD:
POPULATION DENSITY**

People per square mile	People per square kilometer
Over 500	Over 200
250	100
125	50
25	10
2	1
0	0
Uninhabited	Uninhabited

• City with over 3 million people

MAP SKILLS: In which areas are people most crowded? In which areas are they least crowded? How is this shown?

area for only about 300 years. It is a large country with a relatively small population. There has not been enough demand for land to make European and Asian settlers move into the cold climate of northern Canada.

Population Density

Look at the map on page 257. It shows population distribution, or where on Earth people live. The population-distribution map does not show the population density of these areas, however.

Population density is a ratio that shows how crowded or how sparsely populated a particular area of land is. It is the number of people that live on a piece of land of a certain size. For example, 2 people per acre,

10 people per square mile, and 1,000 people per square kilometer are all numbers describing population density.

An example will help you to understand population density. Sweden has a population of 8.3 million people. It has a land area of 173,732 square miles (449,965.8 sq km). When you divide the population by the land area, you will find that Sweden has a population density of about 48 people per square mile (18 per sq km).

$$8,300,000 \div 173,732 = 48$$

The population density of Earth is about 84 people per square mile (32 per sq km). The map on pages 258 and 259 shows the population densities of each continent.

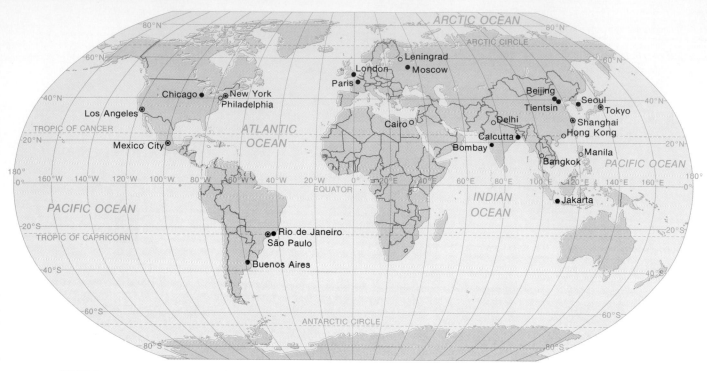

WORLD: 25 LARGEST METROPOLITAN AREAS

⊙ City with over 10 million people

● City with over 7 million people

○ City with over 4 million people

<u>MAP SKILLS:</u> **Which three categories are found on the key?**
In which category are the most cities found?

Rural areas are less densely populated than urban areas. *Rural* means "country." *Urban* means "city." In rural areas, farming is the chief economic activity. In cities, manufacturing and trade are the main economic activities. Urban areas are densely populated; a lot of people live close together.

Knowing that urban areas have denser populations than rural areas, you might think that some areas on a map are urban and like the banquet table with all the food when, in fact, they are not. If you look at the density map on pages 258 and 259, you will see that large parts of Asia are densely populated. You also might think that it would be logical to conclude that they are urban areas, but they are not. Even though there are large cities in Asia, most Asian people still live in rural areas. The way in which they settled the land, however, is different from the pattern of settlement in North America and Europe. In Asia, people live in villages and cultivate tiny plots of land—sometimes, much less than 1 acre (0.4 ha). The villages are small but are close to one another. The proximity, or closeness, of all these small villages results in thickly settled rural areas. In contrast, farms are larger and rural areas are sparsely settled in North America and in Europe.

Nevertheless, urban areas are the most

260

You live in a town of 2,000 people in the hills of rural Connecticut. In the center of town, surrounding the town green, or park, are two churches, several town buildings and shops, and single-family houses.

At the edge of town are a few more shops and a post office. Then, there is countryside—rolling pastures, woods, and an occasional house and a barn. No one is crowded here. Even in town, each family has about 1/2 acre (0.2 ha) of land.

Imagine your first trip to New York City, only 100 miles (160.9 km) away. You visit your cousin who lives in a 20-story apartment house. On each floor are 25 apartments. On the average, in each apartment is a family of four. In this one building live enough people to populate your entire town.

densely populated parts of the world. Most large cities started out as villages. Because of their location—usually close to waterways—they became important trading centers. Look at the map on page 260. You can see that most of the largest cities are located either on the riversides or along the seacoasts.

Since 1900, many cities have grown so large that they have sparked the development of surrounding areas. Like the sun attracting the planets, modern cities draw surrounding communities into their orbits, making them into suburbs. A suburb is a community near a large city. Many people live in suburbs and commute each day to work in nearby cities.

A city and its suburbs make up a **metropolitan area**. A metropolitan area can cross state or national boundaries.

In a few parts of the world, metropolitan areas have grown so much that they connect to other metropolitan areas. A combination of two or more metropolitan areas is called a **megalopolis**. The area between Boston and Washington, including Hartford, New York City, Philadelphia, Baltimore, and other cities, is a megalopolis. In our country, about 172 million people, or about 75 percent of the country's population, live in and around big cities.

Lesson 2 Review

Recalling Information

1. Which is the most populous country?
2. What are two reasons why populations are distributed unevenly?

Interpreting Information

3. What is the difference between population distribution and population density?
4. Why are most large cities located near good harbors along the seacoast or on riversides?

Applying Information

5. When your area was first developed, what factors do you think attracted people to settle there?
6. How are rural areas in your state different from those in Asia?

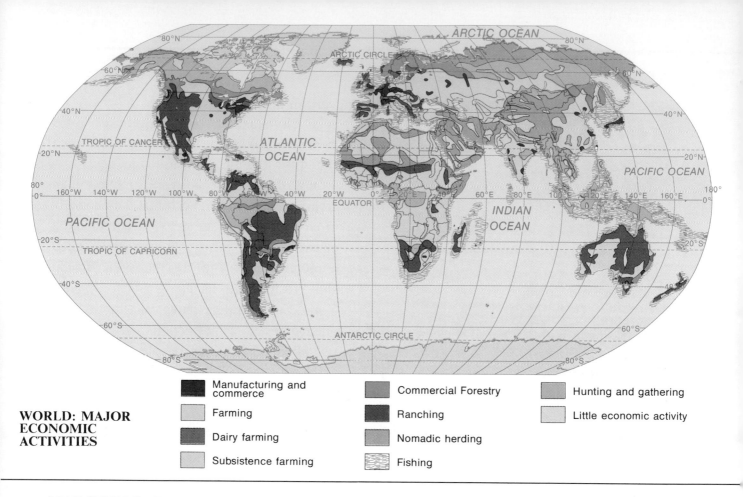

WORLD: MAJOR ECONOMIC ACTIVITIES

Legend:
- Manufacturing and commerce
- Farming
- Dairy farming
- Subsistence farming
- Commercial Forestry
- Ranching
- Nomadic herding
- Fishing
- Hunting and gathering
- Little economic activity

MAP SKILLS: Compare this map to the one on pages 258 and 259. Do many people live in areas where forestry is a main economic activity?

Lesson 3

HOW DO PEOPLE MAKE THEIR LIVING?

To live, people need food, clothing, and shelter. How they obtain these things is the way in which they make their living.

Most of the world's 4.8 billion people make their living directly from the land. In Africa, for example, 65 percent of the people grow crops or raise livestock. In Asia, the percentage is 58. In Latin America, it is 39. Only in the United States, Canada, Europe, and Australia do fewer than 25 percent of the people work in agriculture.

The World of Work

The map on this page shows eight major categories of work that people do. Maps like these are helpful in showing where certain work is done. It is important to remember, though, that not everyone in an area does the same thing. Wherever there are people, there is diversified employment. For example, in the farming areas of the United States, there are towns and cities. In towns and cities, people make their living through manufacturing, trade, and service industries. Service industries do not produce things but, instead, provide things for people: they protect them, teach them, take

The United States harvests so much wheat that it is possible to sell some to other nations.

care of them when they are sick, or help them with their money. Thus, police and fire departments, schools, hospitals, and banks are all service industries.

Farming

Some experts call farming the greatest invention. As you know, when ancient people learned to raise crops, they were able to settle down. Once settled, cultures developed that grew into civilizations. Corn, wheat, and rice are the most important staples, or food crops, grown in the world. A large percent of the world's population exists largely on these three staple foods.

People farm wherever the soil and the climate allow it. The map shows a major farm belt that stretches through the Canadian and the American Midwest. It also shows another farm belt that stretches across the width of Europe and the heart of the Soviet Union. A third major farming area is located in Asia.

In North America and in Europe, large grain fields are planted and harvested through the use of efficient and powerful tractors and other mechanized farm tools. In Asia, people work small plots of land, using "people power" and simple tools. The main crop is rice, which is well suited to the

263

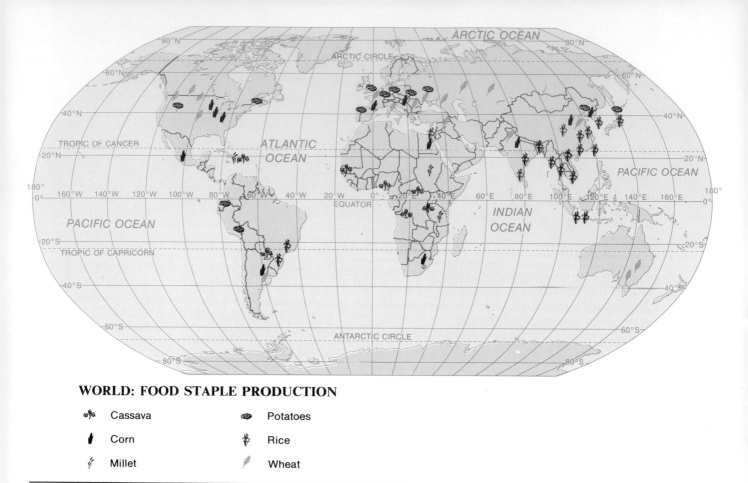

WORLD: FOOD STAPLE PRODUCTION

Symbol	Staple	Symbol	Staple
🌿	Cassava	🥔	Potatoes
🌽	Corn	🌾	Rice
🌱	Millet	🌾	Wheat

MAP SKILLS: Symbols are useful when many products are to be shown. Locate the equator. Which staples are grown along it? Locate the Arctic Ocean. Which foods grow in that area?

tropical climate and the abundant rainfall of much of the area.

The map on page 262 shows that South America and Africa do not have large farming areas. From what you have read about their populations, why is this a problem?

Ranching

Ranching is concerned with the growing of livestock animals for meat or for other products such as hides and wool. Ranching needs grasslands for pastures, but it does not require the best grassland. Hills and dry plains are often used for pasturing animals.

The American West, made famous by the cowhands of a century ago, is one of the great ranching areas in the world. So is an area of Argentina called the pampas. There, the *gauchos* (GOW*chohz*)—Argentine cowboys—are the subjects of legends that rival the stories of their North American relatives, the cowhands.

The map on page 262 shows that ranching is a main economic activity also in both Australia and New Zealand. The map on page 265 shows what kind of ranching is done in these countries. After comparing the two maps, you should be able to understand why lamb and mutton are common in both New Zealand and Australia

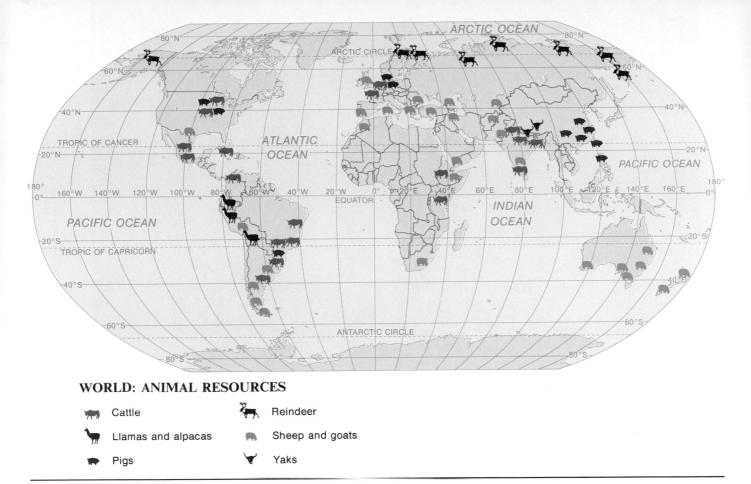

WORLD: ANIMAL RESOURCES

- 🐄 Cattle
- 🦙 Llamas and alpacas
- 🐖 Pigs
- 🦌 Reindeer
- 🐑 Sheep and goats
- 🐂 Yaks

MAP SKILLS: What is the resource shown on this map? How is it represented on the map? In which region is found the greatest variety of this resource? The smallest?

but rarely appear on the dinner table in Chinese homes. With little grazing land, China must import lamb, which makes it too expensive for most Chinese to afford. Besides cattle, what other animals are raised for meat and hides?

Fishing

As you know, people need protein in order to grow strong and to help to maintain their health. Both meat and fish are excellent sources of protein. Many Asian countries rely on fish, rather than meat, for their protein.

Fishing is an ancient occupation. It is practiced by all peoples who live on or near water. However, fishing is a big industry only in coastal regions or in regions that are close either to major rivers or to major lakes. Modern fishers use huge nets to scoop up tens, hundreds, or even thousands of fish at once. Factories have been built to process the fish and to prepare it for sale.

Some places are better than others for fishing. One of the richest fishing grounds is the Grand Banks, off the coast of the Canadian province of Newfoundland.

Study the map on page 262. In what other areas of the world is fishing a most important economic activity?

Fish are a resource with other uses besides food. Their products also provide oils and chemicals. Protecting the oceans also protects the fishing industry.

Forestry and Mining

Forestry is another important industry. Until recently, forests were very poorly managed. For centuries, many people cut down trees with no thought of replacing them. In recent years, the conservation of forests and woodlands has become a matter of necessity. With modern logging machines, any forest on Earth can be cut down for lumber, and as populations increase and as people demand more lumber, our most bountiful forest ecosystems are threatened with destruction.

Mining is also important to the world's economy. Without such resources as iron ore, coal, and copper, most manufactured goods could not be made.

Manufacturing and Commerce

The last category of work—manufacturing and commerce—involves most of the workers of the industrialized countries. This category covers every production and trade occupation from the business executive to the factory worker and computer operator.

Since the Industrial Revolution gained ascendancy in Europe and in North America, it has spread around the world and is increasing its sphere of influence in almost every country. Many people have stopped working the land. In countries such as the United States, this change took place years ago. In many other countries, it is just starting to take place.

Subsistence and Nomadic Activities

Let us take a look at two farmers. Farmer Hess is a **subsistence farmer**. He has a cow, a few chickens, a pig, a garden, and a few acres of farmland. He and his family produce just enough each year for themselves—enough food to eat and enough surplus to trade or to sell for their other needs.

Farmer Young, by contrast, farms 800 acres (323.8 ha) of farmland, using modern machinery to harvest thousands of bushels of corn and wheat. He raises far more wheat and corn than the people who live on his farm can use. He grows these grains as **cash crops**, or crops to be sold for a profit. Farmer Young is a commercial farmer, one who raises crops to sell for a business profit rather than only for the family's use.

Most of the world's farmers are subsistence farmers. Many people around the world also earn their living through other subsistence activities. They fish or hunt-and-gather the foods that their environment provides. Some of these people are living very much as the hunter-gatherers and the fishers of long ago. The modern world has not changed their way of life. They earn their living without benefit of machines and modern know-how. Even so, most people who are engaged in subsistence activities have contacts with people of other cultures. You will read more about their ways of life in Unit 5.

Nomadic herding is another activity that has been practiced for centuries. Nomads travel from one grazing area to another with their herds of sheep, goats, or other animals. The map on page 262 shows that Central Asia, North Africa, and the Middle East are all areas where nomadic herding is still a way of life.

As you will learn, the kinds of work that people do are greatly affected by their environment and by the resources available to them. A people's culture and technology are other important factors that determine how they make their living.

Lesson 3 Review

Recalling Information
1. What is the main crop that is grown by Asian farmers?
2. What are the eight major economic activities? Which of these is the main work category in the United States?

Interpreting Information
3. Why is most farming that takes place in an industrial country commercial instead of subsistence?
4. How has the Industrial Revolution changed the way in which people make their living from the land?

Applying Information
5. How do people make a living in your area?
6. Why do you think that the conservation of natural resources is important?

Skills for Thinking

LISTENING TO A TELEVISION COMMERCIAL

You read in Lesson 1 that demographers can tell us many things about populations. This information can be used in many ways, from telling us how many schools will be needed in the future to how many houses, roads, and shopping areas will be needed.

Population information is also useful to manufacturers. In the United States, 51.5 percent of the population is female and 48.5 percent is male. Almost 50 percent is under 35 years of age. With information such as this, the manufacturers can sell their products to particular groups of consumers.

They can use information about the population as the focus of their advertising. They often use commercials to communicate certain images that they think will appeal to certain groups of people. Can you recall commercials that told you how to

- make your hair more beautiful?
- dress in the most up-to-date way?
- make a snack or a meal more delicious?

By now, you are learning the thinking skill that is called evaluation: You are learning how to judge the *worth* of certain information. When it comes to commercials, you might ask yourself the following question: Is there a good reason to buy this?

You have probably eaten cereal for breakfast many, many times. Cereal companies are always making new kinds of cereal and trying to get more and more people to buy their brands. Your teacher will read a commercial for a new kind of cereal. Listen to the commercial, and then answer the following questions.

- What sounds good to you about the new cereal?
- What information has been left out of the commercial?
- When you find the cereal in your store, what should you check?

Chapter 13 Review

Summary of Key Facts

In this chapter, you learned that

- population has grown dramatically in the past three centuries.
- population is expected to double in 42 years.
- about 70 percent of the world's people live on only 8 percent of Earth's land surface.
- urban areas are the most densely populated parts of the world.
- environment, resources, culture, and technology influence how people earn their living.

Using Vocabulary

The underlined words make the sentences below incorrect. On a separate sheet of paper, rewrite the sentences, putting in the correct words.

1. A metropolitan area consists of a city and its demographers.
2. The birthrate and the death rate are used to find out life expectancy.
3. Subsistence farmers raise enough food for their countries.

Discussing the Chapter

1. Discuss four factors that influence the distribution of world population. Give an example of each factor.

2. What kinds of conclusions about a nation's people have demographers made on the basis of birthrates and death rates?
3. Why have some villages become cities?
4. How does the environment in which people live influence how they make their living?

Reviewing Skills

Answer the questions below about this sentence from a commercial:

"Leading dentists recommend the ingredients in Smile-Free Toothpaste."

1. What sounds good to you about Smile-Free?
2. What do you need to know in order to evaluate this information?

Unit 4   Review

Summary of Key Facts

In this unit, you learned that

- food, water, shelter, and clothing are basic human needs.
- people not only adapt to but also change their environments.
- the culture of a society is defined by material objects and by nonmaterial ideas and customs.
- the domestication of plants and of animals contributed to the development of civilization.
- modern Western technology was the product of original invention and energetic borrowing from around the world.
- the world's population is distributed unevenly.
- population has increased dramatically in the past three centuries due to industrialization and to modern medicine.
- environment, resources, culture, and technology influence the ways in which people earn their living.

Discussing the Unit

1. In what ways does environment influence where and how people live?
2. In what ways are all cultures alike?
3. Do you think that it is difficult to move out of one culture and into another? Why?
4. Explain the advance of technology through history. Give examples to illustrate your points.
5. Explain how population increases.

Activities

1. Interview someone who was born early in this century. Ask about their reactions to some technological changes of the century and how these changes have affected their lives. Report your findings to the class.
2. Choose one of the food staples, either corn, wheat, or rice, to learn more about. Find out how the crop is farmed today and something about its history. Report your findings to the class.
3. As a class, make a chart listing renewable resources.

Test

Using Vocabulary

On a sheet of paper, write the term to which each statement most closely relates.

material culture
renewable resources
nonrenewable resources
average life expectancy
nonmaterial culture
Industrial Revolution
fossil fuels
agricultural revolution

megalopolis
society
custom
reserves
natural resources
migration
demographer
technology

1. These can be biological or mineral.
2. These resources are limited in supply.
3. These resources are unlimited.
4. These minerals are burned for energy.
5. These are known deposits of resources.
6. This is a behavior that is part of our culture.
7. These are visible aspects of a culture.
8. These are cultural elements that you cannot see.
9. This is all of a society's tools.
10. People from Asia came to America.
11. This replaced hands with machines.
12. This person studies population.
13. This is formed when cities connect.
14. Modern medicine has lengthened this.
15. Improvements in farming techniques led to this.

The Big Question

How do a people's technology and culture affect how they live on Earth?

Write your answer in complete sentences. Draw upon the information in this unit to write a good answer.

Using Map Skills

Use the map on page 257 to complete this exercise.

1. What symbol is used on this map, and what does it represent?
2. Are there more concentrated areas of population in eastern or in western United States?

Identifying a Geographic Theme

Think about the geographic theme of **human-environment interactions** as you complete this exercise.

How have people where you live adapted to the natural environment? How have they changed it?

Unit 5 Different Ways of Living

We use our technology to affect how we live on Earth—how we use its resources and how we interact with the environment. Most peoples have had very simple tools. They have lived close to the land and used the resources at hand. They lived by subsistence activities—hunting and gathering, fishing, nomadic herding, and family farming—taking from their environment only what they needed to live.

Many of the world's peoples still live in these traditional ways—very close to their environment.

Concepts

slash-and-burn
   agriculture
sedentary agriculture

native commerical
   forestry
transhumance

The Big Question

How do ways of interacting with their environment compare among traditional societies?

Focus on a Geographic Theme

In this unit you will study the geographic theme of **human-environment interactions**. As you have learned, geographers study how the changes people make in their surroundings affect both them and the environment. Consider the effects of a major oil spill in the Pacific Ocean. How would the environment be changed as a result of the spill?

**Which kind of transport would you prefer
near the North Pole?**

Peoples of Forestlands

Chapter 14

Introduction

The Asmat men crouched over a split log on the muddy bank of the river. Reaching under the bark, they scooped masses of long, wriggling beetle grubs onto palm leaves. The women folded the grubs into the leaves and placed the food in the nearby cooking fire to roast. This delicacy would be added to the main part of the meal, bread baked from the starchy pith of the sago palm. Earlier in the day the women had beaten the plant material into flour after stripping out the stringy fibers.

The Asmat people live along the humid, forested seacoast of southwestern New Guinea. The homes of the Asmat are thatch-roofed huts built on stilts high above the swampy tidal flats of the coastal rivers. The wild sago palm is their symbol of life. From its pith they get their staple food. From its wood they make their houses and canoes and build their fires.

Long ago, many of the people of the world lived in forests. With the growth of farming, the Industrial Revolution, and the worldwide use of timber for building and for fuel, the number of forest dwellers has dwindled. Today, there are few groups like the Asmat. Most forest dwellers no longer live in isolation; they are affected by modern society. In many cases, their traditional cultures are in danger of being lost.

In this chapter, you will learn about past and present forest dwellers. You will discover how the traditional forest societies live in harmony with their environments.

◄ **Iban people of Borneo step from the edge of the rain forest. What human needs can the tree behind them provide?**

275

THE FOREST AS A HUMAN ENVIRONMENT

As you know, a forest is a natural community—a biome—that is dominated by trees. Different climates and kinds of soil produce different kinds of forests.

Forests provide environments for many plants and animals. They form human environments, too. From the earliest time, humans have lived in the forests of tropical and semitropical Asia and Africa. Even before people learned how to make and to use fire, they hunted wild animals and gathered the fruit, the seeds, and the roots of wild plants. They followed nature's ways and lived in harmony with their environment. They changed the environment very little.

The first tools came directly from nature. Sticks were used as spears or as clubs. Stones were used as hammers or as weapons. Sharp stones were used as cutting and chopping tools. As time passed, people began to shape the stones for specific purposes. They also learned to use fire.

Hunting and Gathering

Although forests could supply all the needs of hunter-gatherers, only a certain

In Canada's subarctic forest, an American Indian woman cleans a buffalo hide that she will use to make warm clothing.

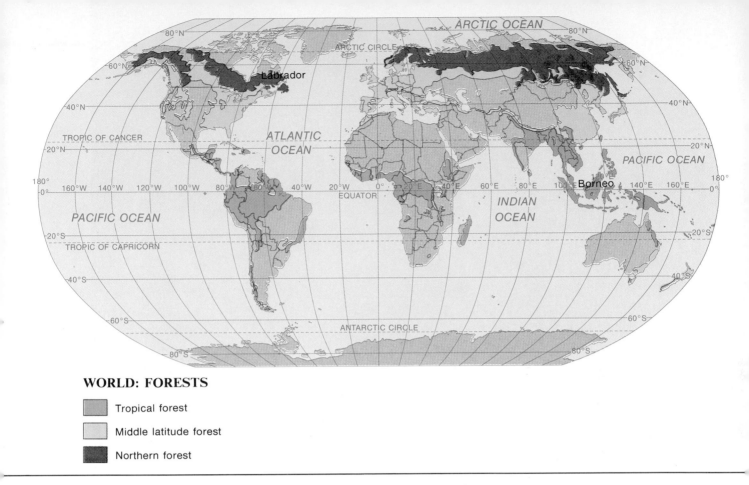

WORLD: FORESTS

- Tropical forest
- Middle latitude forest
- Northern forest

MAP SKILLS: Which areas of middle-latitude forest would you say are the least densely populated? Explain your answer.

number of them could support themselves in a forest region. A growing population had to move into other regions to obtain enough food, shelter, and clothing. The entire Earth was settled in that way. Forest dwellers migrated to other areas of Asia and Africa, to Europe, and, eventually, to Australia, North America, and South America. Before they learned about agriculture, people lived in forests throughout the world.

When Europeans began to settle North America, they found many American Indian groups that lived mainly by hunting and gathering. One such group was the Ojibwa (*oh*JIHB*way*), who were also known as the Chippewa (CHIHP*uh*wah) of Canada and who lived in the forests around the up-

per Great Lakes. The Ojibwa lived in dome-shaped tents that were made of bark. They dressed in animal skins and hunted and gathered food.

Living wholly off "found" resources of a forest is difficult. Over a period of time, most forest dwellers developed other ways of meeting their needs. Only a few isolated groups of people still live by hunting and gathering in forests.

The Asmat people of New Guinea, whom you read about in the introduction to this chapter, are hunter-gatherers. In addition to the food they get from the sago palm, the Asmats spear and net fish in the river and scrape shellfish from the river mud. They catch lizards and hunt wild pigs in nearby

277

Until the Industrial Age, Europe had more dense forest areas than it had farmlands.

forests. Although they have some metal tools from inland peoples, the Asmat still use stone axes and scrapers.

Other hunting-and-gathering peoples include the Kreen-Akarore of Brazil, the Pygmy of the Congo Basin, and the Semang of Malaysia and Thailand.

Each group of forest dwellers adapts its hunting-and-gathering activities to the resources that the forest offers. Each has found different ways to solve the problems of having to live on what can be found—of adapting to its environment.

In Lesson 2, you will learn how the Iban make their living in Borneo's rain forest and then, in Lesson 3, how another group of forest people, the Montagnais-Naskapi

(*mohn*tan*YAY nah*SKAH*pee*) of eastern Canada, make their living. The map on page 277 shows where each of these groups lives.

Clearings in the Forest

As you may have guessed, forests are poorly suited to agriculture. The canopy of leaves prevents needed sunlight from reaching the forest floor. Where the climate permits the growing of crops, however, forest dwellers use an ancient method to grow them. This method is called **slash-and-burn agriculture**.

This process consists of cutting down small trees and grasses and then slicing the bark of large trees, which kills them. When the trees and the "slash" have dried out, the forest dwellers set a fire to clear the land. Then, they plant crops in the clearing. People who live in tropical rain forests use slash-and-burn agriculture to grow cassava, or manioc. This is a plant whose edible roots resemble sweet potatoes and whose starch is an important food in the tropics.

The slash-and-burn method is often called **migratory agriculture**. Because crops drain nutrients from the soil in a few years unless the soil is fertilized, forestlands can be farmed only for brief periods. Thus, forest dwellers migrate when the soil loses its fertility. The clearings from which they migrate are left fallow, or unplanted, in order to regrow and to regenerate.

Using the Forest

Early forest dwellers used the products of the forest only for themselves. They used forest resources to build houses, to make boats, and to feed and to clothe themselves. They used the forest soil to raise a few crops. Their needs were few and they did not take many resources.

Commerce eventually developed. Many forest dwellers found more than they needed and began to sell or to trade forest products to outsiders. People in other areas wanted what the forest provided. They needed wood to build houses, ships, and plank roads and to keep fires burning in stoves and fireplaces. **Native commercial forestry** developed to fill these needs. It remains an important livelihood for many forest dwellers today.

Various other forest products were traded, too. Midlatitude forests produced

Native commercial foresters harvest trees in Brazil's sprawling Amazon rain forest.

honey, wax, resin, and turpentine. In the northern conifer forests, trappers traded furs and skins. Tropical forests provided bananas, palm oil, and rubber.

From Forests to Farms

Forests and forest products have always been of great importance. Nevertheless, the development and the spread of **sedentary** (SEHD'N*tehr*ee) **agriculture** led to the permanent clearing of many forests. Where sedentary agriculture is practiced, people settle in one place to farm. The hard job of clearing dense forests ensures a commitment to working the land long enough to scratch out a living.

COUNTRIES WITH HIGH AND LOW PERCENTAGES OF FORESTLANDS

	Many forests	Few forests
Europe	Finland Sweden Soviet Union	Iceland Great Britain Denmark
Asia	Malaysia Japan Philippines	Saudi Arabia Kuwait Mongolia
Africa	Zaire Ivory Coast Gabon	Egypt Libya Tunisia
North America	Canada United States Guatemala	Greenland Puerto Rico Dominican Republic
South America	Ecuador Peru Brazil	Argentina Uruguay Chile
Oceania	Papua New Guinea	Australia

Name the one continent on Earth that has no forestland at all.

Sedentary agriculture began in the dry, unforested regions of the Middle East. In time, however, farmers began to move to land that was covered by forests. No doubt, the first forests to be cleared were ones that yielded easily to simple tools. The mediterranean scrub forests provide an example of such land. Forests along the Ganges River of India and the great rivers of China were also cleared thousands of years ago. Today, about 30 percent of Earth's land surface is forested. Before people began to cut down trees thousands of years ago, 60 percent of Earth was forested.

Why have people cut down forests for so many thousands of years? There are many reasons. If the cleared land in a region is being used by other farmers, a sedentary farmer has no choice but to clear land on which to plant crops and to pasture livestock. Wood from forests has long been used as fuel and to make houses, barns, furniture, and many other things.

When Europeans began to settle the eastern United States, they cleared the land for farms. This land-clearing process has continued to this day. Even so, a surprisingly large amount—about 30 percent of the land in the United States—is still covered by forest. In contrast, only 7 percent of the land in Great Britain and 10 percent of the land in China is covered by forest. On the other hand, almost 70 percent of Finland is forested, as is more than 80 percent of Malaysia.

The earliest immigrants to colonial America were amazed to see so much forested wilderness. In Europe, the forests had been changed by humans, but in North America, the forests appeared never to have been used by people. Actually, the immigrants were seeing a land that had been used for slash-and-burn agriculture. The Woodland Indians were farmers as well as hunters and fishers. Forests began to grow again after the American Indians abandoned their fields and moved to new homesites. The process of forest regrowth—**reforestation**—began again in the East when people gave up their farms and moved to cities.

Above is a list showing countries with high and low percentages of forestland.

Today's Forest Dwellers

With the spread of sedentary agriculture and the growth of cities, some people came to think of forests as obstacles to be removed. Forests prevented farming on arable land. Forests also proved to be barriers to expansion. The great forests of Central Europe halted Roman expansion. The forested Appalachians were obstacles to American migration westward.

As more and more forests were cleared, the number of forest dwellers also decreased. You have already learned that only a few groups live today solely by hunting and gathering. However, even these societies have been affected by the world beyond the forest.

Imagine that you are a Campa Indian living in a village near the Apurimac (*ahp∗ooh∗*REE*∗mahk*) River in Peru, a tributary of the Amazon. Your village is located in a rain forest, one of the most isolated spots in the world. Your house has cane walls and a thatched-palm roof.

Your father is a fisher-hunter who uses a bow and arrow. He selects the most appropriate arrow for the kind of animal that he is hunting—a pronged arrow for frogs, a barbed arrow for fish, and a blunt arrow for birds. Not long ago, he and other villagers built a fire and drove some wasps out of a tree. You were pleased because you think that roasted wasps are delicious.

Everyone in your family wears a long, brown, sacklike *cushma*, the traditional dress of the Campa. Your mother raises chickens, gathers edible plants from the forest, and grows cassava. She uses cassava to make a variety of foods and beverages.

Visitors to your village might think that little has changed there in thousands of years. They would be wrong. Forty years

In Newfoundland, logs reach a modern paper mill in an old-fashioned way—over water.

ago, your village did not exist. The people who live in your village used to live in separate family groups, deep in the rain forest. In 1948, a group of language students and missionaries from the United States made contact with your people. The students learned the Campa language and eventually persuaded many Campa families to settle in villages that were close to the river. Your people decided to move because they wanted the benefits of education and medical care.

Your life is different because of that change. You go to school in a one-room schoolhouse. Your teacher, a Campa, wears a white shirt and trousers, not a cushma.

You expect to continue your education in Pucallpa, a faraway city of more than 60,000 people.

When you go to Pucallpa, you will see some of the changes that will probably affect the isolated Indian peoples of Peru someday. Lumber mills line the banks of the river. A mill that produces paper from plywood also makes use of the rich resources of the nearby forest.

Manufacturing, too, is part of the economic life of Pucallpa. People who work in the city produce boats and outboard motors. There is a small oil refinery.

Forest dwellers in other parts of the world have been much more affected by outsiders than the Campa. One such group, the Ainu (EYE*noo), live on the island of Hokkaido (hoh*KEYE*doh), the northernmost island of Japan.

For centuries, the Ainu made their living by hunting and fishing. Like most hunter-gatherers, they believed that the forests, the seas, and the rivers belonged to everyone.

Then, in the nineteenth century, Japan took over Hokkaido. Increasing numbers of Japanese immigrated to the island. The new settlers, who were mostly farmers, changed the Ainu way of life. As farms were developed throughout Hokkaido, much of the game disappeared. Hunting became extremely difficult.

Despite resistance from many Ainu, Japanese culture began to dominate life on the island. Young Ainu adults adopted Japanese ways and married Japanese. Today, there are only a few hundred people who have both Ainu mothers and Ainu fathers. Their future as a culture that is separate from the Japanese seems in doubt.

Most forest dwellers in industrialized countries have no experience in living off the forest resources. They have houses in forested areas, but do not make their livings from the forest. Even those involved in forestry do not live off the land in the traditional way. They make money by selling trees, but they buy food and clothing that were produced elsewhere.

Lesson 1 Review

Recalling Information

1. On what does a hunter-gatherer depend for food and clothing?
2. What is slash-and-burn agriculture? Where is it practiced?

Interpreting Information

3. Why did sedentary agriculture reduce the amount of forested land on Earth?
4. Compare the history of the Ainu to the history of the American Indians.

Applying Information

5. Suppose that you were born into a traditional society such as the Campa. You have attended a school that teaches a modern curriculum. Would you want to remain in the traditional society? Why or why not?
6. Why is cassava a valuable resource? What starchy foods do you eat in place of cassava?

The residents of a typical Iban village live together in one long building that is divided into small family-sized sections.

Lesson 2

THE IBAN OF BORNEO

It is a hot July night. A dozen men slash their way through the dense tropical rain forest to make a path.

The men have come to the rain forest to get honey. They have chosen a moonless night, hoping that they will not be visible to the bees that have produced the honey. It is easier to work in the cool of night when the dangerous bees are quiet.

The men locate the honey tree. Its 10 paper hives are found 100 feet (30.5 m) into its leafy canopy.

Several men begin to build a bamboo ladder to reach the hives. They tie the crosspieces with rattan cord, which consists of long, pliable vines from a palm tree. They work quickly and quietly to avoid disturbing the bees.

Two of the bravest men begin the climb. At the top of the tree, they set fire to some branches. They aim the smoke at the hives and chant to encourage the bees to leave the hives.

The smoke drives the bees from the hives. Taking advantage of the bees' confusion, the men scrape the honey from the hives with wooden paddles. They lower a container of honeycomb on a rope. The men on the ground squeeze the honey from the comb. By dawn, the men have collected more than 200 pounds (90.7 kg) of honey.

These men are Iban, one of several groups of people who live on the island of Borneo in the South China Sea.

Down the River Baram

Borneo is a vast island that is about the size of Norway and Sweden combined. It is located at the equator, southeast of the Philippines. Borneo supports one of the largest tropical rain forests in the world. Broadleaf plants cover even the high mountains of the island. Only the top of Mount Kinabalue, which rises 13,000 feet (3,962.4 m), is not covered by plants.

Imagine that you are taking a canoe trip on the Baram River, one of the island's best highways. In a land that is covered by dense forest, it is always difficult, and sometimes impossible, to travel overland. Travel by canoe is the best way to move from place to place. Your trip along this long, slowly moving river takes you past many Iban settlements. For centuries, the Iban have relied on the rain forest for their livelihood.

As your canoe approaches an Iban village that has been carved out of the dense tropical forest, you see boats that are tied to a jetty (protective wall or pier). You notice young children at the oars of other boats. The Iban learn at an early age to navigate the river. Along the banks of the river, you see women who are filling large pots with water. Not only does the river serve as a highway, but it also provides a source of water for drinking, for bathing, and for cleaning.

At the center of the village is a huge structure called a **longhouse** in which the Iban live. Around the longhouse are small vegetable gardens that are partially shaded by broadleaf evergreens. Beyond these gardens are plots of cleared land where the Iban plant rice.

You are invited to visit an Iban longhouse, and, as you enter it, you discover that it is a series of apartments, called *bileks*, that surround an open corridor. You conclude that a longhouse can be compared to an apartment house.

Longhouses are built of wood from the hardwood trees of the rain forest. The houses are raised on stilts that are about 15 feet (457.2 cm) high. This construction keeps the buildings off the damp, often muddy ground. Pigs, chickens, and dogs are kept under the longhouse.

The floors of a traditional longhouse are made of bamboo canes that have been tied together. The stalks rub against one another whenever anyone walks on the floor. You try to step very lightly, but the floor still creaks.

Living in a Longhouse

Each Iban family eats, sleeps, and stores its possessions in its one-room bilek. Sometimes, a prosperous family subdivides its room by using curtains or by using walls that are made of boards. The beds consist of low platforms that are set against the walls or in the corners of the room. Not all of the beds have mattresses.

Woven rattan mats have been spread on the floor or on a slightly raised platform. There, the family sits to eat or to talk. Their

Iban longhouses, built with native forest products, are designed to provide dry, airy shelter in Borneo's steamy rain forest.

cooking pots are made of clay, and their water pitchers are made of bamboo.

A fireplace has been set against the outer longhouse wall. There, the women prepare meals for their families. These meals often consist of rice and salted fish or vegetables. A hinged flap in the roof is raised to let out smoke from the cooking fires. The flap is closed to keep out the heavy rains.

Opposite the row of bileks is a platform, or verandah, that is the same length as the bileks. A section of the verandah is used by each family that lives in the longhouse. On the verandah, people entertain visitors, take naps, weave fish traps, and tell stories in the evening.

Living Off the Forest

For as long as anyone can remember, the Iban have been subsistence, slash-and-burn farmers. The men use machetes and axes to cut through the dense forest undergrowth. Then, they burn the woods to clear a plot for planting. Each plot is planted for a number of years with rice and is then allowed to lie fallow for 10 years or more.

The Iban make use of the other resources from the forest. They gather fruit, such

Turtles captured in the surrounding forest provide an Iban village with fresh meat.

of longhouses because such wooden structures are not fireproof.

Some Iban now wear Western-style clothing instead of traditional clothing, which consists of a loincloth for men and a sarong for women. A loincloth is a piece of material that is wound around the waist and brought between the legs. A sarong is a long cloth that is sewn to make a skirt. Although changes in dress are only superficial changes, they suggest that the way of life of the Iban may change considerably in the years ahead.

as pineapples and coconuts, which they sell or trade for other kinds of food or supplies. An Iban sets as many as 12 traps near trees whose fruit is in season. These traps catch wild pigs that go to the trees to get fruit. A wild pig provides fresh meat for all the villagers.

Changes in Iban Life

The Iban followed traditional ways for thousands of years. The rain forest isolated them from outside influences. Recently, however, their situation has begun to change. The government of Borneo, for example, has tried to discourage the building

Lesson 2 Review

Recalling Information
1. Why are the rivers so important to the Iban?
2. What other resources of the forest are important to the Iban? Why?

Interpreting Information
3. How is a longhouse like an apartment house?
4. Explain how a house that is raised on poles provides a much more comfortable environment in a rain forest.

Applying Information
5. If you were an Iban, what kinds of food might you eat that you do not eat now?
6. Why do you think that Iban culture has changed much more slowly than our culture? Will this rate of change hold true over time? Why?

Lesson 3

LABRADOR'S MONTAGNAIS-NASKAPI

In eastern Canada, just south of the tundra, lies Labrador, where temperatures can drop to -40°F (-51°C) in winter. Labrador is a land of moose and caribou. Only a few kinds of trees, such as spruce and balsam fir, can thrive in the cold climate. Vast forests of these hardy conifers cover the land.

Although the poor soil, the bitter cold, and the ferocious windstorms that are characteristic of Labrador should make the region inhospitable to people, Labrador supports two groups of American Indians. The Montagnais live in southern Labrador, and the Naskapi live in the northern forest of Labrador.

The two groups are similar. They speak the same dialect and have customs that are alike. Both depend on the subarctic forest, on its animals, and on each other. They know that to survive in the taiga, they must take from it only what they need. They waste nothing and always share what they have.

How It Was

Life for the Montagnais-Naskapi involved a year-long cycle of migration, hunting, trapping, and gathering. Groups of families traveled hundreds of miles every year. Each person worked at the job that he or she did best. All shared their food and possessions with the group and with any strangers whom they met.

The Montagnais-Naskapi use the resources of the forest to build canoes for travel.

Imagine that you are taking a traditional journey with a Naskapi hunting party that is composed of your family and friends. It is autumn. You will spend about six months hunting and trapping.

The first stopping place is located upriver on the Canairiktok (*kah∗neh∗*RIHK∗*tahk*), heading inland from the Atlantic Coast. You hunt seal, for seal hide makes the warm, waterproof moccasins that you will need during the bitter winter. You catch fish by placing nets in the river, which is already beginning to form ice. As autumn progresses, the river freezes solid. You go farther inland in search of caribou.

Caribou are large deer that graze on the tundra in the north during the summer and in the taiga to the south during the winter. They are an important resource to the Naskapi. Caribou skins provide tent coverings, clothing, and fresh and dried meat all year. Caribou are respected companions, and their spirits are worshiped by the Naskapi.

Your group has been successful and spends days in camp, tanning hides and drying caribou meat. The Naskapi proudly tell stories of the number of blizzards that they have survived. To survive a blizzard, they say, you must be very clever and resourceful. The best stories will be repeated again and again at future gatherings. That is how the history of the Naskapi is passed from generation to generation.

Caribou are tasty, you think, but are caribou all that you will have to eat? No; depending on the season, the Naskapi will also hunt for porcupines, foxes, wolves, waterfowls, eels, and salmon. One brave hunting party tells the tale of how they trapped a bear last spring as it emerged from its winter hibernation.

Now, it is summertime. Your group joins other groups who have been separated from one another all winter to celebrate on the lakeshore of the taiga. The celebration is joyous, despite swarms of mosquitoes. People share stories with their old friends. Everyone works, too, making the snowshoes, the canoes, and the tools that they will use next winter. The Naskapi do business at the French and the English trading posts, where they exchange animal furs for manufactured goods and for flour. The summer is pleasant. You know, however, that it will not last long. Hunting groups are already beginning to form for the coming season.

"Everyone Must Learn"

The Naskapi's traditional rules of conduct allowed them to survive in the taiga for generations. They understood that everyone's survival depended upon the entire group. A person's ranking in the group was not inherited; it had to be earned by skill. In fact, the Naskapi have no permanent leaders or chiefs. The position of leader rotated among group members. A person became a leader because he could do a particular job better than the other members of the group. When that job was done and another began, the person who was best at that became the leader.

Because they migrated often, the Naskapi traveled light—with very little baggage. They used the abundant supply of wood to make sleds and toboggans every fall. They made canoes of wood and birchbark. They left these heavy pieces of equipment behind when they finished a hunt.

To enable them to live closely in a small group, the Montagnais-Naskapi followed many rules that helped them to cooperate. They tried to be patient with one another. They believed that "everyone must learn," and they welcomed those who worked, shared, and helped. The Naskapi admired and respected the strengths of individuals. They were tolerant of individual faults as long as those did not endanger the group. On hunting journeys, everyone was expected to be patient, hospitable, and

A morning meal simmers at a Naskapi campsite. Which of the things pictured reflect the Naskapi's contact with modern Canadian culture?

generous. The Naskapi shared food with strangers in a spirit of friendship. Women and men made important decisions together and shared jobs, too. Women knew how to hunt and to trap. Men cooked meals and cared for the children.

The Fur Trade Changes Life

The arrival of the French and the English explorers in Canada in the seventeenth and the eighteenth centuries had far-reaching effects on the Montagnais-Naskapi. The Europeans set up trading posts, first near the coasts and then farther inland. The traders were interested in obtaining furs that would bring them high prices in Europe. In exchange for the furs, the Europeans gave the American Indians iron tools, copper kettles, and food.

Fur trapping brought major changes. The Naskapi had to take furs to the trading post. Soon, it became easier and safer for them to obtain food at trading posts rather than to hunt for it in the wilderness.

The change from hunting to trapping required the Naskapi to make adaptations to the environment. For one thing, they had to form smaller working groups. Family patterns changed, too. While men went away to trap, wives and children remained behind. Finally, the migratory life of the Montagnais-Naskapi came to an end.

Many Naskapi now look forward to receiving news and goods that come from other places.

In some ways, the new life was an easier and a more secure one for the Naskapi. They no longer had to depend on the success of the hunt. Food and medical care were more readily available, and people who got medical attention lived longer. Children could go to school. There was more time for leisure activities. Goods were available from stores and could be kept from year to year in permanent housing instead of in tents.

Regardless of these advantages, making a living often proved difficult. Work was not always available. Some people worked in construction, while others worked in the offices of the government.

Returning to Tradition

Today, many Montagnais-Naskapi long for the life of their ancestors. They regret the loss of the close ties to nature and to family. Some Naskapi, especially young adults, have decided to return to traditional ways of making a living from the forest.

Recently, the Montagnais-Naskapi held a meeting. One thousand people attended and pitched tents of caribou skin. They told tales of the old days. The younger people understood the stories because they had studied the language in school. The Naskapi discussed fishing and trapping and how they could live their traditional life with people who had adopted new ways.

Lesson 3 Review

Recalling Information

1. What resources of the forest did the Montagnais-Naskapi use? How?
2. Why did the Montagnais-Naskapi settle in permanent villages?

Interpreting Information

3. Is the traditional use of the land by the Montagnais-Naskapi light or heavy? Explain.
4. How did fur trading change the lives of the Montagnais-Naskapi?

Applying Information

5. Do you think that turning to traditional ways is a move into the future or into the past? Why?
6. What influence do stories of the past have on maintaining your traditions?

Skills for Thinking

COMPARING TWO PHOTOS

If you were writing a letter to someone in a foreign land who had never met you or had never been to your country, how would you describe yourself? How would you explain your home and your culture?

You would probably send a photograph or two, and you would probably request a photograph in return.

Photographs provide information. They can show what people look like and how they dress. They can show people at play or at work. They can show the climate in which people live. Photographs of several people allow you to compare them to one another and to compare yourself to them. If you received the photograph on this page, what information would you have about the child shown in it?

On the next page are two more photographs. Examine each one, and read its caption. Then, answer the questions.

What Do Photographs Show?

1. Where do the people who appear in these photographs live? What can you tell about the climate in these places?
2. Compare the clothing of the people in these photos. How are they alike or different?
3. What kinds of shelters or buildings are shown? Compare the materials used.
4. What contact do you think these people have with others outside their groups? Explain your answer.
5. What other information can you get from the photographs about the way of life of these people?

291

**Above, an Australian woman paints pictures
in the traditional style of her culture.**

**Below, a family in northern India cooks over
an outdoor fire to make a midday meal.**

Chapter 14 Review

Summary of Key Facts

In this chapter, you learned that

- few people today depend solely on the resources of the forests of the world.
- forest people have traditionally made their living by hunting and gathering, fishing, farming, and forestry.
- slash-and-burn agriculture is the simplest kind of subsistence farming.
- sedentary agriculture is practiced where soil is fertile.
- the Iban of Borneo's rain forests farm, fish, and hunt and gather. They also harvest rubber.
- traditionally, the Montagnais-Naskapi of Labrador hunt caribou and trap for furs.

Using Vocabulary

On a separate sheet of paper, write the term that will correctly complete each sentence. Use one term twice.

slash-and-burn	longhouse
sedentary	native commercial

1. A _____ is like an enclosed village.
2. Societies that practice _____ agriculture live in permanent villages.
3. In _____ forestry, people harvest native plants for export and cash.
4. In _____ agriculture, people use fire to clear parts of a forest for crops.
5. In _____ forestry, people harvest trees and sell their wood.

Discussing the Chapter

1. How do traditional forest societies hunt and gather food? Give examples from a few different groups.
2. Compare the clothing and the houses that are used by the peoples of the rain forest and of the northern needleleaf forest.
3. How and why do forest peoples travel?
4. How have the Iban and the Naskapi been influenced by other societies? How have their ways changed?

Reviewing Skills

Look at the photos on page 292. Discuss three details in each photo that reflect the ways of life of the people shown.

Peoples of Grasslands

Vocabulary

pack animal	age grading
transhumance	age set
compound	ger

Lesson Preview

Lesson 1: Grasslands as a Human Environment

Lesson 2: The Masai of East Africa's Savanna

Lesson 3: Herders of the Mongolian Steppe

Introduction

Just before dawn, the Pokot women of Kenya get up and go out to the corral to milk their cows and camels. By sunrise, they will have let out their cattle to graze on the grassy plains of Africa's Rift Valley.

Members of a people who are related to the Pokot also get up with the sun to hoe their terraced fields on a nearby hill. When the rainy season starts, they sow corn.

The valley where the Pokot pasture their animals is too dry to grow crops. The hills of their neighbors are too steep to pasture animals. Thus, each group, living interde-pendently, supplies what the other lacks. The herders supply meat and milk to their neighbors. The farmers give the herders grain and other produce in exchange.

Many people know the savanna of East Africa as the site of spectacular national parks and game reserves. Huge herds of gazelles, wildebeests, zebras, bison, and other animals roam across the broad stretches of this tree-dotted land. Preda-tors—lions, cheetahs, hyenas, wolves, and wild dogs—are abundant, too.

The savanna of East Africa is also the home of a number of groups of people. Some groups, such as the Pokot and their neighbors, have been able to meet all their needs from the resources around them. In this chapter, you will learn about how peo-ple of the past and the present have used the world's grasslands to meet their needs.

For a Masai boy of East Africa, the savanna offers everything—food, water, and all other needed resources.

295

GRASSLANDS AS A HUMAN ENVIRONMENT

When the early explorers of North America first saw a prairie, they were completely overwhelmed by it. Impressed by the expanses of tall, waving grass, the explorers compared the prairie to a "boundless and beautiful" ocean.

Prairies are one of the three kinds of grasslands. Prairie grasses can grow 6 feet (1.8 m) high, or higher. The other kinds of grasslands are the semiarid steppes, with their short grasses, and the tropical savannas, usually with scattered trees.

Hunters on the Grasslands

The first human beings to live on the grasslands were hunters. On the savannas of Africa, they killed such animals as baboons, zebras, giraffes, and elephants. On the steppes of Asia, they hunted antelopes, wild horses, and camels. Later, Indians on the vast prairie, or pampa, of Argentina lived by hunting such animals as the ostrich and the llama.

Nomadic Herders

Hunting on grasslands can provide a good living in some places. In other places, hunters can barely survive. At its best, hunting is not an easy life. The domestication of grazing animals was a great step forward for inhabitants of grasslands.

The domestication of such animals as the horse and the camel aided the grassland dwellers in the search for food by providing faster and more reliable means of transportation. No longer did the people of the grasslands have to walk great distances to hunt and to gather. The ability to travel longer distances enlarged the area in which they could find food.

Domesticating animals also suggested other ways of life. One was that of nomadic herding. By raising their own grazing animals and moving from place to place, following the herds, nomadic herders had solved the problem of finding game by keeping it—raising and caring for it instead of hunting for it.

Among the grazing animals that were domesticated by grassland herders have been cattle, sheep, goats, horses, camels, and yaks. The grazing paths of such animals shift with the seasons. Traditionally, nomadic herders have followed these paths.

The Kirghiz (*kihr*∗GEEZ) people of the Asian steppes have been nomadic herders for generations. If you asked a Kirghiz herder to name the most valuable thing in the world, his answer would probably be "the camel." "A camel is worth 8 yaks or 9 horses or 45 sheep," a Kirghiz would tell you.

The camel is valuable because it provides both milk and transportation. Also, it is a very tough animal that is able to survive the intense heat, the drought, and the bitter cold of the steppes. It is the ideal domesticated animal for this harsh environment.

Camels eat grass, small scrub trees, and even thistles. These hardy animals can digest food that people cannot eat and can convert it into food, such as milk, that people can eat. Some nomadic herders

Prehistoric hunters roamed Asia's grasslands in search of food. They preyed on herds of wild horses and on other native animals.

slaughter their animals for meat. Others do so only for special ceremonies.

Herders depend almost entirely on the animals that they raise. Food is only one of many needs that their animals satisfy. Animals also provide raw materials for clothing, homes, and fuel. They represent wealth and social status. In addition, they can be used as transport and they can be traded to farmers for grain and for such luxuries as tea, coffee, and dates.

Warriors of the Grasslands

Throughout history, nomadic peoples have engaged in fighting—to protect their animals, to assure their pasture. Because nomads are mobile, they have often found that a military kind of organization, with a chain of command, suits their needs.

The Huns, who were pastoral, nomadic people from the Asian steppes, appeared in Europe in the fifth century A.D. They had formed themselves into a military organization. For more than two centuries, they gained the land they wanted to use by driving the other tribal groups away. This mass movement of people eventually played a role in the fall of the Roman Empire.

As warriors, the Huns made effective use of the horse. It was said that they practically lived on their horses. As an old proverb stated, the Hun's country was "the back of a horse."

More than 1,000 years after the Huns invaded Europe on horseback, the horse made its appearance in the grasslands of North America. The first horses seen by the Plains Indians were brought to America by European colonists.

When the Europeans and their horses arrived in North America, the population of the Great Plains was quite small. The American Indians who lived on this grassland had few possessions. When food was difficult to find in one area, they searched elsewhere. The Plains Indians were limited to traveling on foot. Although some groups practiced a simple form of farming, most were hunter-gatherers. The dog was their only domesticated animal. Although sometimes used for food, the dog served chiefly as a **pack animal**, or an animal that carries a load of supplies.

The horse was first brought to North America by the Spaniards. From the lands bordering the Spanish colony of Mexico, the horse gradually moved northward toward the Great Plains. The horse changed life on the Plains. The Plains Indians became highly efficient horseback riders, which enabled them to improve their ability to hunt bison and to fight.

Unlike the Kirghiz, the Plains Indians never became herders. They remained hunters. After the arrival of the horse, the Plains Indians abandoned their homesites and became nomadic hunters, who followed the wild herds over the vast grasslands of the Plains.

The Plains Indians, like the Huns, lived on horseback. A mother and her young child rode together on a horse. Older children, astride their own horses, rode with the adults to hunt and to fight battles. So important was the horse to the Plains Indians that they measured their wealth by the number of horses that they owned.

The Plains Indians hunted four large animals: bison, antelopes, deer, and elks. Hunters on horseback killed large numbers of these animals with bows and arrows. These animals provided the nomads with food. They also provided resources for clothing and shelter. The Plains Indians made dresses, shirts, leggings, moccasins, and robes out of animal skins. They made tents out of buffalo skins. These cone-shaped shelters, which were held up by three or four poles, could be taken down easily and put up again when the Plains Indians moved from place to place.

A band that consisted of between 300 and 500 people was the basic size of the Plains Indians' community. Its territory consisted of the amount of grazing land that was available for its horses. The bands sometimes consulted one another about important matters. The 10 bands of the Cheyenne, for example, sent representatives to a council of 44 "peace chiefs." The decisions of this council were obeyed by all Cheyenne bands. Like other Plains Indians, the Cheyenne lived in very small groups during most of the year. In late spring and summer, the groups, who were often members of more than one band, came together to hunt for the Plains Indian community.

By the time that the European settlers

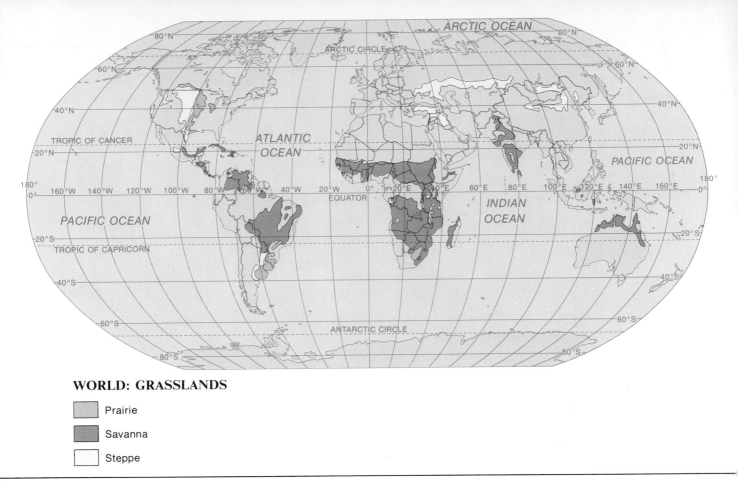

WORLD: GRASSLANDS

- Prairie
- Savanna
- Steppe

MAP SKILLS: Large areas of Earth's surface are covered with grasslands. Which continent has the largest region of prairie? Which continent has the largest region of savanna?

reached the Great Plains, the Sioux, the Blackfoot, the Apache, the Comanche, the Dakota, and the Kiowa—along with many other American Indian groups—had become skillful, horse-mounted foes. Unlike the Huns, however, the Plains Indians were not invaders who drove farmers and forest dwellers out of their homelands. Instead, the American Indians of the Great Plains were Native Americans who were overrun by colonizers from Europe.

Farmers on the Grasslands

Most of the wars that were fought between American Indians and European settlers in North America occurred after new technology had opened the grasslands for agriculture. Until then, most grasslands of the midlatitudes had been used only by nomadic hunters and herders. After the invention of the steel plow and the extension of railroads, however, farming began in the prairies. Do you remember why? Improved methods of irrigation made farming practical even on the semiarid steppes.

Farmers quickly altered the prairies. They replaced the grass with such crops as corn and wheat. They also planted trees. In slightly more than 100 years, many of the world's prairies had become farmland.

During the late 1800s, farmers flocked to America's vast, fertile prairies. Wood was scarce in the grasslands, and so, this Nebraskan farm family built its home with slabs of sod that were cut from the ground.

Today's Grassland Dwellers

Even so, today, the steppes serve as the major grazing lands of the world although nomadic herding is no longer a major activity. In places such as China and the Soviet Union, the development of cooperative farms has affected grazing patterns and the lives of nomadic herders. In other places, such as the United States, nomadic herding no longer exists at all. Instead, animals are grazed on enclosed pastures or ranges. In winter and in times of drought, supplementary food may be trucked to them.

In some grassland areas, the people practice a special kind of herding that is known as **transhumance** (*tranz*∗HYOO∗*muhns*). Transhumance involves a seasonal movement of animals in which only some herders take part. The rest of the group maintains a permanent home in a lowland area. When the weather is warm, herders take the animals into the mountains to graze. The other members of the community stay at home to farm. When the weather turns cold, the herders bring the animals back from the mountains.

Can you think of any other group in

American history that practiced a similar kind of herding?

Transhumance often occurs where former nomadic herders have settled to raise livestock. The Basques of southern France and northern Spain and the Turkomans of Afghanistan practice transhumance.

Lesson 1 Review

Recalling Information
1. Who were the first human beings to live on the grasslands?
2. Why is the camel particularly well suited to living on the steppes?

Interpreting Information
3. What five needs do grazing animals satisfy for nomadic herders?
4. Why do you think that many nomads became warriors rather than farmers?

Applying Information
5. If you had been a Plains Indian in the 1870s, how would you have felt about the coming of the railroad? Why?
6. If you were living on one of the world's grasslands today, what might you do for a living? Explain.

With both ancient and modern tools, farmers cultivate the world's grasslands. A Bolivian farmer tills his field with an ox-drawn plow. In Iowa, a machine makes neat bales of hay.

Lesson 2

THE MASAI OF EAST AFRICA'S SAVANNA

As you know, the savanna of East Africa is the home of a number of nomadic herders. The Masai are one of the most prominent groups. For generations, these Africans have pastured their animals on the grasslands that are part of the present-day countries of Kenya and Tanzania.

The proud Masai have resisted all attempts to conquer them. Centuries ago, they fought off Arab warriors. Later, they withstood European settlers. In the late 1800s, however, an invisible enemy did them great harm: The smallpox virus killed three of every four Masai. Now numbering between 100,000 and 300,000, the Masai cling to their traditional ways.

Before Arabs and Europeans settled in East Africa, the Masai and other groups moved their herds whenever the land had been completely grazed. Now, the Masai are confined to an area of about 60,000 square miles (155,400 sq km). Some Masai grazing land is situated inside the national parks of Kenya.

A Masai legend says that when God separated heaven from Earth, he gave cattle to

A Kenyan Masai watches the sheep drink at a human-made water hole. What problems do Masai herders face?

the Masai. Cattle represent life and prestige to the proud Masai. Wealth is measured by the number of cattle that a Masai owns. Cattle yield meat, milk, and lard. Cowhide is a major source of leather from which many Masai goods are made.

The traditional Masai technique of grazing cattle is considered to be an efficient use of land. During the wet season, the Masai graze their cattle on grasslands near their villages. In the dry season, however, the Masai let their cattle graze farther and farther from the villages. Native breeds of cattle can live in the intense African heat. They are able to penetrate the high grass to graze.

Village Life

A Masai village usually includes several family **compounds**, which are groups of small dwellings that are arranged in a cluster. A village contains two corrals, one for cattle and one for other animals. Each village is surrounded by a protective thornbush fence to keep out predators.

Masai women are responsible for building the houses. For the frame, they use sticks from trees that grow in the scrub. They cover the framework with mud and with fresh manure. They use twigs to make a domed roof. During the rainy season, a house must be repaired almost daily.

Masai houses are low roofed and small. Thus, they are easy to build and to repair. Besides, there is little need for large houses when people spend a lot of time outdoors, as the Masai do in the warm climates of Kenya and of Tanzania.

Despite its small size, a Masai house is usually divided into as many as three tiny rooms. Animals may be kept in the first room; parents sleep in the next room; and children or grandparents sleep in the third. The few and simple furnishings include beds with grass mattresses, cowhide sheets, blankets, a few clay or plastic pots, and drinking vessels made of gourd.

Masai villages are semipermanent. The people move every three or four years, to give their cattle and themselves a fresh living area to use. In the dry season, the Masai set up temporary villages wherever the cattle are grazing.

Each day, herders take the animals out of their corral and graze them in the open savanna. They return at dusk to the safety of the village. Each family has its own herd. The animals are herded as a single unit, but the owners can easily identify their own cattle in the group. The Masai also keep sheep and goats, although they do not value them as highly as they value their cattle which, of course, are larger.

In each village, the children perform specific tasks. Masai boys are trained to herd and to care for cattle and for smaller animals. They must know, for example, how to help a mother animal to give birth on the plains and when to move the animals to new grazing land. Often, the boys work alone for half a day.

Masai girls work mostly in the village. They are taught to help their mothers to milk the cows and to distribute the morning milk. Later, they fetch water from a stream or gather firewood from the scrub. They also do housekeeping chores and have been taught to care for younger children.

Young Masai men who are training to become warriors dye their hair, skin, and clothing red. ●

Organizing Society

Every society develops a way to govern itself. The Masai way is centered on a system of **age grading**. In this system, each adult male progresses through a number of stages.

At about the age of 14, a Masai boy is initiated into the *moran*, or warrior, group. He and the other boys who are initiated with him form an **age set**. This is a group, somewhat like a school class, whose members identify with one another for the rest of their lives.

Each moran leaves his home to live with other moran in a rough camp that is called a *manyatta*. Each moran takes with him some of his father's cattle and a senior female relative to look after him. The moran do not assume adult responsibilities. Instead, they are expected to develop their fighting skills by throwing spears and by shooting bows and arrows. They also learn the history and the traditions of their people.

For many years, the Masai have not used their moran as warriors. The moran now form a corps of young men who can be called on to do hard work.

After 12 to 15 years, the group of moran returns to its village. All the members of this age set then advance to the second stage, that of junior elder. At the beginning of this stage—in his late twenties—a Masai marries and sets up his own household. At this time, he also becomes a member of the village council.

The council is a democratic governing board for the village. The elders settle disputes, administer pastures, and organize rituals.

All the elders belong to the council, and each has a voice in its decisions. The meetings of elders take place in the shade of a tree. The association between the elders and the site of their meetings may explain the saying that "a wise elder gives out shade."

After a period of years, the age set of junior elders moves into the next category: senior elder. Senior elders have more influence than junior elders in the village council because they are more experienced and have proved to have better judgment more often.

Members of the next stage—retired elders—are often consulted about village matters. The few old men who reach the fifth stage take part in ceremonies but do not play an active role in village life.

Masai Clothing

The usual garment of the Masai is a *shuka*, a capelike garment that is tied over one shoulder. To keep warm at night, a Masai adds another shuka. Shukas were once made of cowhide. Today, the Masai wear cotton ones as well.

The Masai wear more jewelry than clothes. Girls and women wear many necklaces and headbands and several pairs of long, looped earrings that are made of tiny beads. Men, too, wear earrings.

Distinctive forms of decoration and of hairstyles indicate differences in status. Only the moran are permitted to carry spears and to wear elaborate headdresses. When they become elders, they shave their heads. They no longer carry spears because they are no longer warriors.

Other Masai Customs

The Masai have many ceremonies. Most involve the progress of an individual from one age set to the next. (Women belong to an age-grading system, too, but play no role in governing the village.)

Death is the only stage in the life cycle that is not marked by ceremony. The death of the oldest villagers is simply accepted. The death of anyone younger, however, is regarded as an insult. Such a death is ignored out of respect for the family.

Ceremonies are blessed by *laibons*, or prophets. A laibon decides when a group of moran should be initiated, and when the moran should be promoted to junior elders. Formerly, laibons gave advice about the best time for cattle raiding and for warfare. Today, they are expected not only to bless ceremonies but also to help individuals to solve personal problems. If a person is sick a great deal, for instance, a laibon is expected to help.

Lesson 2 Review

Recalling Information

1. What functions do cattle serve in Masai life?
2. Describe how the Masai use the land for grazing.

Interpreting Information

3. What are the main parts of a Masai village? How do these structures reflect the Masai way of life?
4. Describe the tasks that Masai children are taught to perform. What special responsibilities do American children of your age assume at home? At school?

Applying Information

5. American schools have grade levels. They admit students at a certain age and promote them at regular intervals. How is this system like that of the Masai? How is it different?
6. Compare the government of a Masai village to the government of your own community.

On a windy steppe, a Mongol herder tends his grazing flocks. Camels provide the Mongols with meat, milk, and transportation.

Lesson 3

HERDERS OF THE MONGOLIAN STEPPE

His jacket is dusty, for he has just dismounted after riding many kilometers. The sun shines brightly over the dry, flat plain where he lives. Tavutai lives in a countryside where few people live, but he has visited the city. "It's so noisy, and you can't move because there's no space!" he exclaims. "I would never leave the grasslands for *that*."

Tavutai is a Mongol. His homeland, Mongolia, is located in east-central Asia. It is bordered on the north by the Soviet Union and on the south by the People's Republic of China.

About the size of Alaska, Mongolia is a land of steppes and desert. It has a continental climate, with long, cold winters and short, humid summers. Rainfall is scant and unpredictable.

The southern half of Mongolia is part of the huge Gobi Desert. The rest of the country consists of broad expanses of steppe. Grasses vary in height according to the amount of rainfall and the amount of moisture in the soil. Trees grow only where rainfall is abundant or where they have been planted near water or on slopes.

Making a Living

The harsh climate, scarce precipitation, and poor soil discourage farming in Mongolia. For centuries, Mongols have lived as nomadic herders. Most still live the traditional life of their ancestors. Most of the steppe—82 percent—is suitable only for pasturing. Not all pastureland is equally good, however. One-fourth of the country contains excellent pastureland; one-half has average pastureland. The poor pasturelands are located in the drier Gobi region.

The steppe vegetation that grows in much of Mongolia supports more than 25 million grazing animals. There are about 24 grazing animals for every person. The ratio of livestock to people in Mongolia is the highest in the world.

Mongolia has been called the land of five animals. Although other animals are raised there, cattle, sheep, goats, camels, and horses are the most abundant and the most important to the livelihood of the Mongols.

Herders rely on their animals for almost everything that they need.

Animals provide the Mongols with milk and meat, their daily food. The source of milk varies. It may come from a goat, a cow, a yak, a mare, or even a camel. Yak milk and slightly fermented mare's milk are the favorite drinks of adults in most parts of the country. Butter, cheese, and yogurt are other staple dairy products.

Meat comes from sheep, cattle, yaks, camels, and horses. Goats are the least val-ued animals because they have little fat.

Mongols do not often eat meat in fresh form. Usually, they allow the flesh of slaughtered animals to dry before they eat it. Mongols consider fat from a sheep's tail to be a great delicacy.

Although lacking in grains, in fruit, and in vegetables, the Mongol diet is quite rich in protein.

One of the few food items that Mongols cannot get from their animals is tea, which they drink with milk, butter, and salt. They trade for tea as well as for such staples as rice and flour.

Animals are also used as sources of materials and as beasts of burden. Their dung, when dried, is used as fuel. Cattle are grazed mainly in the northeastern and north-central areas of Mongolia, where grass and water are more abundant than in other parts of the country.

Sheep are raised throughout the country. Sheep account for 40 to 50 percent of all livestock production in Mongolia. They are an important source of wool and fat. (Mongols apply fat to their bodies—just as cold-water swimmers do—to help to maintain body heat during the cold winters.)

Goats are numerous where scrub vegetation is scarce. They live in all mountainous areas and in desert and semidesert regions.

The two-humped camel is common in the desert areas.

Of all animals, the horse is the most important to traditional Mongol society. It can be found everywhere in the country. Like North American cowhands, Mongol herders use horses in roundups, as beasts of burden,

Like other peoples who live in cold climates, the Mongols use fabrics and animal furs to create warm clothing and shelter.

and as a major form of transportation across their vast land. Mongols domesticated the horse in about 2000 B.C. They also invented the saddle.

Mongolian horses are well adapted to the extreme heat and cold of the land. In winter, for instance, their sweat turns to ice and thus stops the escape of body heat. This protects the horses from freezing.

Livestock serve as the measure of wealth and the medium of exchange in Mongolia. Payment for goods and for services is made in a unit of measurement that is known as a *bot*. A horse or a cow equals 1 bot. A camel is worth 1 1/2 bots. A sheep is worth

only one-seventh of a bot and a goat is worth only one-tenth.

Way of Life

Life on the steppes of Mongolia is hard. In order to find new grazing land for their animals, herders often have to travel great distances in the course of a year. Each time they move, they have to pack their goods and then settle themselves again. Nomadic life, however, has its rewards. It provides freedom, which Mongols cherish above all. Their work is geared to the seasons as much as to a daily schedule. Mongol herders live in portable shelters called **gers.** A ger is a light, round tent that is shaped like an old-fashioned beehive. The wooden frame for the side walls, which are fastened by animal-hide loops, is about 4 feet (1.2 m) high. It can be expanded or pushed together, like the wooden gates that are used to prevent children from falling down stairs. The walls are attached at each end to the door frame. Two sturdy poles support a wheel-like roof ring. Rafters rise from the walls to the roof ring.

The framework of the ger is covered with sheets of felt, a fabric that is made of matted wool or hair. These sheets, in turn, are covered with a white waterproof canvas. The number of felt layers that are used depends on the season. More are needed in winter to provide insulation against the bitter winds of the steppes. In pleasant weather, the canvas cover can be opened to let in air and sun.

The walls of the ger are hung with cloth or with bright woolen carpets. Woodwork, doors, and rafters are painted, sometimes in intricate patterns.

The traditional outer garment that is worn by a nomad is a long, flowing robe that is made of animal fur or hide. Buttoned at the throat, at the right shoulder, and down the right side, it reaches to 1 foot (30.5 cm) above the ground. In winter, men and women line their robes with sheepskin or with red-fox fur. They tie colorful sashes around their waists.

Beneath their robes, Mongols wear heavy trousers of wool or of felt. They tuck their trousers into high leather boots. In winter, their boots are made of felt for warmth. Fur

caps with ear flaps complete their winter outfits.

Mongol clothes are well suited to the harsh climate of the country. They are also practical for a nomadic life.

Lesson 3 Review

Recalling Information

1. Which five animals are the most herded in Mongolia?
2. What are the staple foods of the nomads' diet?

Interpreting Information

3. Why is a Mongolian shelter appropriate for nomadic life?
4. How does the cold-weather dress that is worn by Mongols compare to the typical winter clothing that is usually worn by Americans?

Applying Information

5. Mongol nomads like Tavutai, quoted at the beginning of this lesson, value the open spaces of the grasslands where they live. Does your environment provide you with enough open space? If so, how does it affect your life? If not, in what ways do you think that more open space would change the manner in which you live?
6. How do the Mongols' ideas about moving compare to the views of most Americans?

Special Feature
Celebrations: Rites of Passage

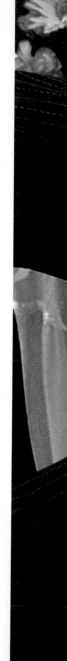

Almost every culture has special ways of celebrating a person's passage into different stages of life. Like the Masai, Australian aborigine boys who are about to become adults must leave their homes for a short time. The boys' relatives and other adults celebrate by singing songs and performing special dances. The boys remain for several days in the desert without food. This experience symbolizes their new independence as adults. When they return to their homes, they are considered men.

Such celebrations are called rites of passage. Marriages, births, and graduations are all rites of passage.

A marriage is a rite of passage that is common to cultures all over the world. The family is one of the oldest and the most important organizations in human society. Because of this, almost every society in the world encourages men and women to marry. The marriage ceremony emphasizes the bonds between husband and wife.

The wedding ring is an important symbol in this rite of passage. The roundness of the ring is said to represent eternity. Its presentation symbolizes that the man and the woman are united forever. Wearing the ring on the ring finger of the left hand, as is done in the Western Hemisphere, stems from an old belief that a vein or a nerve ran directly from this finger to the heart.

From the time of coming-of-age ceremonies to the time of marriage ceremonies, rites of passage have played an important role in unifying societies throughout the world.

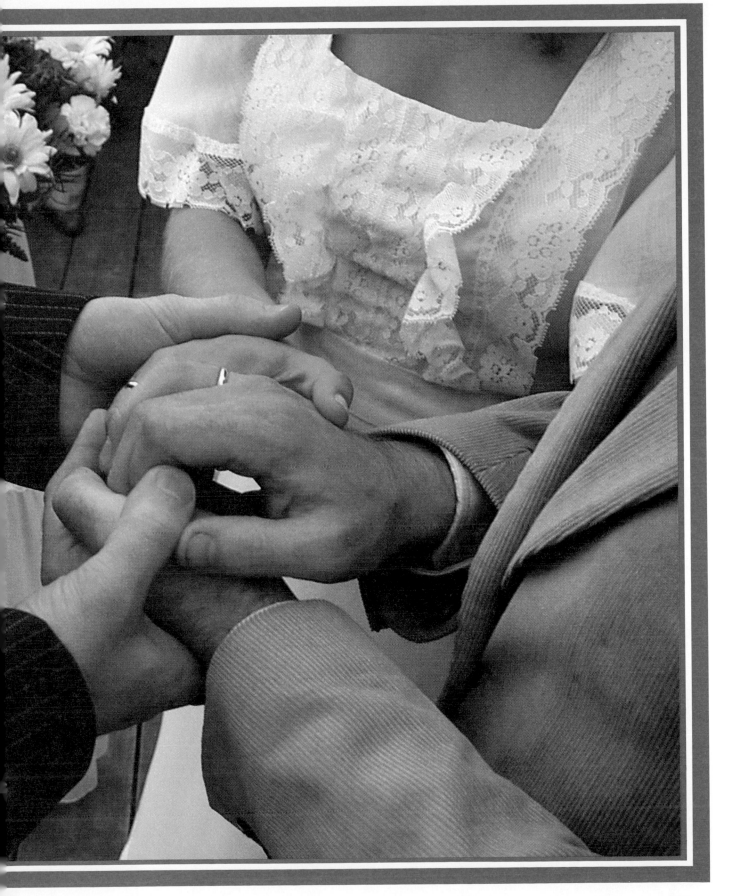

Skills for Thinking

USING A GAZETTEER

Mozambique! Casablanca! Madagascar! The world is full of famous places with exotic names. How can you find out quickly where they are? By using a gazetteer, a geographical dictionary that lists place names alphabetically, you can locate any place in the world.

Some gazetteers are complete books. They include many details about a place. Other gazetteers are parts of atlases or history books.

How Is This Organized?

Part of a gazetteer is shown below. Use it to answer the following questions.

1. Name three things that are listed about places.

2. Would the gazetteer from which this information was taken list the capital of North Dakota? Explain your answer.

3. Which country has the larger population, Mozambique or Mongolia?

4. This gazetteer is part of a world atlas. Where in the atlas would you look to find Montserrat?

Country or place	Area in square miles	Population	Capital or main town	Page number
Mauritania	397,954	1,700,000	Nouakchott	22
Mauritius	787	1,000,000	Port Louis	23
Mexico	761,601	71,300,000	Mexico City	26
Michigan, United States	58,216	9,109,000	Lansing	114
Midway Islands	2	2,256	. . .	25
Minnesota, United States	84,068	4,133,000	St. Paul	118
Mississippi, United States	47,716	2,551,000	Jackson	120
Missouri, United States	69,686	4,951,000	Jefferson City	125
Monaco	368 acres	26,000	Monaco	10
Mongolia	604,090	1,700,000	Ulan Bator	21
Montana, United States	147,138	801,000	Helena	126
Montserrat	38	11,600	Plymouth	32
Morocco	172,413	22,495,000	Rabat	22
Mozambique	302,308	12,700,000	Laurenco Marques	23

Chapter *15* Review

Summary of Key Facts
In this chapter, you learned that
- in the past and in the present, people have found similar ways of solving the special problems of living in a grassland environment.
- traditionally, people of the grasslands have been nomadic herders, hunters, or farmers.
- the Masai are nomadic cattle herders of the East African savanna.
- cattle provide food, clothing, and other necessities.
- nomadic herders who live on the steppes of Mongolia primarily raise five kinds of animals.
- horses, their most important animals, are used for transportation and herding and as beasts of burden.

Using Vocabulary
On a separate sheet of paper, write the number of the statement and then the term that most closely matches each statement.

compound	age set
transhumance	ger
pack animal	

1. This hut is made of sheep or yak wool.
2. This is a cluster of small groups of buildings.
3. This is a group whose members are of the same age and identify with one another throughout their lives.
4. This is a kind of herding that involves the seasonal movement of animals in which only some herders take part.
5. This is an animal that is used to carry supplies.

Thinking About the Chapter
1. How do the differences in the climates in which these grassland societies live help to explain the differences in their cultures?
2. How do grassland societies use available resources for clothing, for homes, for food, and for fuel?
3. How do groups in Masai society look, act, and work in ways that are different from one another?
4. How do Mongol herders and their horses adapt to the climate of the Mongolian steppes?

Reviewing Skills
1. Would the gazetteer from which this information was taken list the population of New York City? Explain.
2. Which country that is listed here has the largest area? The largest population?

Peoples of Deserts and Tundra

Chapter *16*

Introduction

In the 1300s, the explorer Muhammad Ibn Batuta set out on a journey across the great desert of northern Africa. He wrote:

> We used to go ahead of the caravan, and when we found a place suitable for pasturage we would graze our beasts. We went on doing this until one of our party was lost in the desert; after that I neither went ahead nor lagged behind. We passed a caravan on the way and they told us that some of their party had become separated from them. We found one of them dead under a shrub....The water was only about a mile away from him.

Almost 500 years later, Sir John Franklin explored northern Canada. Robert Hood, a member of the expedition, wrote:

> We were forced to make many circuits, to avoid the lakes, and rambled late in search of bushes for our fire, but without being successful....During the night the tents were overthrown by a storm of wind and snow from the northwest. It continued with such violence the next day that we did not deem it prudent to march....

Both explorers were writing about environments where life has always been difficult. In this chapter, you will learn about how people traditionally have lived in lands of little precipitation.

For this Arab, a business trip means crossing part of a desert. What things here are desert necessities?

315

DESERTS AND TUNDRA AS HUMAN ENVIRONMENTS

Deserts and tundra are two very different kinds of environments. Deserts are dry and often, although not always, hot. The tundra is cold. Although it receives little precipitation, it is often damp and marshy. Nearly all of the plants and the animals of one of these regions would be unable to survive in the other. Humans, however, with their adaptability to heat and to cold, have managed to survive in both environments.

What the desert and the tundra have most in common is harshness. They are not hospitable environments. The plants and the animals that survive there, as you learned in Chapter 9, have adapted to their environment. Humans, too, have adapted to these harsh environments by using their intelligence and their technology.

You may well wonder why people ever bothered to try to live in such difficult places. We do not know very much about life in very early times, but we know enough to make some guesses and to form some conclusions.

In some cases, it is probable that people began to live in both regions when these environments were far less hostile. Climates have changed gradually over many thousands of years. More than 10,000 years ago the vast desert region of the Sahara was a grassland. It received more precipitation than it gets today. Its plant and animal life were similar to those that can be found on the African savanna of today.

Very slowly, the climate changed, becoming drier and drier. Some people moved on to other areas. A desert environment cannot support a very dense population, but the people who remained in the Sahara region adapted to the new conditions and learned to survive there.

The tundra regions of the world, on the other hand, were mostly covered by ice and snow more than 10,000 years ago, during the last Ice Age. It was at the end of the Ice Age that the final groups of travelers from Asia crossed the land bridge that once connected Asia and North America. These were the Innuit and the Aleut peoples. The Innuit had already learned to survive in the freezing conditions of the north by the time that they moved into the North American tundra region.

Living in a Hostile Environment

Forests provide an abundant supply of plant and animal food. Even grasslands have a great variety of food sources. Many of these areas, too, have soil that is suitable for farming. Desert and tundra regions offer far less food, both in variety and in quantity. This is why these regions are among the least densely populated areas of the world.

Grains, for example, provide an important food for much of the world's people. Yet, grains, either wild or cultivated, cannot exist in the desert or tundra. The tundra is too cold, and its growing season is too short. Deserts are warm enough, but they are too dry. Only where there is enough wa-

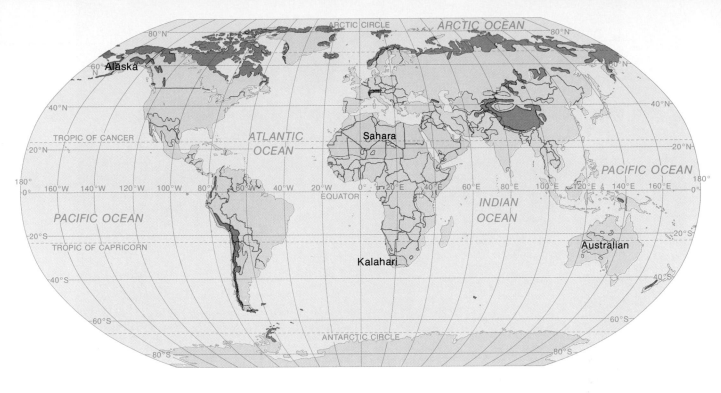

WORLD: DRY LANDS

Desert

Tundra and alpine tundra

MAP SKILLS: **Notice the pattern of desert climate across the world. What does this imply about world weather patterns?**

ter for irrigation can people who live in the desert grow wheat, rice, or corn.

In general, edible plant life is scarce in both regions. Mosses, lichens, and a few flowering plants and shrubs of the tundra provide food for some grazing animals but little for people. Plant food is also scarce in most deserts. Animal food, therefore, traditionally has made up the major part of the diets of desert and tundra people. Meat, fish, and animal products such as milk and cheese traditionally have been supplemented with whatever plant foods can be gathered, grown, or traded.

Getting enough water is the greatest problem that most desert people must face.

Underground water can be tapped in a few places by digging deep wells. In other places, it flows to the surface in a small spring that feeds a few trees and other plants. These small patches of green, called oases, provide drinking water for both people and animals. These oases are usually surrounded by miles and miles of barren rock or sand.

The need for protective clothing and shelter in a hostile environment is obvious. Desert dwellers need protection against the burning sun and the hot, dry winds during the day. Nights in the desert can be cool, even quite cold in some areas. In the cold tundra, people would freeze without proper

These Lapp herders live above the Arctic Circle in Norway. They rely on their reindeer for food, clothing, and shelter.

clothing and shelter. Because there is so little plant life available, animal skins and woven animal hair provide the main materials for clothing.

Neither deserts nor tundras support enough trees for people to be able to use much wood for building shelters. Even finding enough wood to make frames for tents that are covered with animal skins has proved to be difficult. As you will see, people have come up with some ingenious solutions to the problem of providing shelter in these hostile environments.

Hunter-Gatherers of the Desert

The earliest desert dwellers survived by

hunting and gathering. Since there has always been little to hunt and to gather in a desert environment which is usually inhospitable to life, hunting and gathering has always been a hard way to make a marginal living. Only a few small bands of traditional hunting-and-gathering societies can still be found in isolated desert spots of the world today. These traditional societies include the Bushmen of the Kalahari in southern Africa and the aborigines of the Australian desert. You will learn about how the Bushmen survive in their desert environment in Lesson 2.

As you know, hunters and gatherers cannot remain in one place very long because the food supply in desert areas is exhausted very quickly. Therefore, they lead a nomadic existence, moving in small groups from place to place in search of food and water. They carry all their belongings as they move about. As a result, they have few possessions, only those things that are essential, such as cooking utensils and hunting implements. Each time they stop at a new place, they must find materials to use in building shelters, usually simple, one-room structures or lean-tos.

Through experience, recounted from parents to children, the desert hunter-gatherers know where to look for water. Where an outsider, for example, would see only dusty earth, an aborigine would see clues that indicate the remains of a drying stream. By digging only a small hole, hunter-gatherers may be able to obtain enough water for a day's journey or for a few days. They carry water with them as they move across dry areas, using available materials as containers. The intestines of an animal can serve as a water container, as can an ostrich eggshell.

Herders of the Desert

In the Sahara and in Arabia, many groups have made their living as nomadic herders. Most of them raise sheep, goats, horses, and camels.

The North African and Arabian herders, called *bedouin*, satisfy almost all of their needs from their animals. The animals provide meat, milk, and milk products. They also provide hair and skins that are used to make clothing and tents for shelter. Using their animals—especially camels—to carry loads, the desert herders travel with plenty

Identify some crafts and clothing of the desert in this busy Cairo marketplace.

of belongings, including their tents, which can be taken down quickly and packed for a move.

The camel is especially suitable for desert living. It can carry heavy loads, go for days without water, exist on sparse vegetation, and provide milk for herders. A slaughtered beast provides meat and also skins for tents and for other uses.

You have undoubtedly seen pictures of Arabs, especially from the oil-producing nations, in their native dress. Have you ever wondered why they wear such long, loose-fitting garments? Actually, these robes are quite practical. They cool the body by providing protection against the sun's rays

Once a home to desert shepherds, Israel's Jordan Valley is well irrigated today.

and the desert's heat. The headdress protects the head from the sun and can also be wrapped around the face as protection during a sandstorm. Although very few bands of genuine bedouin exist today, clothing and many other aspects of modern-day desert life are carry-overs from the days when desert herders roamed the sands.

Traditional Tundra Cultures

In the tundra, too, people traditionally have survived either as hunter-gatherers or as herders. The Innuit of North America are hunters and gatherers. You will learn more about them in Lesson 3. In the tundra regions of Europe, most traditional people are nomadic herders who survive by following herds of reindeer as they migrate. These groups include the Lapps of Scandinavia and several groups in the northern region of the Soviet Union.

Whether hunters or herders, the people of the tundra have had to learn to live in a bitterly cold climate. The tents of the desert nomads would not provide the people of the tundra with sufficient protection against such cold. Some Innuit build ice houses—**igloos**—in areas where no other building materials are available. They also dig pits in the ground and erect over them structures that are made of animal skins that are stretched over a frame. Lacking wood, they have used whalebones for frames.

Lapps who live in the mountains and herd reindeer use tents made of reindeer skin for shelter. The tents are cone shaped and large enough for an entire family to live in. When the Lapps move their herds to another area, the tents are easily packed and carried. Lapps who live along the coast live in wooden dwellings. They insulate these dwellings by covering them with sod.

Clothing, too, must provide protection against the cold. In winter, the people of the tundra wear several layers of clothing. The Lapps dress in clothing that is made of reindeer skin. To keep their feet warm as they trudge through the snow herding their reindeer, the Lapps line their shoes with sennegrass, a plant they gather in summer that grows in the mountains.

Tundra herders, like herders of other environments, get most of what they need from their animals—meat, milk, cheese, and skins for leather, fur garments, and other items. Herders in deserts and in other environments usually lead their animals to pasture. The tundra herders are more likely to follow their animals. Reindeer migrate yearly between the northern tundra and the southern tundra. In some places, the reindeer even leave the tundra in winter and move into the northern forest. The herders follow, stopping where the animals stop and moving when the animals move on.

Changing Traditions

The ways of life that are described in this lesson were once the only ways of life for people in desert and tundra regions. Yet, even centuries ago, people began to change their traditional ways of life. In less arid areas, some bedouin, for example, gave up nomadic herding for farming. Others, who were used to traveling long distances over dry lands, put their skills to use as traders. Those who remained herders found that they could trade to obtain products from outside the desert. Thus, they no longer had to depend on only what they themselves could produce.

More recently, few people anywhere have been untouched by the technology of industrial societies. Today, some Innuit use snowmobiles. Some bedouin watch color television in their tents.

In other areas, traditional ways of living have given way completely to modern ways. In desert areas, where water can be piped in or pumped from the earth, cities and large commercial farms cover former hunting and herding lands. Even in the tundra, technology has enabled people to build towns. Only in a few spots have groups of desert or tundra people maintained the traditional ways of their ancestors.

Lesson 1 Review

Recalling Information

1. Explain how nomadic herders provide for their needs of food, clothing, and shelter in a desert and in the tundra.
2. What problems do desert people and tundra people have in common? What makes them different?

Interpreting Information

3. Describe at least two ways in which their environments have led to differences between desert hunter-gatherers and forest hunter-gatherers.
4. What environmental factors might determine why people in a desert or in a tundra region would take up hunting and gathering rather than nomadic herding?

Applying Information

5. Suppose that you and your class were suddenly transported to either a desert or a tundra and had to survive there for a long period of time. What are some of the first things that you would do? What kinds of things would you try to find in your new environment?
6. What would you like best about a nomadic herder's life? What would you like least?

THE BUSHMEN OF THE KALAHARI

Dasina sliced off the top of a melon. It was ripe and watery. She set the bottom part onto hot coals. Soon, the melon began to boil like water in a pot. She then dropped some pieces of meat—her share of an antelope—into the boiling melon juice.

Dasina's brother sat nearby in the sand. He was preparing a tortoise for cooking. First, he stuffed the dead tortoise with leaves for flavor. Then, he dug a hole in the sand about the size of the tortoise and lined the hole with burning sticks. Next, he placed the tortoise, on its back, in the hole. Finally, using his sister's discarded melon top as a cover, the young Bushman raked hot coals over the tortoise.

These are two ways in which the Bushmen of southern Africa cook without kettles or water. As nomads with no beasts of burden, they carry as little as possible.

A Hot, Dry Land

The Bushmen live in the Kalahari (*kah*∗*luh*∗HAH∗*ree*) desert. The desert covers 200,000 square miles (518,000 sq km)—an area larger than California. Much of the Kalahari is covered with reddish sand. There are clumps of tough grass, low shrubs, and occasionally, tall, thick *baobab* (BOW∗*bab*) trees. Few towns exist in this barren desert.

The Kalahari is not always dry. In early spring, heavy rains fall. Downpours can go on for days. When they do, water fills the shallow bowls in the sand, which are known as **pans**. Some pans are the size of a football field and others are 20 times as big. From the coming of the spring rains until they go dry, pans provide the Bushmen with water for bathing and for drinking.

Bushmen live in only a few places in southern Africa. A few hundred years ago, Bushmen lived in a much larger area. We know this because paintings that were made on rocks long ago by Bushmen have been found throughout southern Africa.

In the mid-1600s, Europeans landed at the Cape of Good Hope and began to move northward. At the same time, African cattle herders were moving south into Bushman territory. The Bushmen were caught in the middle. They fought both invading groups, but they lost most of their land. Today, about 44,000 Bushmen live in Africa. About two-thirds of them have moved out of the desert to work on farms in the plain (known in Southern Africa as the *veld*). The rest live in the traditional way, as nomadic hunter-gatherers in the Kalahari.

The Kalahari Bushmen travel in bands of 25 to 60 people. The leader of each band is called the headman. He is wise about the land and its resources. He decides when his band has taken enough from a certain part of the desert.

Most visitors see the Kalahari as an empty wasteland that shimmers with heat. The Bushmen, however, notice things that others miss—the tracks of an animal, the signs of hidden roots. They know, too, when spring rains will flood the pans. This knowledge of their environment helps them

Bushmen hunters carefully study the animals that they hunt. They learn to stalk and to kill their prey at close range.

to hunt and to gather the food that they need for survival.

Hunting is the men's responsibility. A hunt begins when a Bushman comes upon a gemsbok (GEMZ*bahk*), a kind of antelope, drinking at a waterhole. The hunter moves closer. He is careful to stay downwind. As long as the wind blows away from the gemsbok and toward the hunter, the animal will not pick up the hunter's scent and can be taken.

The hunter carries only a small bow and four arrows. The arrows are tipped with poison that is made from beetle eggs. The hunter shoots, and two of his arrows find their mark. The hunter returns to camp to get two other men to help him to carry the animal back to the band.

When the hunters bring the gemsbok to camp, they give everyone some meat to eat. They use all parts of the animal. The hooves sharpen knives. The skin is used to make a *kaross* (*kuh*RAHS*), a long leather cape that is worn by a woman and can be formed into a pouch to carry a baby and food. The animal's tendons are used to make traps and bowstrings.

Women do most of the food gathering among the Bushmen. They may walk more than 10 miles (16.1 km) a day, gathering roots, berries, and other things to eat. Their tool is a digging stick. During the long dry

During rainy seasons, Bushmen build domed, waterproof huts with branches and thatching.

season, from August to December, they look for *bi* (BEE), a large, watery root. Sharp eyes are needed because only a slight crack in the earth shows where a root lies hidden. Bushmen know of about 100 plants that are safe to eat. They also gather insects, toads, and lizards.

The smooth, green melons that women tuck into their kaross pouches have many uses. Besides serving as pots for cooking, the melons also contain fluid for cooking and nutritious seeds. Their rinds are used as mixing bowls, they serve as targets for the children's arrows, and they can even be used as drums.

There are no sources of sugar in the Kala-

hari because the land is usually too dry for sugar-cane to grow. The Bushmen have, however, developed ingenious ways of gathering honey. They pound pegs into the trunk of a large tree in which there is a beehive. Using the pegs as steps, they climb to the hive. Like the Iban of Borneo, the Bushmen thrust a smoking stick into the hive to stun the bees and to flush them out. Then the Bushmen will gather the honey, bringing down some of the honeycomb from which to extract it.

Lesson 2 Review

Recalling Information
1. Where do the traditional Bushmen live? Describe their land and its resources.
2. What are the traditional responsibilities of a male Bushman? Of a female?

Interpreting Information
3. Compare ways of hunting that are used by the Iban of Borneo to the methods of the Bushmen.
4. Using an animal or a plant as an example, show how the Bushmen make maximum use of their resources.

Applying Information
5. Tell how you would use Bushman ways to live in a dry area of your state. What would you need to carry? To learn?
6. If you were going to spend time in a desert, what would you wear during the day? At night?

THE INNUIT OF THE TUNDRA

What can you eat when the land is a sheet of ice for eight months of the year? How can you put up buildings or dig cellars when the permafrost makes the ground as hard as concrete? How do you stay warm when the winter cold of -20°F (-28.9°C) causes frostbite in seconds? Where do you get drinking water when the annual precipitation totals 6 to 10 inches (15.2 to 25.4 cm)? These questions are very real problems for people living in the tundra.

Among the people who have long known the answers to these questions are the Innuit. Their ingenious technology has helped them to survive for a long time in a very harsh environment.

Centuries ago, the ancestors of the Innuit lived in northeastern Asia, in what is now the Soviet Union. Then, groups migrated eastward to North America. You may remember that the ancestors of the American Indians also came from Asia. The Innuit, however, came later, many years after the land bridge between Siberia and Alaska had disappeared.

For a long time, the Innuit lived entirely by hunting the animals of the tundra. Even when outsiders brought guns in the 1800s, the Innuit continued to follow their traditional economy. Today, although life has changed for many of the 92,000 Innuit of the tundra, hunting still plays an important part in their lives.

A Hunting Economy

Hunting animals is a year-round activity for a traditional Innuit family. Their prey and their hunting methods change with the seasons because the tundra itself changes. When the tundra is covered with snow and ice, hunters can move across the land easily. After the spring thaw, however, the land becomes a muddy marsh, and the sea is filled with dangerous ice floes.

Animals migrate with the seasons. Innuit hunters must know the animals' habits and hideouts.

Most important to the traditional Innuit economy are the polar bear and such sea mammals as seals, walruses, and whales. Of all these, the seal is the Innuit staple.

After a seal is killed, an Innuit woman skins it right away. She uses an *ulu* (OO∗*loo*), a knife with a wide, crescent-shaped blade and a handle in the middle. She cuts the meat into chunks. She puts the flippers into a soup. The Innuit eat liver cold, as a snack. They use seal oil to preserve fish and for light and for fuel. Sealskin is made into clothing. It also makes good rope and tents. Every piece of the seal is useful. Even the bladder can be made into a window for a house.

Learning to hunt seals is an important accomplishment for an Innuit boy. When a boy brings home his first large seal, his mother gives a party in his honor.

Seal hunting goes on all year, but other animals are caught in different seasons. In the late fall, when the ice is 4 inches (10.2 cm) thick, everyone goes ice fishing. Each person digs a hole in the ice the size of a basketball hoop. Hooks, with or without

The Innuit have learned to make full use of the Arctic's limited resources. This Innuit woman catches fish through the ice.

bait, are lowered into the water and jiggled to attract the fish. Children in schools go ice fishing at recess and keep their fish in plastic bags. When the ice is too thick to go fishing, winter has come. Men trap mink and otters and shoot Arctic hares and foxes.

In the spring, women and children look for bird eggs in nests on the marshes. Men and boys hunt ducks, geese, and ptarmigans (a kind of Arctic bird).

In the summer, families work together to catch salmon and herring. They often camp in tents with relatives to add fun to the work. They net the fish and dry them on racks for winter eating.

The Arctic summer, with 24 hours of daylight, brings people outdoors. It also brings clouds of mosquitoes, but these insects are soon eaten by all the newly hatched birds. Women pick grasses for weaving. They also gather other plants that grow wild on the spongy tundra—celery, spinach, willow, and rhubarb. Boys go muskrat hunting. Girls pick berries. Some of these berries are frozen in a cellar that is dug down to the permafrost to make *akutaq* (AH*koo*tahk) for parties.

In the fall, children collect driftwood in the cold, wind-driven rain. Hunters repair their tools and their sleds. Women sew and mend winter clothing and make sealskin boots.

Tundra Living, Traditional Style

In former times, the Innuit developed a technology that was well suited to their needs. Hunting, for instance, required special techniques. Sea mammals are large and move fast. The Innuit figured out a way to slow them down so that they could kill them.

Hunters made a harpoon with a barbed head and a long line. When a hunter hurled a harpoon at an animal, the head pierced the skin and caught in the blubber (fat). The hunter pulled the line to slow the mammal and then struck again. He often fastened an inflated sealskin to the end of the line. The float let the hunter know where the wounded animal had dived.

How could a hunter get so close to such large animals? He had good transportation. In the summer, he paddled the sea in his one-person canoe, a **kayak** (KEYE*ak*). It was lightweight. Its sealskin cover was waterproof. Salt water did not damage it. Icy water could not get into it. When a storm came, a hunter put on a gut hood that fastened him tightly into the kayak.

In the nine winter months of the year during which snow covered the ground, an Innuit family relied on its dog team and sled. Sometimes, people rode on top of the loaded sled. The driver stood at the back.

A team was made up of from 5 to 15

Above, an Innuit woman collects wild greens from the tundra in summer. Below, an Innuit hunter scouts for more seals, using a telescope that was paid for with a previous catch.

huskies—as many as a hunter could feed. The husky was the only domestic animal that the Innuit had, but it was hardly tame. It was so wolflike that a hunter felt safer throwing food to it. A dog could go three or four days without food. After a hunt, the team gorged itself on fresh meat.

The Innuit also developed effective protective shelter and clothing. These were of life-and-death importance in weather so cold that skin freezes in seconds. A family's winter home in Canada was the igloo. Sod houses were common in Alaska. Families slept together on skins on a platform because there was more warmth in the upper part of the house. Summer houses consisted of tents that were supported by frames of either bone or driftwood.

Traditional Innuit clothing was made of fur. Rabbits, foxes, seals, and other animals were used to make warm, snug clothes. One layer of fur was placed against the body. Another layer of clothing, with the fur turned outward, was worn on top. Men and women wore trousers, hooded jackets, fur mittens, and sealskin boots.

Modern Ways

Mining, commercial fishing, and oil drilling have brought outsiders, money, and jobs to the Innuit of today. Modern ways have taken the place of many traditional customs.

Modern Innuit life mixes the old and the new. Gas-powered snowmobiles are replacing dog-powered sleds. Traditional arts such as soapstone carving are still practiced skillfully.

The Innuit still use sleds to cross the tundra. Usually, the sleds are pulled by snowmobiles, not dog teams. Snowmobiles skim quickly over the ice and snow, but they need fuel, which has to be bought. Old men shake their heads over snowmobiles. They worry about what would happen if a snowmobile broke down in a storm. They tell stories of how dogs saved hunters' lives in the old days. A snowmobile, they say, "won't keep you warm, and you can't eat it."

Most Innuit no longer live in igloos or sod houses. Now, their houses are built of lumber that has been shipped from places outside the tundra. Innuit houses have electricity and televisions, sewing machines, and citizens-band radios. Yet, the wooden buildings are not so well insulated as the traditional ones.

The old-style clothing of fur and sealskin has been replaced by nylon and down jackets. This clothing is very colorful and serviceable, but older Innuit insist that only fur provides real warmth.

Many of the old Innuit ways do survive, however. For instance, the Innuit in Alaska catch and dry fish for winter just as a gardener freezes green beans. Young people still enjoy traditional pastimes—storytelling for the girls, wrestling for the boys. The old Innuit art of carving soapstone and ivory is very much alive. Family support and sharing still mean a great deal. Respect is paid to the elderly and to the land and its resources. Traditions which have served the Innuit for centuries are still alive and are passed down from one generation to the next. "The tundra is the very best place to be," says one Innuit. "Here, there are no restrictions, such as where to cross the street—or the river."

Lesson 3 Review

Recalling Information

1. How do the Innuit make use of the seal? What other animal resources are important to the Innuit?
2. How did the kayak, the harpoon, and the dogsled make living in the tundra easier?

Interpreting Information

3. Compare the hunting methods of the Bushmen to the hunting methods of the traditional Innuit.
4. Think about the kinds of transport that are used by the Iban, the Mongols, and the Innuit of earlier times. Explain how the climate affected each group's choice.

Applying Information

5. Innuit life has been changed by modern technology, especially the snowmobile. Is there a modern invention that has changed your life? If so, tell what it is and how it has affected you. If not, what modern invention would you like to own? How would it make your life easier?
6. What do you like best about the traditional way of life of an Innuit? Why? What aspect of Innuit traditional life would you change? Why?

Skills for Thinking

INTERPRETING STATISTICS

Much information about our planet comes from measuring and counting. For example, we measure the elevation of mountains and we count the number of people in different regions. To show the results of such studies, we often use statistics. Statistics present information in the form of numbers.

What Do These Facts Mean?

Study the chart on this page. Notice the word *normal* in the chart headings. *Normal* means "average." The numbers on statistical charts are often the results of averaging numbers. For example, to find the normal temperatures and precipitation in various places, the National Weather Service keeps a 30-year record.

To find the normal high temperature for July in a particular year in Winnemucca, Nevada, a record is made of the highest temperature reached on each day of that month. These high temperatures are added. The sum is divided by 31 (the number of days in July). The answer shows the average high temperature of *that* July.

After 30 years the averages are added, and *that* sum is divided by 30. The result is the final average. Based on 30 years of study, the normal high temperature for July in Winnemucca is 92°F (33.3°C).

Like many statistical charts, this one provides a summary of facts. Tell how the numbers relating to precipitation that are shown on the chart were developed.

NORMAL TEMPERATURE AND PRECIPITATION CHART

Place	Normal temperature range, January		Normal temperature range, July		Normal annual precipitation
	Low	High	Low	High	
Phoenix, AZ	38	65	79	105	7.05 in.
Winnemucca, NV	15	40	50	92	8.63 in.
Albuquerque, NM	24	47	65	92	7.77 in.
Alert, Canada	− 33	− 19	34	44	6.15 in.
Yellowknife, Canada	− 27	− 12	53	69	9.84 in.

Chapter **16** Review

Summary of Key Facts

In this chapter, you learned that

- for humans, tundras and deserts are difficult environments to adapt to because of their extreme climates and their limited food resources.
- traditionally, most desert peoples have been nomadic herders; others have been hunters and gatherers.
- getting water is the greatest problem that desert people must face.
- about one-third of the 44,000 Bushmen live as nomads in the Kalahari.
- the Bushmen hunt and gather food.
- traditionally, people of the tundra have been herders; others have been hunters and gatherers.
- protecting themselves from the cold is one of the greatest problems that people of the tundra face.
- for the peoples of both the desert and the tundra, many traditional ways have been replaced by modern technology.

Using Vocabulary

On a separate sheet of paper, write the term that will correctly complete each sentence.

pans   kayak
oases   igloos

1. Places in the desert where there is a permanent water supply are called ____ .

2. When no other materials were available, some Innuit built ____ for shelter.

3. When it rains in the Kalahari Desert, the ____ are filled with water.

4. A ____ is a one-person canoe.

Discussing the Chapter

1. Explain the difficulties that are involved in living in a hot, dry region.

2. What characteristics make the tundra a harsh environment?

3. How do the Kalahari Bushmen solve the problem of getting enough moisture in their dry land?

4. How do Innuit hunters adapt their searches for food to the seasons?

5. What traditional Innuit ways of living in the tundra have changed in modern times?

6. Do modern ways make the Innuit more or less dependent on the world beyond the tundra? Explain your answer.

Reviewing Skills

Use the climate chart on page 330 to answer the questions.

1. What is the average low temperature in January for all five places?

2. What is the average annual precipitation for the places in the United States? For the places in Canada?

Peoples of Lands Near Water

Chapter 17

Introduction

Early on a summer morning, a small boat heads into the Sea of Japan from the island of Hekura, 30 miles (48.3 km) off the coast of Honshu—the main island of Japan. In the boat are a woman and a man. Soon, they drop anchor, and the woman dons a wetsuit and goggles. She hangs egg-shaped weights and a long piece of rope from her waist. The rope is her safety line. Carrying an iron bar, the woman dives deep into the cold, dark water. Beneath her, she sees a forest of giant kelp, a kind of seaweed. Clinging to a rock is the domed, reddish shell of an abalone. The woman inserts her iron bar

under the shell and pries it from the rock. Quickly, she swims upward to the boat, where her husband is waiting.

This woman is called an *ama*, a diver who hunts in the sea for shellfish. Each year, 7,000 Japanese women harvest 4 million pounds (1,814,400 kg) of abalone.

Japan is a small, densely populated, mountainous country that is composed of islands. Lacking large amounts of arable land, or land that is fit for plowing, the Japanese have exploited the resources of the oceans for thousands of years. In this way, they have helped to solve the problem of feeding themselves.

In this chapter, you will read about other peoples who make their livings from water or from the lands near water. All have learned to use their technology to exploit the resources of coasts and shores.

Smelt fishing along the coast of the state of Washington. How else could you make a living in a coastal community?

Lesson 1

LANDS NEAR WATER, AS A HUMAN ENVIRONMENT

People who live near coasts and shorelines have close ties to the water. It affects their lives in many ways. It affects their climate. It affects what they eat and how they earn a living. It even affects their relations with other peoples.

Rivers, lakes, and oceans play larger roles in people's lives than we may realize. As you know, these bodies of water offer

Bass Harbor, Maine. Lighthouses were among the first navigational aids that were used to help merchant ships as they approached land.

many resources. They also can separate the people who live on their opposite sides, or they can bring people together by providing a highway for both communication and trade.

Using Water

As you know, water is necessary for all living things. Water, particularly fresh water, therefore, is a valuable resource. People use water for drinking and for cooking. They use it for washing and for bathing. They use it for making things such as roads, houses, and pottery. Water has thousands of uses. People who live near lakes and rivers are fortunate to have a ready and abundant supply of fresh water.

Besides using water for drinking, cooking, and the like, people who live along rivers and lakes can use the water for irrigation. You read about some early users of irrigation in Chapter 12. Today, irrigation is used in many places. Farmers in the Imperial Valley of southern California benefit from an irrigation project that uses water from the Colorado River. In the warm climate of their valley, they grow vegetables which are shipped to the northern United States in the winter. Without irrigation, the land would be desert.

Since salt water kills plants and cannot be drunk, water that is used in homes and on farms must be fresh water. In some coastal areas, people have developed processes to get the salt out of seawater. To do this on the very large scale that is required by modern societies, however, is a difficult and an expensive procedure. For example, in Saudi Arabia, there is a factory that can remove

What does the size of this pier in Buenos Aires, Argentina, tell about the volume of goods that travel here by sea?

salt from water. The process is so expensive, however, that salt-free water can be used only for drinking and for a few household needs, not for farming.

Waters as Highways

People who live along shorelines and coasts can use bodies of water for transportation. Before the invention of trains and cars, boats and ships were the quickest means of transportation. The Huron traveled by canoe along the rivers of Canada and the Great Lakes, trading furs with other American Indians. Early European fur traders from companies in Montreal used the same routes. Like the Huron, many peoples in river valleys have used rivers as highways.

Later, when roads and the railroads were built, the roads and railways frequently followed the flatlands along the rivers.

For many thousands of years, the oceans were barriers rather than highways. People did not have boats that were suitable for crossing the ocean safely. Nor did they have instruments to navigate, or find their way from one place to another.

People such as the Pacific Islanders, about whom you will learn more in Lesson 3, began to learn about travel on the oceans as they searched for fish. Most of this travel was always within sight of land. People used the sun and the stars to navigate.

Then, in the Renaissance, the Europeans gathered together a number of technological

What river-leaping fish do you think this man from Canada's coastal region is trying to catch?

instruments: the compass, a better astrolabe, firearms, and a new way of rigging sails. Then, they were able to sail out of sight of land without losing their way. This enabled them to sail across the oceans and around the world. Today, the oceans are great highways of trade.

The ships that sail the seas and the oceans need harbors. Great port cities such as New York, Boston, New Orleans, and San Francisco all have fine natural harbors. Where there is no natural harbor, however, people can sometimes make one. Los Angeles's harbor, built over many years, is now the busiest port on the West Coast.

Resources From Water

Water itself is a valuable resource. It also contains many valuable resources. Many fish and other animals live in aquatic environments. People have eaten these animals for thousands of years. Some people also eat plants from the sea, such as kelp. Seafood provides an important source of protein in countries where meat is scarce and expensive. In such countries as Great Britain, Japan, and Portugal, people eat a lot of fish, and fishing is a large industry.

Since the 1700s, fishing has been an important industry in the New England States. For hundreds of years, whaling was, too. Ships from New England hunted whales in waters all over the world. Besides their meat, whales were valuable for their oil, which was burned in lamps.

People who live far from the sea catch fish in lakes and in rivers. Whitefish, trout, pike, and bass are some freshwater fish that are preferred by Americans. In Austria, carp that is caught in rivers is the traditional food for Christmas Eve dinner.

Using Land Along Water

Most people who live along coasts and shorelines also use the resources of the land. Some of the best farming areas in the world are located in river valleys and on coastal plains. The valleys of the Ganges River in India, the Mekong River of Vietnam and Cambodia, and the rivers in China are among the world's great rice-producing lands. You will read about another such area in Thailand in Lesson 2.

The coastal plain along the Atlantic

Many nations once competed on the sea in the whaling industry. What factors have greatly reduced the number of whale hunters?

Ocean and the Gulf of Mexico in the United States is another important agricultural area. Its farms produce vegetables, cotton, fruits, and nuts.

In some coastal areas, the natural vegetation is an important resource. Along the Pacific Northwest Coast of Washington and British Columbia, the land is too mountainous for farming. Yet, heavy precipitation has produced dense forests of cedar, fir, and spruce trees. The American Indians who lived there hundreds of years ago lived comfortably because they were able to catch the salmon of the sea and to gather the products of the forests. The resources of their environment were so plentiful that they did not have to uproot themselves to find food. Thus, they built large, permanent villages of wooden houses.

Coastal Areas in Ancient Times

In Chapter 12, you read about early civilizations in Mesopotamia and in Egypt. These lands have almost no rainfall. Without the Tigris-Euphrates and the Nile rivers, they would be deserts. Civilizations were able to grow and to flourish there because the water of the rivers could be used for irrigation of the surrounding lands and agriculture could be developed.

Phoenicians load timber—cedars of Lebanon—for export to Egypt in 700 B.C.

The Nile gave other gifts, too. Every summer, it rains hard in the mountains far to the south where the Nile begins. So much water flows, that the Nile floods every year. These floods watered the fields of early Egyptians and left a rich layer of topsoil. The gentle flood was an annual delivery of fertilizer.

The Nile also served as Egypt's main highway. Boats sailed up and down and across the river. People in different parts of Egypt used the river to form trading links with one another.

Some time after the civilizations of Egypt and of Mesopotamia arose, another civiliza-tion started to develop in Phoenicia (*feh∗NEESH∗uh*). Phoenicia was located about where the country of Lebanon is to-day, on the coast of the Mediterranean Sea. The Phoenicians, who used the Mediter-ranean as a great highway, sent trading ships to every shore. Their ships even sailed into the Atlantic Ocean and traded with peo-ples in such faraway lands as the British Isles.

The Greeks and the Romans also used the Mediterranean as a great highway. The Greeks developed colonies all along the shores of the Mediterranean. From these colonies, their ideas spread throughout the region. The Romans conquered most of the shores of the Mediterranean. The Romans even called the Mediterranean *mare nos-trum*, which means "our sea."

Coastal Areas in Modern History

As you have read, the modern wave of ocean travel and exploration began in Eu-rope during the Renaissance—roughly from 1400 to 1600. Europeans sailed around the world and established colonies on almost every continent.

In what is now the United States, these colonies stretched along the Atlantic coast. Colonists used resources from the ocean in many ways. You have read about how fish-ing and whaling became important industries in New England. So did trade. From its many natural ports, New England shipped and received goods from countries across the Atlantic. Fishing industries grew up in other colonies, too.

Chesapeake Bay in Maryland and in

Acapulco's warm climate and beautiful beaches make it a popular vacation resort.

Virginia became an important fishing area as well as a trading highway. Great swamps and forests and broad rivers, which flowed into the bay, made land travel around the bay very difficult. The colonists found it much easier to journey by boat. They developed large farms in the area. Many of these farms had private docks along the bay or on rivers. Wealthy farmers traded with English merchants without having to travel to town.

Changing Resources

In some coastal regions, one resource may be important at one time and another may be important at another time. For example, the city of Acapulco in Mexico was an important port in the 1600s and the 1700s. After Mexico won its independence from Spain in the 1800s, the great Spanish ships no longer went to Acapulco. The only vessels that used the harbor were small fishing boats.

Then, in the 1920s, a road was built from Mexico City to Acapulco. By the 1930s, people began to go there on vacation to enjoy the warm weather and the beaches. Today, tourism is the main industry of the people in Acapulco.

Lesson 1 Review

Recalling Information
1. Name three ways in which bodies of water can be resources.
2. Why are bodies of water often called the first highways?

Interpreting Information
3. Why were our early colonies located close to the Atlantic Ocean?
4. Why is it important to protect the oceans from pollution?

Applying Information
5. Make a list of things that you use that come from the water.
6. If you were to spend your vacation at a shore, how might you use that body of water as a resource?

Another bushel of rice is bound for the granary in a remote Thai village.

Lesson 2

THE RICE GROWERS OF THAILAND

Raek Nah, the Plowing Ceremony, is about 2,500 years old. Each year, the court astrologer of Thailand determines the day on which the ceremony will take place. Farmers travel to the cities to participate in the ritual.

After making offerings to the gods, the lord of the festival selects one of three folded *panungs*, which are traditional costumes that are worn by men. The garments are folded so that no one can tell their length. Thais believe that if the lord of the festival chooses a long panung, rain will be sparse. A panung of medium length means that there will be average rainfall. A short panung signifies that there will be heavy rainfall and a good harvest.

Raek Nah is a serious matter to Thai farmers. As in most Southeast Asian countries, rice is Thailand's staple food, and rice cannot grow without water. Rice is also the basis of the nation's economy. Thailand sells more rice than any other country in the world, except the United States. About 90 percent of the farmland in Thailand is planted with rice. The average size of a family farm is about 10 acres (4 ha); these are among the largest farms in Asia. Seventy-five percent of the Thais live, as their ancestors did, on the produce of the land. Others work in teak forests, on rubber plantations, and in lumber mills.

The Central Plain

Thailand's most important agricultural region is its Central Plain. Located about 15°N of the equator, in the path of monsoons, the plain has a warm climate, moderate rainfalls, and a year-round growing season. The region contains just less than half of Thailand's rice acreage.

The Central Plain of Thailand is between 75 miles and 150 miles (120.7 km and 241.4 km) wide from east to west. A horseshoe-shaped range of hills borders it on the north, the east, and the west. To the south, the plain reaches the coast of the Gulf of Thailand.

Each year, between May and October, the southwest monsoon brings about 55 inches (139.7 cm) of rain. Each day, downpours alternate with sunshine. On these rains depends the vital rice crop, for lowland rice needs 2 inches to 6 inches (5.1 cm to 15.2 cm) of standing water in which to grow. Thus, the Plowing Ceremony developed great importance.

The Central Plain is also the flood plain of the Chao Phraya (CHOW *prah*∗YAH), a wide river that flows south to the Gulf of Thailand. Each year, it floods its banks and replenishes the topsoil, adding deposits of silt and clay at the river's mouth. Because of this continual flooding, the land has extended gradually seaward. Its elevation is still low. Half of the plain is less than 100 feet (30.5 m) above sea level.

The main transportation system of this flat plain is a network of waterways. Ocean-going ships can travel up the Chao Phraya River from the Gulf of Thailand to Bangkok, which is the Thai capital and one of the major ports of Southeast Asia. The river, with its tributaries and the network of **klongs**, or canals, forms a vast highway system for small boats.

Between klongs, squares of rice fields stretch as far as the eye can see. Klongs are used to irrigate the rice fields. They also supply drinking water and fish that are part of the Thai diet. Children play in klongs, and everyone washes in them. People travel klongs in **sampans**, or small, canoelike boats. It is no wonder that people live near klongs and that villages have grown up where they intersect.

Cultivating Rice

Life for Thai farmers, who make up three-quarters of the country's population,

Thai farmers harvesting rice near Ayudhya. What is the next step in their work?

revolves around the rice crop. Each family member helps with some part of the farming process.

The head of the household begins the work when the monsoons start in May. After rain has soaked the land for a few weeks, the farmer plows a field or two to be used as **seedbeds**, or areas where plants are raised from seeds for transplanting. A water buffalo pulls a wooden plow through the muck. A farmer who does not own a water buffalo borrows one from another villager.

Next, the farmer harrows, or plows, the earth to break it into smaller pieces. The stalks and the roots from the previous crop are cleared from the field at the same time.

341

Then, the field is drained, and the mud is leveled, usually with a banana stalk.

The next step is broadcasting, or scattering, the seeds. While these take root and sprout, the farmer begins to prepare the other fields.

Then comes the hard work of transplanting. About six weeks after sowing, the farmer uproots the seedlings, ties them in bundles, and plants each one in several inches of water. Relatives share this muddy work, the hardest of the year. They sing and joke while their hands rhythmically push each grasslike plant into the oozing muck. Soon, the fields are a bright, reflecting green. Once or twice after the early August planting, the neat rows must be weeded.

By November or December, the rice panicles, or heads, are heavy with grain. The fields are drained to let the stalks dry for harvesting. In some areas of the Central Plain that flood heavily, farmers plant long-stemmed, flood-resistant varieties of rice. They harvest such rice from boats or while standing in water up to their chests.

For harvesting, farmers cut the stalks close to the ground. Then, the grain is tied in bundles and carried to the village threshing floor. The bundles are hit against the earth to knock the heads of grain off the straw. When the rice is tossed into the air, the wind takes the chaff, or tough outer skin, away.

Above, farmers at work planting rice in Thailand. The care of livestock such as water buffalo (below) is an important task in this farming community.

The family rice supply is stored in baskets in the **granary**, or storehouse for grain, on the family compound. Surplus rice goes to merchants who ship it by canal boat to Bangkok. From the capital's warehouses, thousands of tons of rice are exported to the Philippines and to other Asian countries, such as Malaysia and Indonesia.

Besides growing rice, the family raises vegetables and fruits and catches fish for food. Children look for small crabs and freshwater shrimp in the flooded rice paddies. Everybody spends time netting and trapping fish in the small klongs. Thais like fresh food and go to the market each day to trade, to buy, and to sell. Any surplus does not go to waste.

Daily Life

To see how the people live, let us visit a Thai village. A village may have 10 to 100 houses with small wooden jetties that face a klong. Inside a bamboo fence is the compound where trees—bamboo, fruit, and palm—shade the house. The dwelling, which is made of both wood and woven materials, stands 5 feet to 8 feet (1.5 m to 2.4 m) above the ground on teakwood stilts. The raised house provides safety from flooding. Animals live under the house. A ladder leads to an open porch for sitting and for eating. The roof is peaked so that rain can roll off it quickly.

Inside the house, you smell the spicy aromas that come from the small cooking stove. A seasoning called *nampla* is being made by fermenting silverfish that were caught in the gulf. Spicy sauces are used for dipping vegetables and meat, which Thais eat with their rice. Lemon grass, curry, and chilies are also used. Thais like spicy, hot foods which have been either steamed or stir-fried.

Most villagers live their entire lives within a few miles of home and are virtually untouched by the hustle and bustle of the industrial world. Yet, they may be only a short distance from Bangkok, one of the busiest cities of Southeast Asia and one which has been feeling the touch of the industrial world for some time.

Lesson 2 Review

Recalling Information

1. On what natural resources do the Thai rice farmers depend for their livelihood? Explain.
2. What is the process by which rice is cultivated and harvested?

Interpreting Information

3. How might life in Thailand change if rice were not the staple?
4. How would life be different without the resources of Thailand's canals?

Applying Information

5. Do the farming families in your area work together as families do in Thailand? Explain.
6. Upon what water resources do people in your region depend?

Imagine yourself a member of this Trobriander group. What
skills might the adults be helping you to develop?

Lesson 3

THE TROBRIANDERS OF
THE SOUTH PACIFIC

The ocean has shaped the land of the Trobrianders. It has also shaped the lives of
these island dwellers of the South Pacific.
So tied to the ocean are they, that they mark
off land distances in **fathoms**, a measurement used for water depths. As easily as
you bike a few miles, they paddle a canoe
from one island to another. They can navigate by "reading" the swell of the waves,
the position of the stars, and the flight of
birds.

The Trobriand Islands consist of a large
coral island, which has been named Kiri-
wina (*kihr*∗*uh*∗WEE∗*nuh*), and several
other islands that make up an archipelago,
northeast of New Guinea. Locate these islands on the map on pages 488 and 489.
None of the islands is wider or longer than
50 miles (80.5 km).

Coral is a limestone formation that is
made of the skeletons of tiny sea animals.
The Trobriand Islands arose during an era
when the ocean was several hundred feet
lower. A reef of coral surrounds the islands.
Between the islands and the reef is a lagoon
of calm, shallow water.

As do most islands in the tropics, the

Trobriand Islands receive abundant rainfall and much sunshine. Water temperatures range between 64°F (17.8°C) and 74°F (23.3°C) all year. The land temperature is even warmer. Rain forest covers most of the flat coral islands. A year-round growing season and waters that are filled with an abundance of fish and shellfish have made it easy for the Trobrianders to provide for their basic needs.

The first Trobrianders probably came to the islands from nearby New Guinea 25,000 years ago. That was during the time of the Ice Age, when the distance between the islands in the Pacific was not so great. When the ice melted and the level of the ocean rose, the people on each island became more isolated. Since that time, the people of the Trobriand Islands have depended on the sea.

Making a Living

The sound of water—the lapping of the lagoon against the beach, the crash of the breakers over the reef—can be heard everywhere. The westerly winds swish through the palm trees that grow at village sites. Wind and water are both important to the economy of the Trobrianders. The winds bring rain, the only source of fresh water on a coral island. From the sea, the people get fish and shellfish, which are eaten or traded to other islanders. The sea also serves as a highway for travel and for commerce.

Fish and other sea animals seek the calm lagoons around the islands. The islanders have many ways of catching them.

Very young children learn how to fish in the lagoon with a seine net, or a vertical net weighted with shells. Men use long canoes to go fishing near the reef where they use a round net that is bordered by long strands of coconut fronds. The fish swim into the net to get away from the coconut fronds, which look to them like a solid barrier hanging into the water. Men, women, and children work together to catch fish in a large, encircling net that is attached to a rope. Those who are holding a part of the rope stand close to shore; others who are holding other

Can You Imagine?

Among the Trobrianders, a gift is repaid with one of similar value. The giving and receiving of the gifts themselves is not the goal of this exchange. The goal is the cementing of friendships.

Imagine that you are a Trobriand chief. Villagers from a neighboring island have caught a surplus of tuna, which they have smoked and brought to you by boat. What should you do in return?

You call a meeting of your people. One person suggests sending coconuts. Another suggests sending coconut twine. Yet another says that taro, which is abundant this year, would be the best gift. The group decides to send coconuts.

Your people gather the coconuts and arrange them in open baskets. A delegation of men loads the baskets into canoes and sets off for your neighbor's island.

When the men return, they are happy because your neighbors gratefully accepted the coconuts. How do you feel?

A Trobriand yam-house shares center space in the village with the chief's house.

parts have to tread water or to work from small canoes. Guided by the older men, everyone pulls the net toward the shore. After a half-hour's work, there may be a few dozen fish or many more if a school of fish has been located.

As important as fishing is to the Trobrianders, they value farming even more. A man's prestige depends on how well his gardens produce. Trobrianders spend about half their time at work in their gardens.

As in many tropical lands, the soil is fertile but easily depleted, or worn out. New plots of land must be prepared every year. Trobrianders clear the land by the slash-and-burn method. Villagers work as a group

to clear their land and to build their fences.

The yam is the most important crop. Trobrianders also raise bananas and taro, a starchy root.

Using a pointed digging stick or a knife with a steel blade, a Trobriander plants the tops of yams that the family has saved from the previous year. As the vines grow, they are staked. A good gardener arranges the foliage so that the sun reaches each leaf. The number of leaves determines the growth of the tuber, or root, under the ground. A yam's size is very important to Trobrianders. A man who raises the year's prize yam, which may weigh as much as 30 pounds (13.6 kg), receives many compliments from the other villagers.

Women weed the crops, and men do all the rest of the work. After the yams are harvested, they are stored in yam houses whose sides are open. Yams are arranged so that passersby can see and admire the biggest ones.

Villages trade with other islanders for the raw materials that they need. Grass for baskets, wood for carving, and shells for necklaces are all objects of trade. The exchange of vegetables for fish is an important part of commerce.

Village Life

In each village, the houses are arranged in a large circle. In front of the houses is a smaller circle of storehouses for yams. These storehouses are more carefully made than the dwellings. In the center of the circle, there are always two additional houses, one the house for the chief, and the other his storehouse for yams.

Yams are the most important food crop grown in the Trobriand Islands. Here, a farmer uses a long knife to harvest his crop.

From the rain forest, the Trobrianders get many essential resources. Wood is used to build houses and the long canoes that Trobrianders use for fishing and for transport. Wood is also used for fuel. Cooking utensils are made of materials that can be gathered from the rain forest. Leaves are used to line shallow pits in which Trobrianders bake their food.

In Trobriand villages, men are expected to carve axes, adzes, and other tools. They make water bottles from coconuts. Women are taught to weave floor mats for sleeping. They cook and do domestic work. The women also make fiber skirts, sew mats, and plait baskets.

Trade

Using the sea as a highway, the Trobrianders and other islanders carry on a circle of trade that is known as the *kula*. Hundreds of boats run a double circuit that includes the eastern tip of New Guinea and all the small neighboring archipelagoes. These circuits involve the trading of necklaces and of armbands. Each person who trades goods receives a gift and passes it or another gift on to another trader. The exchange suggests a kind of partnership among the participants. It serves to unite members of different groups and islands. The bond that is created among these peoples continues during the lifetime of the participants.

Along with necklaces and armbands, green stones that are used as blades in ceremonial hatchets, ebony sculpture, and other items are traded.

The *kula* provides not only an exchange of trade items and gifts but it also provides an opportunity for social contact among the islanders who are surrounded by the sea.

Lesson 3 Review

Recalling Information
1. What are the resources of the Trobriand Island environment?
2. How do the Trobrianders obtain food from the land? From the sea?

Interpreting Information
3. How does the sea influence the culture of the Trobrianders?
4. Compare the agriculture of the Trobrianders with that of the Thais.

Applying Information
5. How do you think that living on an island is different from living on a mainland?
6. How is the culture in the region where you live affected by the environment?

Each house in a Trobriand village (top) is occupied by a single family. Men from the village celebrate the annual yam harvest with a colorful dance (below).

Special People
Queen Salote Tupou

Salote Tupou, queen of Tonga, ruled that island kingdom from 1918 until her death in 1965. The kingdom includes about 150 islands in the South Pacific.

Salote Tupou was an enlightened and progressive ruler. She gave great support to public health and education programs. During her reign, education became free and compulsory for all Tongans.

During World War II, the people of Tonga contributed heavily to the Allied war effort. When the troops landed, Salote Tupou urged the people of Tonga to go back into the forest. Thus, according to a report in *The New York Times*, "she protected (her people) from the ills that befell many other island peoples from too close association with an alien civilization."

Salote Tupou belonged to one of the world's oldest ruling families. Her royal ancestry could be traced from modern times back to the tenth century A.D.

Skills for Thinking

MAKING ANALOGIES

Two scientists are about to leave on different expeditions. One says, "I'll be comparing the altitudes of different peaks in the Himalayas."

The second scientist says, "Our work is similar. I'll be measuring the depths of different parts of the Indian Ocean."

The second scientist has made an **analogy**, or has shown a relationship. An analogy pulls ideas together to show the similarity between them. In this case, both *mountains* and *oceans* are things to be measured. Each measurement is expressed in a special way: *altitude* (mountains): *depth* (oceans).

Here is a short way of expressing the analogy: *Altitude* is to *mountains* as *depth* is to *oceans*.

How Are These Ideas Related?

To complete any analogy correctly, ask yourself how the ideas are related.

From what you have learned about climate in this book, you can probably complete the following analogy. Choose the correct word to use in the blank. Then, explain your choice.
Prevailing winds are to *mountains* as ____ are to *coastal regions*.
(a) sand **(b)** currents **(c)** tides

The ability to see relationships is an important thinking skill. Many tests include analogy sections. Study the following examples.

- Prevailing winds : mountains
  ____ : coastal regions
  (a) sand **(b)** currents **(c)** tides
- depth : oceans
  altitude : ____
  (a) snowfall **(b)** length **(c)** mountains

Practice your skill at making analogies by completing the ones that follow.

1. channels : ships
   ____ : vehicles
   (a) wheels **(b)** power **(c)** roadways
2. catch : fish
   harvest : ____
   (a) crops **(b)** farmers **(c)** sow
3. shore : coast
   lowlands : ____
   (a) soil **(b)** grass **(c)** mountains
4. pastures : flocks
   feeding grounds : ____
   (a) sheep **(b)** fish **(c)** shepherds
5. migration : animals
   ____ : hunters
   (a) movement **(b)** food **(c)** tools

Chapter *17* Review

Summary of Key Facts
In this chapter, you learned that
- bodies of water are natural resources that are used for food, for transportation, for irrigation, for recreation, and for many other purposes.
- seafood may be an important protein source for people in countries where meat is scarce.
- rice is grown on Thailand's coastal plains and is the country's staple.
- Thais rely on their waterways for irrigation, for transportation, for fish, and for fresh water.
- the Trobriands are coral islands that form an archipelago.
- the Trobrianders fish, farm, and trade with neighboring islands.

Using Vocabulary
On a separate sheet of paper, write a word that will correctly complete each sentence.

1. A fathom is a measure of water ____ .
2. Coral is a limestone formation that is made of the tiny ____ of sea animals.
3. A granary is a place to ____ grain.

Discussing the Chapter
1. How do people who live in coastal regions depend on the sea for their needs?
2. How do the customs and the beliefs of the Thais reflect their dependence on water and on the rice harvest?
3. How do the Trobrianders cooperate as a group to survive in their environment?

Reviewing Skills
Write the word that will correctly complete each analogy.

1. fathom: water
   foot: ____
   (a) shoe   **(b)** ocean   **(c)** land
2. klong: canal
   sampan: ____
   (a) boat   **(b)** Thailand   **(c)** ocean

Unit 5 Review

Summary of Key Facts

In this unit, you learned that

- many of the world's peoples still live in traditional ways—very close to their environment—though few of them are completely untouched by the industrial world.
- traditional societies base their economies on the resources that are found immediately around them.
- each type of region—forest, grassland, desert, tundra, and land near water—offers different resources and poses different problems to be overcome.
- societies adapt their cultures to the demands of their environments.

Discussing the Unit

1. How has fire been used for agriculture by people in traditional societies?
2. What are some useful resources of a forest? Of a grassland? Of lands near water? How do people traditionally use these resources?
3. What are some of the special problems that are faced by people who live in deserts? In tundra?
4. How are traditional societies being influenced by the modern world, including national governments?
5. Compare how the following peoples traditionally make their livings—the Iban and the Montagnais-Naskapi, the Masai and the Mongolians, the Bushmen and the Innuit.

Activities

1. Research and report about the culture of another traditional society.
2. Find a legend or a tale from a traditional society. Read it aloud to the class. Then, lead a discussion about what the story reveals about that society's culture.

Test

Using Vocabulary

On a sheet of paper, write the term that will correctly complete each sentence.

oasis
reforestation
pack animal
native
commercial forestry
transhumance

coral
pan
rite of passage
slash-and-burn agriculture
sedentary agriculture

1. A(n) _____ is a place in a desert where there is a permanent supply of water.
2. A kind of farming that uses fire to clear land is called _____ .
3. A(n) _____ island is created of the skeletons of tiny sea animals.
4. In _____ , some people follow their herds while others stay at home in permanent settlements.
5. A(n) _____ is one that is used to carry loads.
6. _____ is an economic activity that involves the sale of forest products.
7. In _____ , people settle in one place to farm.
8. A marriage ceremony is a _____ .
9. The process of forest regrowth is called _____ .
10. In a desert after a rain, look for water in a shallow _____ .

The Big Question

How do ways of interacting with their environment compare among traditional societies?

Write your answer in complete sentences. Draw upon the information in this unit to write a good answer.

Using Map Skills

Use the map on page 277 to complete this exercise.

1. Between which parallels can most of the world's midlatitude forests be found?
2. What is the predominant forest along the equator?
3. What types of forest primarily grow in Australia?

Identifying a Geographic Theme

Think about the geographic theme of **human-environment interactions** as you complete this exercise.

What advantages can be found in the life styles of traditional societies? What are the disadvantages?

Unit 6 The Modern Industrial World

When our nation was young, most people obtained food and vital resources from the land. Few people worked far from home because land transportation was slow.

Today, in the United States and elsewhere in the industrial world, few people are tied to the land. They are separated from nature by modern technology and its products. Forests, grasslands, and deserts are, to most people, places to visit, not places in which to live or to make a living. The modern industrial world is a human-made environment, not a natural one.

Concepts

exports   standard of living
imports   high tech

The Big Question

How has industrialization changed the world and the ways in which people live?

Focus on a Geographic Theme

In this unit you will study the geographic theme of **movement**. For people to get what they do not have, they interact with one another through travel, trade, and communication. Geographers study the changes that result from these interactions.

**Japan's Bullet Train links several major
industrial cities.**

The New Industrial Environment

Chapter *18*

Introduction

Fireworks lit the sky over the southern end of Manhattan Island one night in 1883. New Yorkers were celebrating the opening of the Brooklyn Bridge. No longer would they have to depend on ferryboats to take them across the river to Brooklyn. Now, they could drive their carriages, push their carts, and ride their bicycles across the new bridge.

In 1883, the Brooklyn Bridge was the highest point in New York City. Supported by thick steel cables that were attached to tall pillars, it was called the eighth wonder of the world.

The technology and the techniques that built the Brooklyn Bridge were products of the Industrial Revolution. By 1883, the United States was industrializing at a rapid rate. Farming was becoming mechanized, too, and so were communications. Telegraph cables, telephone lines, and railroad tracks put people and businesses across the country in instant communication with one another.

With their new technology, Americans increased their power over the resources of their rich environment to solve many problems. In doing so, they created an important phenomenon—world modernization—and another age of human history.

◀ **Now more than 100 years old, New York's Brooklyn Bridge proves that industry and art can be combined to beautify a city.**

THE INDUSTRIAL LANDSCAPE

The Brooklyn Bridge is still a famous American landmark. It looks about the same as it did a century ago, but the area around it looks much different.

The Environment of a Metropolis

The Brooklyn Bridge is no longer the highest point in New York City, nor is it the only great bridge. Other even more spectacular bridges now connect Manhattan Island to the other four **boroughs**, or political divisions, of New York City. The newest, the Verrazano Narrows Bridge, stretches over the New York Harbor to connect the boroughs of Brooklyn and Staten Island. It is so long that engineers had to figure in the curvature of Earth as part of the bridge design. A half-dozen or so railway bridges also cross the waterways of New York City. Tunnels under the rivers and under the ground provide transit for subway trains, cars, trucks, and buses.

Transportation systems are not the only developments that have changed the look of New York City since the 1880s. From the Brooklyn Bridge, you can now see hundreds of tall buildings. The technology of the continuing Industrial Revolution has created an artificial environment, one that is built of steel, glass, plastic, and concrete.

South of the Brooklyn Bridge, tall buildings tower over Brooklyn's central business district. Even taller skyscrapers are situated at the other end of the bridge, in Lower Manhattan. There, the twin towers of the World Trade Center soar 110 stories high, a quarter of a mile (402.3 m) above ground level. Within these buildings are thousands of acres of work space.

It is an exciting walk from the Brooklyn Bridge to the World Trade Center. The city seems to be at work every step along the way. During the week, the flow of commuters into the city swells the population density of Manhattan from 65,000 persons per square mile (about 25,000 per sq km) to 200,000 people per square mile (80,000 per sq km) every day. Taxis, cars, and buses often jam the city streets. The roar of traffic mixes with the clank of jackhammers and pile drivers to make conversation difficult. The building of the city never stops. Old structures are torn down. In their place arise steel skeletons that outline taller buildings to be built. Machines of every imaginable variety are used everywhere.

You ascend swiftly to the top of the World Trade Center in a quiet elevator, the invention that made tall buildings practical and, therefore, usable. The view from the top of the tallest building in New York City includes New York Harbor and parts of all five boroughs. The greenery of Central Park, to the north in Manhattan, shows you what little is left of grass fields to walk across, of trees to climb, and of growing flowers.

Manhattan Island has the greatest collection of skyscrapers in the world. They are the headquarters of both large and small businesses, of banks, of financial institutions, of oil companies, and of advertising

Skyscrapers crowd the streets of lower Manhattan. This high-rise urban environment is a product of modern industrial technology.

firms. Located among them—and in the other four boroughs—are many other buildings in which manufacturing is done. New York is a leading center in the manufacturing of clothing and other products of **light industry**, or industry that does not rely on heavy equipment or heavy materials.

Deep and sheltered harbors help to make New York a leading trading center. Docks, truck terminals, and warehouses line its shores. Tugboats guide oceangoing ships into and out of the harbor. The ships transport cargo to and from all parts of the world. Barges pass slowly under the bridges and carry food and raw materials to the city.

Beyond the City

New York City is part of a megalopolis that extends along much of the Atlantic coastal plain. Look at any map of the United States. As you can see, New York City is bordered by New Jersey on the west. Across the Hudson River, set among the sprawling marshlands along the shores of New Jersey, are refineries and factories that process many raw materials. These **heavy industries** manufacture gasoline and chemicals and refine copper and oil.

Other areas in the New York metropolitan region are highly industrialized. The nearby counties of New York State contain

Industrialization changes urban landscapes in large and in small ways. Compare these two views of London's Thames River. In which view is the city older? How do you know?

business headquarters, plants that specialize in light industry, and research centers. Connecticut is noted for fine tools, for precision instruments, and for insurance companies.

Streets and highways of concrete and of blacktop, plus steel railroad tracks, form a grid across the landscape. They connect commercial, industrial, and residential districts. The typical housing near business districts consists of apartment buildings with little greenery around them. Nearby suburbs have enough space for single-family houses and small, open yards.

Toward the outskirts of the New York metropolitan region, the landscape becomes

Past and Present

Much of the growth of New York City was caused by the continuing Industrial Revolution. Yet, as you have read, many of the cities that are part of today's biggest metropolitan areas bustled with activity long before the days of industrialization.

One such urban center was the London of Shakespeare's day, in the late 1500s. Most of its 200,000 inhabitants lived on the north bank of the Thames (TEMZ) River. A single bridge, the London Bridge, connected the north and the south sides of the city.

London was a city of wooden dwellings that were four or five stories high. These dwellings were divided into small, dark rooms. Only a few church steeples rose above their peaked roofs. London's streets—most of them unpaved—were dirty, crowded, and unsafe. There was no system of garbage removal, nor was there a police force. People moved about the city on horseback, in horse-drawn carriages, or on foot. Farmers with carts that were full of vegetables and grains came to the city to sell their produce.

London was a busy port, and ships from many lands could be seen at its wooden docks. It was a government center, too.

London is still a center of commerce and government. It is also a manufacturing center. Although many buildings average only about four stories in height, steel and glass skyscrapers now rise above them. Like all modern cities, London has the trappings of industrialization—mechanized transportation, advanced communications, and the like. Its industrial landscape stretches over miles of what was once broadleaf deciduous forest.

less and less urban. Concrete and steel give way first to suburban villages and finally to woods and farmland.

Although the landscape is no longer urban, signs of industrialization can be seen everywhere. Asphalt roads and steel rail lines thread through rural areas. Electric power lines and telephone lines edge many roadways. Television antennas sprout from the roofs of farmhouses and homes in small towns. In dairy barns, machines that are run by electricity milk cows. In open fields, farmers who are sitting in enclosed cabs operate machines that plow, cultivate, and harvest. Crop-dusting planes spray chemicals over fields and orchards to control insects that would otherwise destroy crops. So, even rural areas that are far from cities are part of the industrial environment.

The New York–New Jersey–Connecticut megalopolis is typical of megalopolises everywhere. Human beings, not nature, designed it. The landscape has been shaped by humans, and it, in turn, has shaped them.

Growing industries contribute jobs and change the skylines in major cities. Which industries center around Houston, Texas?

In the next lesson, you will see how the industrial environment has shaped the economy of the modern world. Economy, as you know, has to do with the way people make a living and use their natural resources.

Lesson 1 Review

Recalling Information

1. Why was the Brooklyn Bridge considered to be unusual in 1883?
2. Describe how New York City has changed since the building of the Brooklyn Bridge.

Interpreting Information

3. What features of the rural landscape near New York City indicate that it is situated in an industrialized country?
4. What are some important ways in which a preindustrial city differed from an industrial city?

Applying Information

5. Think about your trip from home to school each morning. What things do you see or experience that are part of the industrial landscape?
6. Look around you. What elements do you see that are part of the natural environment?

Lesson 2

THE INDUSTRIAL ECONOMY

In earlier chapters, you read about peoples who live in many kinds of environments. You saw how their surroundings have shaped the lives of the Iban of Borneo, the Masai of East Africa, the Bushmen of the Kalahari Desert, and the herders of Mongolia.

As different as their ways are, these traditional societies have at least three things in common: (1) Their economies are basically local and self-sufficient. (2) Their use of the environment is light, and they do not significantly reshape the land and the water around them. (3) Therefore, their environment is a sustainable environment, one that is stable and can be sustained year after year for the benefit of its inhabitants.

Although people in traditional economies trade surplus food for produce that they cannot grow, such as sugar, most people can survive without trade. These traditional societies can use the resources of their environment to meet their needs for food, shelter, and clothing, and they have been doing just that for centuries.

Large ships are essential for international trade. They carry raw materials to manufacturers and finished products to consumers.

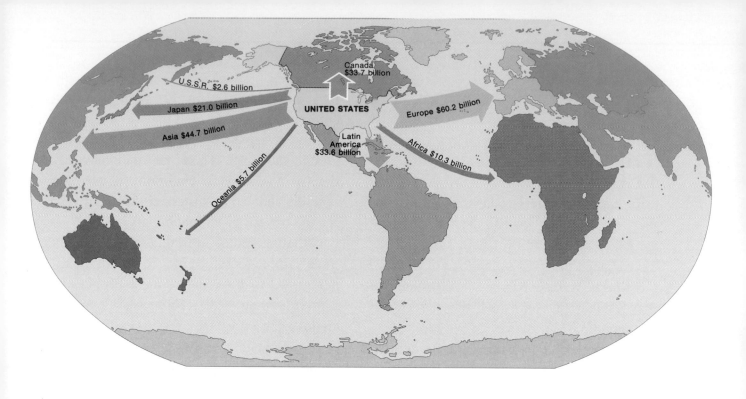

UNITED STATES: 1982 EXPORTS

MAP SKILLS: To which region of the world did the United States export the largest amount of goods in 1982?

Resources From Many Lands

The situation is very different in the industrial world. People depend on a great many resources and products that they cannot provide for themselves locally. The people of New York City, for instance, depend almost solely on resources that are available outside the city's borders. In fact, they utilize resources from around the world. Their food is trucked in from other parts of New York State, from the neighboring states of New Jersey and Connecticut, as well as from many more distant points. Oranges, grapes and lettuce come from California's valleys, grapefruit arrives from Florida, and bananas are imported from the countries of Central America.

Similarly, people in industrial societies no longer use only local resources to build or to furnish their homes and workplaces. Unlike their ancestors who chopped down nearby trees to build their houses, today's industrialized people use building materials that they may import from the whole world. Steel for city buildings may come from Pennsylvania, from West Germany, or from Japan. Their wood may come from New England, from the northwestern part of the United States, or from such faraway countries as Indonesia and Brazil. The fabrics for clothing and bedding may also come from distant parts of the globe.

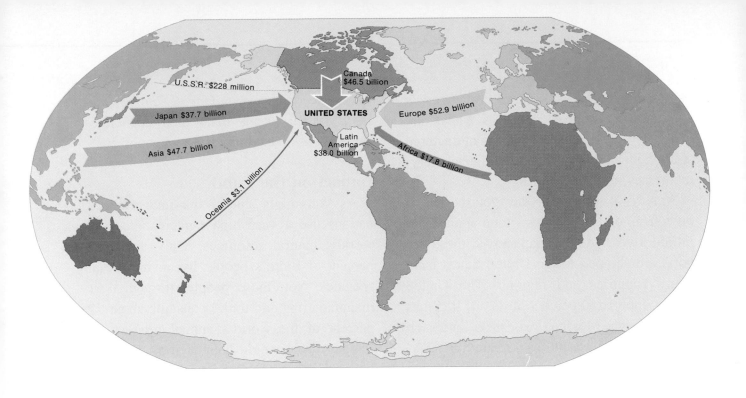

UNITED STATES: 1982 IMPORTS

MAP SKILLS: Compare this map with the map on page 364.
In 1982, did the United States import or export more goods?

A Global Economy

New York City and other centers of the industrial world, then, cooperate in a global economy. To meet their needs, industrial nations draw on the natural and the human resources of the entire world. They rely on a worldwide trade network to obtain resources and goods, and they trade their own resources, goods, and services to obtain the money to pay for them. You, too, are a part of this global economy.

Take your new jeans. The cotton for the fabric may well have been grown and woven in China. From there, a ship may have carried it to Indonesia, where workers cut and sewed the cloth into the proper design and size. The machines that the workers used for cutting and sewing may have been made in France from steel that was manufactured in West Germany. The jeans then may have been packed in cardboard boxes that were made of wood from the forests of Oregon, and, from Indonesia, they may have been shipped across the Pacific Ocean to San Francisco. From there, they were sent to your local store and were bought by you.

The maps on these two pages show how involved the United States is in world trade. Its **exports**—the goods that the United States sells to other nations—are worth more than $200 billion a year. About one-third of these exports are raw materials and natural resources, such as wheat and coal. The rest consists of manufactured goods, including aircraft, farm machinery, medicines, and electronics.

America's **imports**—the goods that it buys from other countries—total about $270 billion a year. As the map shows, these imports are shipped to the United States from many countries and regions. The United States imports 40 percent of its oil. It comes from Canada, Mexico, Venezuela, and such Middle Eastern countries as Saudi Arabia. Look at the map on page 365. From what other countries might the United States buy oil?

Every nation on Earth exports and imports goods. Resources, money, goods, and services continuously flow between nations. Because of this worldwide trade network, every country's economy is affected by the economies of other countries. The nations of the world are *economically interdependent*, which means that "their economies depend on the economies of one another."

Impact on the Land

As you might guess, the industrialized nations use a very high percentage of the world's natural resources. Only about 25 percent of Earth's people live in industrial societies. Yet, those people, through their manufacturing and trade, consume about 75 percent of the world's annual production. Imagine what would happen if all the people of Earth were to use resources at that rate. Some of the world's nonrenewable resources would be gone almost overnight. In what other ways would the environment be affected?

Industrial societies make heavy use of the environment. Every year, for instance, the United States consumes billions of tons of iron for steel, billions of barrels of

Which nations are major importers of fuel? Which export machinery? Which import more than they export?

TABLE OF STATISTICS FOR SELECTED NATIONS				
	Total value of exports (1982)	Total value of imports (1982)	Major export product (1981)	Major import product (1981)
INDIA	8,446	14,088	Textiles	Fuels
IVORY COAST	2,235	2,090	Coffee	Manufactured goods
JAPAN	138,911	131,932	Machinery	Fuels
PERU	3,230	3,787	Minerals	Machinery
SOVIET UNION	86,912	77,752	Fuels	Machinery
TANZANIA	480	1,046	Coffee	Machinery
UNITED KINGDOM	97,028	99,723	Machinery	Manufactured goods
UNITED STATES	212,275	254,884	Machinery	Fuels
WEST GERMANY	176,428	155,856	Machinery	Manufactured goods
VENEZUELA	16,443	11,670	Fuels	Machinery

millions of U.S. dollars

petroleum, and billions of tons of sand for making concrete. All these products have to be dug from the earth. In many places, great open scars have been left. Often, when land is so altered, it can no longer sustain natural growth. The cycles of nature are so disrupted that the environment cannot return to its natural, productive state.

Early settlers in America dug for mineral ores and built roads, but without heavy equipment, they could not make massive changes in the entire landscape. They built dams, but these small dams only diverted water to turn mill wheels. Today, with power machinery and with access to vast amounts of concrete, people can build huge power dams that flood entire river valleys and drown the natural landscape.

The massive use of resources is one part of the global economy. Such use depends on another part of the global economy, the use of money. Money is needed to buy resources, goods, and services.

Money and Trade

Money makes world trade flow smoothly. Money and goods change hands many times during the trading process. Not all nations use the same unit of money, of course. The basic unit of money in the United States and in Canada is the dollar. In West Germany, it is the mark; in France, it is the franc; in Mexico, it is the peso; in India, it is the rupee; and in Japan, it is the yen. None of these units is worth the same amount as any of the others. Not only are the values of various units different from one another, but the value of any one unit changes often.

Banks exchange one country's money for another so that the flow of goods and services can proceed.

International trade is a two-way street. Nations buy what they need from other nations, and, in turn, they sell to other nations what those nations need. International banking is also a two-way street. All international purchases and sales involve transactions of money from one kind of currency to another.

Lesson 2 Review
Recalling Information

1. What are the major economic differences between traditional societies, such as the Iban and the Masai, and industrial societies?

2. What is an import? An export?

Interpreting Information

3. Why have nations developed ways to exchange money with other nations?

4. How do goods that are used by industrial societies differ from those that are used by traditional societies?

Applying Information

5. Look at labels in your clothes and the underside of your shoes. Were any of them made outside the United States? (The law requires most manufacturers to indicate where a product was made.) If so, from where did they come?

6. Look at a bicycle, skates, or a skateboard. What resources were used to make it? From where might they have come? Did these products come from these countries 15 years ago? Why?

Skills for Thinking

READING AN EDITORIAL

Imagine that you are visiting an industrial fair. At the Personal Robot Display, you hear this conversation:

First Person: "What an expensive toy!"

Second Person: "Think how useful a robot could be to older people or to handicapped people."

These two people have different points of view. One sees the robot display as a toy, and the other sees it as a tool.

Very often, people want to express their points of view, and they try to persuade others to agree with them. Newspapers do this by publishing **editorials**. An editorial is a statement of opinion. The writer chooses one side of a subject or an issue, states a point of view about it, and uses facts to support that point of view.

What Is the Point of View?

Read the following editorial, and then, answer these questions.

1. What does the writer caution us about in the first paragraph?
2. The writer presents two facts in question form. What are they?
3. What is the writer's point of view about sharing technology?

The recent World's Fair of Technological Advances stunned us with its wonders of computerized toys, gadgets, and complex machines. Yet, as industrialized nations race into an electronic future, let us not overlook the problems that such achievements can bring to the peoples of nonindustrialized countries.

Too often, the marvels of technology are introduced in areas that are not prepared for them. What good are computers in areas that lack the power to run them? For how long is a machine useful if the know-how to repair it is not available? If we sell transistor radios to people in a rain forest society, shouldn't we also make replacement parts available?

Certainly, there is reason to share the advances of technology on a global basis. Yet, trading goods simply for economic gain would be both shortsighted and unfair. The responsibility of industrialized nations to the rest of the world is far greater than that. Well-thought-out programs are needed to spread the benefits of technology without undermining the fabric of other cultures and societies.

Chapter *18* Review

Summary of Key Facts

In this chapter, you learned that

- the United States was industrializing rapidly in the early 1880s.
- an industrial environment is one that is shaped by large-scale human technology.
- New York City is a leading manufacturing and trading center.
- rural areas near cities show many signs of industrialization.
- industrialization depends on large quantities of raw materials, broad networks of transportation, a large, organized supply of skilled workers, and large markets.
- unlike traditional societies, modern economies are not self-sufficient; they use many more raw materials, and they change their environments as well.
- the nations of the world are economically interdependent.

Using Vocabulary

On a separate sheet of paper, write the word that will correctly complete each sentence.

exports   imports   editorials

1. ____ are statements of opinion.
2. ____ are the goods that a nation sells to other nations.
3. ____ are the goods that a nation buys from other nations.

Discussing the Chapter

1. Explain why New York City is an example of an industrial environment.
2. Which of the following would not have existed before the Industrial Revolution: steel bridges, skyscrapers, sailboats, tugboats, wooden bridges, castles, jackhammers, railroad tracks, telephone lines, asphalt highways, stone highways, TVs, cars, carriages, tractors?
3. Explain to the class how the global economy is interdependent.

Reviewing Skills

Use the editorial on page 368 to answer the questions.

1. What two examples are used in the editorial to support the writer's view?
2. What does the writer propose as a solution to the problem that is discussed?

Living in the Industrial World

Vocabulary

mass produced	agribusiness
prefabricated	high tech
standard of living	new town

Lesson Preview
Lesson 1: At Home in Industrial Society
Lesson 2: Ways to Make a Living
Lesson 3: New Problems, New Possibilities

Introduction

Kam Ba was seven years old when she came to the United States. Born on a small farm in Laos in Southeast Asia, she can remember the rice paddies that provided food for her family. She can picture her father plowing behind the water buffalo. She recalls her mother weaving cloth.

During the Vietnam War, Kam Ba's entire family was killed. Later, she was adopted by a family in White Plains, a city north of New York City. Although she had heard of the United States, she had never heard of White Plains, New York.

Kam Ba's new world was far different from that of rural Laos. She noticed right away that few people in White Plains grow any food. Instead, they buy most of it at large supermarkets. She was amazed, too, when her adopted father told her that he commuted by train to work. To Kam Ba, a train ride to a city was a special experience, not something you did every day.

In Laos, Kam Ba was surrounded with things that had been made by hand. Her father made the plow he used. Her mother made many of the family's clothes. In her White Plains apartment, Kam Ba uses things made in factories all over the world.

In this chapter, you will read how everyday life in the industrial world reflects the many different changes that were caused by the Industrial Revolution.

This apartment complex in Munich, West Germany, once housed Olympic athletes; local citizens now share it.

Lesson 1

AT HOME IN INDUSTRIAL SOCIETY

Kam Ba's adopted family, the O'Days, had moved into a new apartment shortly before she joined them. Before that, the family had lived in Brooklyn. Both the old neighborhood and the new are industrial environments in which people have altered the natural landscape in significant ways. Yet, each community is distinctive. Kam Ba notices differences each time the O'Days visit friends in Brooklyn.

Both Brooklyn and White Plains began as small villages during colonial days. Because of its deep port facilities and its location across the river from New York City, Brooklyn grew much faster than White Plains. Eventually, Brooklyn became a borough of New York City.

When George Washington's retreating army fought the British Army in 1776, White Plains was a small farming community that was several hours by horse or wagon from downtown New York. It was too far away for people to live in White Plains and to work in the growing city to the south.

Today, Mr. O'Day rides a commuter train that takes him to Manhattan in 30 minutes. At Grand Central Station, he boards a crowded subway that speeds him underground to the financial district. About an hour after he leaves home, he's at his desk.

Technology makes it possible for him to live in one city and to work in another. It gives him options that he would not have had in a preindustrial society. He and his family could live in Manhattan or across the Hudson River in New Jersey or near the ocean beaches of Long Island. The family could choose a single-family house, a downtown apartment, or a suburban townhouse. They might even live on a houseboat in one of the region's many harbors.

Kam Ba's family in rural Laos did not have such a variety of choices. People there lived where they worked. Their homes were made of materials found locally. Most homes were made by hand with simple tools.

An Artifical Environment

At work, Frank O'Day is reminded constantly that he is part of a machine-made artificial environment. The windows on his office building cannot be opened to obtain fresh air. Machines pump warm air through the offices in winter and cool air in summer. Since he is a history buff, he knows that a small stream once flowed along the street where his 57-story office building now stands. The creek disappeared underground more than a century ago as cement gradually covered the city streets.

Years ago, New Yorkers drew their water from wells or from the rivers, just as Kam Ba's family drew water from a well. Today, water is piped into the city over many miles from reservoirs elsewhere. White Plains draws its water from the same distant sources. The same giant electric and gas company provides energy for both cities. An electric power failure, a water shortage, or a railroad strike interrupts the lives of people in both communities because technology links them together.

How Neighborhoods Change

We take rapid change in our communities for granted since, all our lives, we have watched roads being built, houses and apartments being constructed, and businesses being opened. In Kam Ba's old community, change occurred very slowly.

Rapid change is typical of industrial regions. You have seen how a megalopolis develops. At first, people usually build single-family houses. As more businesses and factories open, land becomes more valuable. People squeeze larger buildings onto less land. Larger buildings replace one-story buildings in sections where businesses and industries are concentrated. Prices and rents there increase, and some people begin to look for less costly land on the outskirts.

The O'Days moved to White Plains because they could rent a three-bedroom apartment there for less money than they would pay for a two-bedroom apartment in Brooklyn. They live on the eleventh floor of a new apartment building.

Mass-Produced Buildings

In the O'Days' old Brooklyn neighborhood, most apartment buildings were five stories tall. Their height shows that they were built before important advances in technology.

The building in which the O'Days lived was built in 1880, which was after the start of the Industrial Revolution but before machine-made materials had replaced most handmade items in buildings. Bricks for the outside walls were laid by hand by skilled bricklayers. Skilled carpenters carved the fireplace mantles. Other workers applied a

High-speed electric trains such as this one in Japan make commuting between cities easy.

smooth coat of plaster to inside walls.

By contrast, the White Plains apartment building is built with many **mass-produced** items. *Mass produced* means "made in large numbers." Walls are sheets of ready-made plasterboard. Shower and tub stalls are single units of molded plastic that were made in a factory in the Midwest. Windows are also factory-made in a standard size.

Visiting the O'Days' relatives in Arizona one summer, Kam Ba saw whole neighborhoods of factory-built homes. Cousins of the O'Days live in a mobile-home community. Their house was assembled in a factory from parts made in many places. Then, it was shipped complete to Arizona.

Paris is famous for its wide, sunny boulevards. Why is it good to have wide streets between tall buildings?

Since it is mass produced, such housing tends to cost less than modern housing in which most work is done on the spot. By 1980, nearly four million Americans lived in mobile homes, and many more Americans lived in houses or apartments that had been partly mass produced.

Kam Ba's adopted grandparents recently bought land for a vacation house on the North Carolina coast. Now, her grandparents are studying brochures for **prefabricated** houses. *Prefabricated* means "built in standardized sections for shipment and for quick assembly." What examples can you give of mass-produced buildings in your community?

Homes Around the World

If you saw photos of new apartment buildings in Paris, Houston, and Hong Kong, you might have trouble guessing which building was in which country. Industrial environments are similar all over the world.

Yet, up close, you would see many differences. Even if a house is factory built, the builders take into account the geography and the climate of their region. Styles of building reflect both local and national tastes. Japanese houses have delicate Oriental features. In contrast, a single-family house in Sweden has spare, clean lines that are typical of the Scandinavian look.

Other Homes, Other Times

Many large and excellent buildings were built long before the coming of the machine age. Four thousand years ago, well-to-do Mesopotamians built large two-story town houses with kitchens, stairways, guest rooms, and beautiful courtyards. The elaborate Palace of Versailles, which is located outside Paris, is another example of a vast structure that was built before the industrial age. Such structures were for the wealthy, however. Ordinary people could not afford to build elaborate or costly homes for themselves.

Industrialization of itself did not make large buildings possible, but it did make better housing available to great numbers of people.

Higher Standards of Living

Industrialization raised the **standard of living** for millions of people. Standard of living is the general level of goods and services that are available to a group or a country. Before industrialization, the rich could live very comfortable lives, but many others could not. Industrialization made good housing, a variety of food, and affordable clothing available to large numbers of people. Mass production lowers the cost of many goods. Consequently, the standard of living of the great masses of people in industrial lands has been raised.

As part of the industrial world, Kam Ba now has access to many things that much of the nonindustrial world would consider luxuries. She has plenty of food and a home that is warm in winter and cool in summer. Kam Ba also has access to advanced medi-

What elements of this modern kitchen design suggest a high standard of living?

cal care. She has a telephone, a stereo system, a television, and a dozen other conveniences. She has access to information from all over the world through the city's libraries, television and radio stations, and newspapers.

At home in rural Laos, Kam Ba would have expected to live a life much like that of her ancestors. Her life would have been full of rich traditions, but it would have been simpler and clear-cut. It is quite possible that she would never have left the family farm, taken a train ride, or used a telephone. Here, Kam Ba has many more choices and opportunities. One of them is the choice of a career.

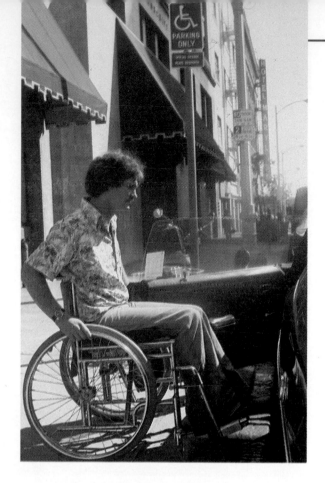

Lesson 1 Review

Recalling Information
1. List some parts of buildings that can be mass produced.
2. In what ways has industrialization raised standards of living?

Interpreting Information
3. Why are prefabricated houses less costly than similar houses that were made individually?
4. What reasons can you suggest why large apartment houses are more likely to look similar throughout the world, while single-family houses are more likely to show local styles?

Applying Information
5. What is the source of water in your community? Of electricity? If the water source failed, how could you obtain clean water? What kinds of problems would you have during an electric-power failure?
6. How could you determine if certain buildings in the community in which you live were built before or after the Industrial Revolution?

In what ways has industrialization improved the quality of life for many people? Relate your answer to the Bostonian who is headed for work, above, and to the British Columbians, below.

Computerized word processors have replaced the older mechanical typewriters as standard office equipment. How has this technological advance changed the nature of office work?

WAYS TO MAKE A LIVING

Bill Corcoran's mother designs educational games for computers. Her special field is producing games that teach mathematics. Five years ago, she worked for a firm that prepared tax returns. She drove to work in downtown Austin, Texas, from her home in the suburbs, a trip that took a half hour each way. Now, she works at home three or four days a week. The other days, she drives to an office.

Mrs. Corcoran calls herself a telecommuter. Her home office is equipped with many electronic devices that range from a telephone-answering machine to a sophisticated computer. Another machine, called a modem, links the computer by telephone lines to data banks that can provide a vast amount of information.

Not many people are telecommuters, but many people's work is shaped by new technology. Advanced technology has changed the places where people work and the kinds of work that they perform. Even farming, one of the most traditional occupations, has been changed greatly by new methods and machines.

As you learned in Chapter 12, about half the world's population consists of farmers, but the percentage is much smaller in industrial countries. Technology makes it possible for fewer people to grow much more food. Only about 8 percent of workers in the United States, Canada, and Europe are farmers. Yet, these 8 percent produce nearly 45 percent of the world's crops.

Power-driven machines such as reapers, threshers, cultivators, and combines reduce the need for human labor on farms in industrial countries. They help to make farmers far more productive than those in traditional societies.

Most of today's farmers tend to specialize in a single product. Farm owners have found single-product farms more efficient. The wheat fields of Kansas, the cornfields of Iowa, and the cotton fields of Mississippi all represent specialized agriculture. Specialization is a characteristic of industrial jobs that has spilled over into agriculture.

In preindustrial societies, farms usually produce all the kinds of food that are needed for the family. Families do their own canning and preserving and do not buy many food products in stores.

Because it requires a huge investment in machinery and in land, large specialized farming is big business. It is sometimes called **agribusiness**.

As you might guess, there are problems associated with industrial farming. In dry regions, one-crop farms use great quantities of water for irrigation. They also tend to wear out the soil faster than farms on which different crops are rotated. Industrial farms use far more resources than nonindustrial ones. Giant farms make heavy use of water, chemical fertilizers, pesticides, and energy to power farm machines.

Changes in the Workplace

You recall how the Industrial Revolution led to the creation of jobs in factories, in mines, and in mills. A large number of people no longer worked at home or on the family farm as they had in traditional societies and as they still do in less-developed areas. Instead, people became wage earners. Their work involved such activities as assembling parts on an assembly line, operating power-driven tools and machines, welding metal and metal parts, or operating printing equipment.

Millions of workers still do these kinds of jobs. Nevertheless, the old assembly-line manufacturing jobs have been decreasing throughout the most advanced industrial nations. There are several explanations. First, automatic machinery took over some of the tasks of workers. Second, some of the old manufacturing industries have shifted to areas of Asia and Latin America where labor costs are less. Today's workers are more likely to be employed in *non*manufacturing industries, or service industries. Before 1982, there were more jobs in manufacturing than in any other industry in the United States. After 1982, more people worked in service industries.

Because of this shift, new office buildings are familiar features of both urban and suburban landscapes. In some areas, old factories have been boarded up or torn down. San Francisco's popular Ghirardelli Square was once a chocolate factory. Today, the people who work there are employed in restaurants, bookstores, and other shops. All of these occupations are part of the booming service industry.

Modern technology can reduce the need for human labor or make the labor easier. Today, mechanized sprinklers irrigate vast fields, while computers assist in manufacturing.

You can observe another kind of shift from old-style manufacturing in a brick factory in Maynard, Massachusetts. In the 1850s, workers there used the machinery of the Industrial Revolution to make carpets. During World Wars I and II, the Maynard factory produced army blankets. Today, noisy machines no longer clank out woolen goods. Assembly-line workers are no longer at work. Instead, in the same building, engineers work in offices of the second-largest computer manufacturer in the world. It is one of the new **high-tech**, or high-technology, companies that are creating different kinds of jobs. You will read more about high-tech industries in Chapter 21.

Many jobs in new industries require specialized training. Therefore, people who lose their jobs on assembly lines may need retraining to find other work. Unemployment that results from vanishing jobs has been one price of industrial society.

An industrial economy, however, provides frequent opportunities and vast resources to start enterprises. An average of a half million United States companies opened for business each year in the early 1980s. A 30-year record was broken in 1983, when 600,400 new businesses filed papers to become corporations. The flip side of opportunity, however, is the failure of some business enterprises.

People who study the job marketplace predict only one thing. It will continue to change rapidly. "The transformation of our jobs, the movement of our people, the improvement in our skills over the first 80 years of this century have been stunning," says Delaware Governor Pierre du Pont IV. "But it is entirely likely that those changes will be matched and exceeded during the final 20 years of the century."

Lesson 2 Review

Recalling Information

1. How do preindustrial farms and modern agribusinesses differ?
2. Why has there recently been a shift away from assembly-line jobs? What kinds of jobs have replaced them?

Interpreting Information

3. Compare the advantages and disadvantages of large-scale agriculture.
4. Why does industrialization sometimes lead to unemployment? What steps could be taken to correct the problem?

Applying Information

5. Make a list of 10 adult workers. What kinds of jobs do they have? What needs do they fulfill in your community?
6. Suppose that you became a *telestudent*, or a person who stays home and does all schoolwork through a computer network. What would be some of the advantages and the disadvantages?

Lesson 3

NEW PROBLEMS, NEW POSSIBILITIES

In 1936, Charles Chaplin made a movie called *Modern Times*. In it, a gigantic machine trapped and devoured the character played by the famous comedian. The machine, with its fierce-looking gears, was a mechanical villain.

Fifty years later, two popular movies again pitted humans against machines. This time, the villain was Darth Vader, a man who ruled an empire of machines. Some critics see George Lucas's *Star Wars* and *The Empire Strikes Back* as fables of our times.

"Are the machine and the machine maker going to dominate the human spirit, or is the human spirit going to be served by the machine?" asks Joseph Campbell, a noted scholar who studies myths. "Luke Skywalker and his father, Darth Vader, represent the two positions."

Professor Campbell points out that the father gave in to the machine empire and almost became a robot himself. His son Luke refused to give in. He kept his human values. The Chaplin and the Lucas films, which were made a half century apart, reflect a fear that humans could lose control of their machine environment.

At the start of the industrial age, some people thought that technology would solve most of humanity's serious problems. Technology created better homes and more goods for most people, but it also led to industrial blight. Technology created energy resources but also fouled Earth's air and

**This photograph of modern Cairo shows how overcrowding is
a very serious problem in some industrialized cities.**

water. As you read in the last section, high technology makes jobs for some people and destroys the jobs of others. It offers fast transportation and excellent communication systems. Yet, it also makes cities noisy, crowded, and hectic.

Crowded Cities

The problems of cities did not begin with the Industrial Revolution. At the time of the Roman Empire, the writer Juvenal complained of Rome's noise. Wealthy Romans often built villas, or country estates, outside the city to escape the noise and the crowds.

The Industrial Revolution improved cities in some ways and made them worse in others. At first, modern transportation systems helped large cities to grow outward. Railroads, trolleys, and buses brought people to the cities and moved them efficiently within them. So did automobiles, for a while. More people bought cars, which resulted in too many vehicles entering already clogged city streets. Today, stalled traffic is common in every major city in the world.

Cairo, Egypt, has been a city for more than 1,000 years. It has always had some problems. Yet, the problems seemed manageable before the industrial age.

As Egypt began to modernize, millions of people flooded into Cairo. They came to Cairo to find work and because the city

This row house in Brooklyn, New York, is due for repairs under an urban renewal program.

offered more opportunity and excitement. The city's population was about 2.3 million in 1950. By 1984, at least 14 million people used the city's resources.

Cairo's sewer and water systems were built early in the century to serve about two million people. Now serving seven times that many, the old lines often break. In 1982, a sewer break sent raw sewage flooding through one neighborhood for two weeks.

The city's water resources cannot always meet the needs of so many millions. Often, pressure is too low to pump water to faucets on the top floors of new skyscrapers. Water has always been precious in Egypt, which is

a desert country. In preindustrial parts of the country, however, people still draw their water from wells or from the Nile. They do not have to rely on a big system that can break down.

Pollution and Waste

You can see another problem of industrial life at a traffic circle near Cairo's main railway station. At the center of the circle stands a 65-ton (60-MT) statue of an ancient Egyptian ruler, Ramses II. For thousands of years, the statue had survived in the Egyptian desert. After it had been moved to Cairo, the statue's granite began to chip and to pit. Chemicals in the polluted air are eating into the granite.

Old cities all over the world face similar problems. Fine old buildings in Paris, London, and Rome are being damaged by chemicals in the air from industrial smokestacks and auto exhausts.

As you know, industrial societies use large amounts of natural resources. They also throw away staggering amounts of waste. Fleets of garbage trucks prowl the streets of industrial cities in a vain effort to keep up with the trash.

One possibility of treating some of the mountains of waste is recycling, or reusing, resources. A power company in Zurich, Switzerland, for instance, burns garbage to provide power for the city.

Manufacturing wastes pose a serious problem. Some of them are poisonous. For many years, companies dumped such wastes into rivers or buried them in the ground. Few people realized that the environment could not absorb them safely.

When there are few people and a great deal of open space, disposing of trash is not much of a problem. People burn or bury it. They may feed edible garbage to their animals. Rivers can cleanse themselves of small amounts of waste. When many people create a great deal of waste, however, the problem can be critical. Interestingly, many groups of traditional peoples do not have problems with waste. Can you figure out why this is true?

Saving Unspoiled Places

Ray Sanchez can remember when Orange County, California, did not have a garbage problem. He worked as a cowhand on a vast ranch in the area. He remembers when the area that is now Disneyland was covered with orange groves. That changed in the 1950s. People were drawn to Orange County by the warm mediterranean climate and the long Pacific coastline. They could find work in nearby Los Angeles. Between 1960 and 1980, the population tripled.

Similar rapid growth has changed hundreds of once rural areas all over the world. In the late nineteenth century, a few far-sighted people began to worry about the loss of open space. They wanted to keep some places unspoiled so that later generations could experience environments that had not been changed by humans.

John Muir, President Theodore Roosevelt, and others began working to set aside some places as parks. In the United States, the National Park System was begun with the creation of Yellowstone Park. At the same time, other people worked hard to save open space in the heart of cities.

Would you like to live in this planned community in South Miami, Florida? Why?

Frederick Law Olmsted designed many well-known city parks, including Manhattan's Central Park.

Since then, many individuals, groups, and government agencies have saved and set aside natural areas. The federal government passed a Wilderness Act to keep some places free of humans. Other areas have been set aside as wildlife preserves. You will read more about efforts to save natural environments in Chapter 23.

New Towns and Urban Planning

Ray Sanchez's Orange County environment did not happen by accident. He now lives in the city of Irvine, California, a **new town**, or a new community, that was planned and laid out before anything was built. It was carved out of a section of the 77,000-acre (31.2-ha) Irvine Ranch, where Sanchez used to work.

Sanchez's parents live in a nearby town in another kind of planned community that was designed for older people. Individuals must be at least 52 years old to buy a home in Leisure World. Sanchez is welcome to visit, but he would not be allowed to live there. Families with children are barred.

Planned communities like Irvine and Leisure World drew some of their ideas from new towns in Scandinavia and in England. They also drew ideas from the new towns of Reston, Virginia, and Columbia, Maryland.

The developer who shaped Columbia bought several farms between Washington, D.C., and Baltimore, Maryland. There, he planned a city where people could live, work, and study and where they could enjoy many forms of recreation. He planned a city that would have a university and offices.

In most suburban developments, builders simply put up housing. In contrast, Reston, Columbia, and Irvine were planned to be total environments. They were designed to blend the best features of industrialization with open space and cultural facilities.

In Reston, open land surrounds all the neighborhoods. The Reston Home Owners Association operates 50 miles (80.5 km) of walkways and bike paths, 15 public swimming pools, 4 lakes, 44 ball fields, and 51 tennis courts. There is a 70-acre (28.3-ha) nature center, and 850 acres (344 ha) of land have been saved as open space.

Although Reston is located outside Washington, D.C., it is not a typical suburb. You do not have to leave to find a job. In 1984, 20 years after the town was founded, the community newspaper reported that there were more jobs than households in Reston. More than 700 firms have plants or offices there.

Lesson 3 Review

Recalling Information

1. List some ways in which industrialization has created problems in cities.
2. Why are waste and garbage greater problems in industrial societies than in preindustrial communities?

Interpreting Information

3. Why might it be more difficult for an older city such as Cairo to build sewer and water lines than for a new city such as Irvine?
4. What features of life in an adult community such as Leisure World are different from those in a more typical community?

Applying Information

5. Is your community gaining or losing jobs? Are the kinds of jobs changing? For what evidence could you look to answer these questions?
6. If you could plan an entirely new city, what features would you want it to have?

Special People
Noel Brown

Noel Brown calls himself a frustrated botanist. He likes to see things grow. As the director of the United Nations Environmental Program at United Nations headquarters in New York, he has been able to do more than that. He has been able to help things to grow.

Since 1972, when the first United Nations international conference on the environment was held, Brown has helped diplomats to understand their role in conservation. As he has said, "Environment is a diplomatic issue. We must now negotiate for the protection and the enhancement of our common heritage."

Brown points out that many of the problems that face people of industrial areas affect people all over the world. Such problems as air and water pollution have no national boundaries; they are global. Only by working together can the people of the world solve shared environmental problems.

IDENTIFYING TRENDS ON A GRAPH

Did you know that in 1910, a young man could expect to live to the age of 47? By 1920, that figure had increased to 55, and by 1970, it had increased to 67.

Such general patterns of change are called trends. A trend can be shown on a line graph. As you know, a line graph records specific information by means of dots or points that are drawn on the graph. These points are connected by a line, and the line's direction, either up or down, shows the trend.

What Does the Graph Show?

Analyze the line graph below, and answer the questions about it.

1. What trend does this graph show?
2. Why are there two lines?
3. How long could men expect to live in 1940? Women?
4. Which 10-year period had the largest increases for both men and women?
5. By about what year could women expect to live to be 70 years old?
6. What conclusion can you draw about average life expectancies?

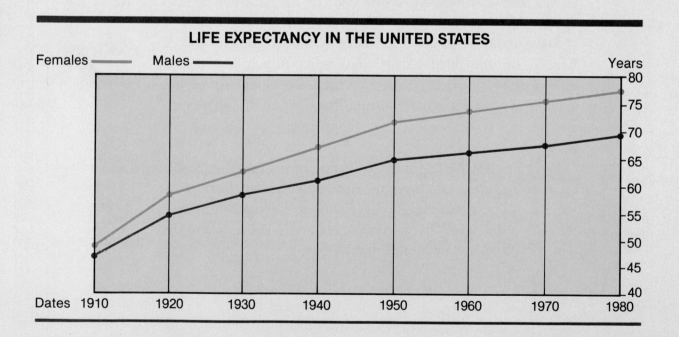

LIFE EXPECTANCY IN THE UNITED STATES

Females ——— Males ———

Years

Dates 1910 1920 1930 1940 1950 1960 1970 1980

Chapter 19 Review

Summary of Key Facts
In this chapter, you learned that
- technology has changed the ways in which people live and work in industrial societies.
- industrialization raised the standard of living for great numbers of people.
- communications and transportation widen the choices that people in industrial societies have in both where to live and where to work.
- rapid change and increasing density are both typical of industrial regions.
- technological developments continually change the job market.
- technology solves some problems and creates others.
- urban planning is one solution to problems of rapid growth.

Using Vocabulary
On a separate sheet of paper, write the term that will correctly complete each sentence.

standard of living new town
prefabricated high tech

1. Parts of a ____ house are made in a factory to be assembled elsewhere.
2. Designers of the ____ wanted to save open spaces in the planned community.
3. The ____ is higher in industrial societies than in preindustrial communities.
4. Computers and spaceships are examples of ____ .

Discussing the Chapter
1. What examples can you cite to show differences in standards of living between industrial and preindustrial societies?
2. Describe why it is possible for a company to move its manufacturing plants to another country and still sell goods in the United States.
3. In what ways does a city such as Cairo show both the benefits and the problems of industrialization?

Reviewing Skills
Use the graph on page 386 to complete this exercise.
1. Which 10-year period has the smallest increases for both men and women?
2. How long could men expect to live in 1950? Women?

The Major Industrial Centers

Introduction

Samuel Slater was an ambitious young man. At the age of 14, he went to work in a factory that made cotton cloth. By the time that he was 21 years old, he knew the business well. Yet, in England, where Slater lived, he did not see much of a future for himself in cotton manufacturing. He thought that too many men, who were richer than he, were already involved in the industry.

Across the ocean, in the newly independent United States, the situation seemed different. Slater had read newspaper notices in which Americans offered benefits to ex-

Is this ship empty or full of goods? Explain. It handles about 61 million tons (55 MT) of cargo annually.

perienced workers who understood the workings of textile machinery. He decided that America was the place for him.

Slater memorized the details of the machinery on which he worked. He sailed for the United States where he went to work for a Rhode Island cotton manufacturer, Moses Brown. Slater helped manufacture the first cotton yarn in America.

Samuel Slater helped to introduce the Industrial Revolution to the United States. Within a few decades, his adopted country became highly industrialized. In less than a century, it surpassed the country of his birth as the major manufacturing nation of the world. Since the mid-1800s, the continent of North America has been an industrial leader among the countries of the world.

Lesson 1

INDUSTRIAL REGIONS OF NORTH AMERICA

North America is a diverse continent. It has interesting natural features and a vast array of resources. The continent is divided into the three large nations of Canada, the United States, and Mexico. It also contains the seven nations of Central America and a number of island nations and territories.

North America has seven major land regions: the Pacific Coastland; the Inter-mountain Range, an area of basins and high plateaus; the Interior Plain; the Canadian Shield, a flat, rocky area that rings Hudson Bay; the Coastal Plain; the Appalachian Mountains; and the Rocky Mountains.

The Rockies run from northern Alaska to Mexico, where they divide into two ranges—the Sierra Madre Oriental (eastern) and the Sierra Madre Occidental (western). In southern Mexico, the two ranges come together again and continue through Central America. The Appalachians run parallel to the Atlantic coast from the Gulf of St. Lawrence to northern Alabama.

The East Coast and the West Coast of North America are very different from each

North America's many rivers are often centers of industry and manufacturing. Hull, Quebec, is located on the Ottawa River in Canada.

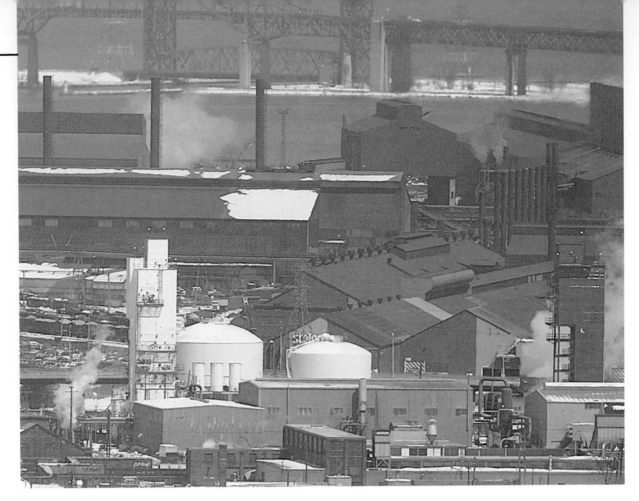

Pittsburgh, Pennsylvania, stands at the meeting point of three rivers. A fifth of the U.S. steel supply comes from this place.

other. On the West Coast, mountains range right down to the sea. In contrast, the Atlantic and the Gulf coasts are bordered by a large coastal plain. Good harbors exist along both coasts, but they are more numerous along the Atlantic.

Deserts exist in northern Mexico, in the southwestern United States, and in portions of the Caribbean islands.

In North America, 12 major rivers and 11 lakes provide water and inland transportation systems. The largest river is the Mississippi, and Lake Superior, one of the Great Lakes, is the largest freshwater lake in the world.

Beneath the mountains and the plains of the continent lay rich mineral resources that North Americans have used to develop their industries. Look at the map on pages 212-213. As you can see, many deposits of ores which are used for making metals are found in mountain areas and in the Canadian Shield. In addition, coal deposits are found in mountain areas, especially in the Appalachians, and in the Central Plains. Some oil and natural gas deposits are situated in mountains, but, like coal, these sources of fuel are also found in plains regions and even under the sea. Great forests still stand, covering about one-third of North America.

The United States and Canada have some of the richest and the largest agricultural areas in the world. In contrast, large areas of Latin America are too dry or too wet to

Mexico's industrial output has developed rapidly since the 1940s.

practice agriculture with success.

By applying modern technology to their vast resources, North Americans have become some of the most productive people on Earth. North America's "giants," the United States and Canada, account for more than 40 percent of the industrial output of the world.

The First Manufacturing Center

The first manufacturing center in the United States was New England—the states of Maine, New Hampshire, Vermont, Massachusetts, Connecticut, and Rhode Island—where enterprising Samuel Slater set up what turned out to be the first suc-

cessful cotton mill. Soon, cotton mills were scattered all over New England.

Cotton mills were not located in New England because cotton was grown there. As you know, New England is too cold to produce cotton. The mills were located in New England because the region had waterpower to run them, **capital**, or money or wealth, to invest in building them, and the workers to operate them.

New England is still a manufacturing center. Even though many textile factories have moved to the South, other kinds of manufacturing have replaced them. New England remains the center of a huge industrial area known as the American

A festival in New York City's Chinese community reflects the ethnic diversity of many North American industrial cities.

Manufacturing Belt. This region extends west from the American Northeast to Illinois and north into southeastern Canada. This center produces almost every kind of manufacture you can think of, from tiny electronic components to giant locomotives.

Transcontinental Industry

As you know, iron and steel are the basic materials that are needed to produce industrial goods, and for construction. An industrial society must have an abundant supply of iron and steel. It also needs reliable sources of power to run its industries, efficient transportation to move raw materials and products, and skilled and semiskilled people to operate industries. In the Middle Atlantic states of New York, Pennsylvania, and New Jersey, iron has been made since colonial times. The hills of Pennsylvania and northern New Jersey and the swamps of southern New Jersey contain deposits of iron ore. In addition, trees provide charcoal for smelting. Iron-making centers were built where these resources were found.

Eastern Pennsylvania contains deposits of **anthracite** (hard coal). A process for using this kind of coal to smelt iron was discovered in 1833. More iron can be made with coal than with charcoal because coal produces more heat. Canals and railroads brought coal to the ironworks.

After the Civil War, a way of changing **bituminous coal** (soft coal) into coke was developed. Coke is used to make steel. Pittsburgh, Pennsylvania, became the country's major steel center. Situated where two rivers join in the midst of great soft-coal fields, Pittsburgh contained both the ore and the coal that were needed to make steel.

The Middle Atlantic states still produce iron and steel. Even more important than industries that produce these metals, however, are hundreds of other kinds of industries. The Middle Atlantic industrial region, which includes New York City, is the leading clothing manufacturing center in the country. Other industries in and around New York include oil refining, printing and publishing, chemicals, food processing, and aviation.

Steel centers also were set up along the shores of the Great Lakes in such cities as Chicago, Detroit, Cleveland, and Buffalo, as well as in Hamilton, Ontario, in Canada. Coal and iron for making steel were brought to these cities from northern Minnesota by ship.

At the time that steel mills were being set up, railroads were being built across the country. Railroads helped the growth of industry in several ways. They provided a fast means of transporting both large amounts of raw materials to factories and finished goods to markets. In addition, the railroads bought iron and steel (for rails), railroad cars, watches and clocks, tickets, maps, and other items that were produced by many different industries.

The steel industry in the Midwest received another boost from major inventions that used large quantities of steel. Detroit, the hometown of Henry Ford, became the center of the automobile industry, which uses large quantities of steel in all parts of auto making. Other midwestern industries grew by supplying the automobile industry. For example, the rubber industry, which makes tires for cars, situated itself in eastern Ohio.

While all these industries were growing, the Prairies and Great Plains of the Midwest remained a major farming region. Factories were located in the Midwest, especially in Illinois, and were built there purposely to produce a great deal of farm machinery, which also uses steel.

Other factories in the region were built to process the farm products that were raised there. Chicago and Kansas City (Kansas) became meat-packing centers, and Minneapolis, Minnesota, became a flour-milling center. Today, these cities have attracted a wide range of additional industries, from printing to electronics.

The Pacific Coast states of Washington, Oregon, and California did not become industrialized until the 1900s. These regions developed only after transportation links to the large population centers of the East had been formed. This new transportation system, as well as the lure of the West's beauty and climate, brought many people to live in the region.

Because southern California receives much sunshine and has many kinds of scenery, pioneering moviemakers found it to be a good location for their new industry. There were more good days for filming than

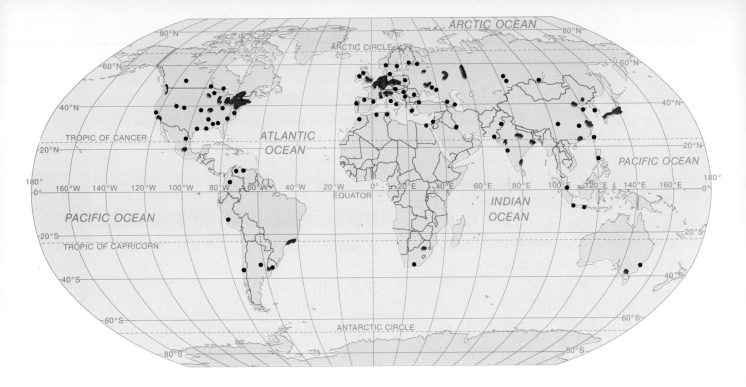

WORLD: INDUSTRIAL REGIONS

 Manufacturing region

• Smaller manufacturing center

MAP SKILLS: What region of the United States is the most industrialized? Which country of the Far East shares this distinction?

in most other places. Actors and other skilled workers flocked to the movie industry in southern California. Later, the producers of television programs located their studios in California.

Another industry that has grown in California is the computer industry. You will read more about it in Chapter 21.

The warm, sunny climate that brought moviemakers to California attracted companies that build airplanes. Airplane factories have to be huge because the planes themselves are so large. Locating immense factories in regions of warm climate means low heating costs. The warm, sunny climate provides consistent conditions for testing

airplanes that are fresh out of the factory.

Most recently, manufacturing has begun to grow in the Southeast. Except for Birmingham, Alabama, which has long produced iron and steel from local coal and iron ore, the Southeast has traditionally been a rural farming region. Then, the Gulf Coast was discovered to have rich reserves of oil for gasoline, heating fuel, and chemicals. Many companies in these industries have moved to the Gulf Coast and to other parts of the South because of the presence of these substantial energy resources and the mild climate. Air conditioning has made working and living comfortable in the hot summers. Furthermore, the winters, when homes and factories must be heated, are short, minimizing fuel costs. People can also enjoy outdoor sports and recreation for much of the year. The pace of living can be relaxed. People who move to the southeastern part of the **Sun Belt** are both the workers and the customers of these industries. They have created a thriving economy out of what was once a less profitable farming region.

Industrialization in Canada

Canada's Great Lakes–Saint Lawrence lowland in southern Quebec and Ontario was becoming industrialized at the same time that the Sun Belt was developing. The Great Lakes–Saint Lawrence lowland has more people than any other region in Canada—people who are both workers and customers. Like the Sun Belt, the lowland is centrally located.

It is not surprising that many of the industries in Canada are similar to those in the United States, for many of them are owned by American companies. Canadians prefer the goods that they use to be made in Canada rather than outside the country, and so, companies from other nations build factories in Canada to make things to sell in that country. You will read more about Toronto, one of Canada's industrial cities, in Chapter 21.

Industrialization in Latin America

Mexico, the countries of Central America, and the islands of the Caribbean are in the process of developing industries of their own. You will read more about them in Chapter 22. Around Mexico City, there are factories that produce a great

variety of goods for the people who live in the area. These are **consumer goods,** which are things people need to live. To the north, in Monterrey, is another industrial center that includes the country's major steel mills.

Lesson 1 Review

Recalling Information

1. Name the region that was the first manufacturing region in North America. Which resources made manufacturing possible?
2. In what regions did colonial iron-making develop? Why?

Interpreting Information

3. Why is transportation necessary for industrial development?
4. Which resources helped Canada and the United States to develop industries more quickly than Mexico? Explain.

Applying Information

5. Which industrial center is nearest your community? Is it an old or new center? How does it affect your life in terms of school and recreation? How does it affect your environment?
6. Would you prefer to live in or near another industrial center? If so, which one? How might moving there change your life?

Lesson 2

INDUSTRIAL REGIONS OF EUROPE AND ASIA

As you have read, Europe and Asia together form the large landmass called Eurasia. The Ural Mountains form the dividing line between the two continents, which are geographically and culturally different from each other. Here are some facts to remember about the two continents.

Europe can be divided into two political and geographic regions, Eastern Europe and Western Europe. Western Europe consists of the continental, or mainland, nations of Andorra, Austria, Belgium, France, West Germany, Greece, Italy, Liechtenstein, Luxembourg, Monaco, the Netherlands, Switzerland, Spain, Portugal, San Marino, and Vatican City; the Scandanavian countries of Sweden, Norway, Finland, and Denmark; Iceland; and the United Kingdom, Ireland, Cyprus, and Malta. Eastern Europe includes the European part of the Soviet Union, Albania, Bulgaria, Czechoslovakia, East Germany, Hungary, Poland, Romania, and Yugoslavia.

The northern part of continental Europe consists of a large plain. South of the plain, in France, Switzerland, and Austria, lies the Alps mountain system. There are also mountains between France and Spain (the Pyrenees) and in Czechoslovakia, Romania, Yugoslavia, Bulgaria, Greece, and Italy. Much of Spain is a plateau. Western Great Britain contains many ranges of hills and some low mountains.

Europe has a very irregular coastline; that is, it has many bays and small seas. In addition, it has many rivers that form good harbors and transportation highways.

Europe is rich in mineral resources. England, Wales, Belgium, West Germany, and the Soviet Union contain major coal deposits. Northern Sweden, the Saar in West Germany, and the Soviet Union contain iron ore. Small deposits of iron ore exist in many other places. The Soviet Union has oil along the western shore of the Caspian Sea, and several countries share the oil that lies under the North Sea.

Asia, the largest continent, is also the most geographically diverse. It has some of the highest mountains, the largest deserts, and the thickest forests in the world. Geographers often divide the continent into six geographical and political regions.

The Asian part of the Soviet Union makes up North Asia. This is a plateau region that is rich in mineral resources such as iron. Forests cover the most northern areas of the region, and farmlands characterize the southern portions.

East Asia and Central Asia include China, Mongolia, Sinkiang, Tibet, Japan, North Korea, South Korea, and Taiwan, plus two nonindependent political units, Hong Kong and Macao. Asia's poorest land lies in Central Asia, where mountains, deserts, and plateaus are the dominant land features. The plains of East Asia contain some of Asia's richest agricultural land. Through these plains flow some of China's great rivers—the Huang He, the Chang, and the Si. East Asia also contains many forest resources.

South Asia includes the countries of

the Indian subcontinent—India, Pakistan, Bangladesh, Nepal, and Bhutan, plus Sri Lanka and the Maldive Islands. The northern parts of South Asia are extremely mountainous. Some of the southern parts contain fertile farmland.

Nine independent nations make up most of Southeast Asia—Vietnam, Cambodia, Laos, Thailand, Malaysia, the Philippines, Indonesia, Burma, and Singapore. Southeast Asia is a land of many resources, including fertile soil, large forests, and important minerals such as tin.

Southwest Asia, or the Middle East, consists of Afghanistan, Turkey, Iraq, Iran, Israel, Jordan, Lebanon, Syria, Cyprus, and the eight nations of the Arabian Peninsula, including Saudi Arabia, the largest. Southwest Asia is a land of deserts, plateaus, and mountains. It has little good farmland but is rich in mineral resources, especially oil.

Thousands of miles of rivers flow through the regions of Asia, irrigating them and serving as transportation routes. Although Central Asia lacks good inland water resources, some important rivers originate in the mountains of the region.

Industry in Western Europe

As you know, by the early 1700s, England was a wealthy manufacturing and trading nation. The invention of the steam engine by Robert Fulton and of power

How does Switzerland's rugged alpine geography contribute to and limit the development of Swiss industries?

machinery made increases in productivity possible. Increased profitability was the incentive to make English money available to build factories. England also had a relatively large population of skilled and semiskilled workers. Some designed and others operated industrial machines. Many other workers knew how to produce goods. From this population, factory owners drew a competent **labor force**, or a collection of industrial workers. They also manufactured many products that appealed to customers for their convenience or comfort.

Fortunately, some essential raw materials were available in England. Iron and coal, the basic metal and the basic fuel for the first industries, were both mined in England. Colonies in almost every part of the world provided the raw materials that England lacked. For instance, during the 1800s, England obtained copper, tin, gold, diamonds, and other minerals from its colonies in Africa.

The first industrial centers were located near coalfields because coal was heavy and expensive to transport. Thus, it made no sense to set up factories far from the coal. The Midlands of England, which also contain deposits of iron ore, became a center for ironmaking and steelmaking and for the products that were eventually forged from these metals: railroad engines, automobiles, machinery, pots and knives. Manchester and York to the north were among the first English textile centers.

Other countries of Western Europe have also used their natural resources for industry. The Industrial Revolution developed in the western part of the continent later than in England, during the middle 1800s. By that time, railroads had been built to transport ore from Central European iron mines to the coalfields of the West, just as railroads had moved raw materials in North America. Steel making and other kinds of industrial manufacturing began to operate in Belgium, France, the German states, and other Western European countries.

Like the Midlands of England, the Ruhr region of West Germany, which you will read about in Chapter 21, became and remains today a major center for the manufacture of iron and steel. Industrial regions in Belgium and in northern France are considered to be extensions of the same industrial district. France's automobile and textile industries are centered in and around Paris. The Saar is another West German center for the manufacture of iron and steel, machinery, and automobiles.

Italy's major industrial region is located in the north, in the valley of the Po River. Automobiles, typewriters, sewing machines, motorcycles, espresso machines, and many other consumer products for domestic use and for export are made there.

Many factories were destroyed during World War II. When industries were rebuilt after the war, however, they manufactured their products in modern and efficient factories. In the postwar period, therefore, Western Europe resumed its former role as one of the major industrial producers in the world.

Industry in Eastern Europe

Compared to the countries of Western Europe, the Soviet Union got a late start in

Busy rail lines link modern European cities. Here, passengers in Denmark wait for trains.

industrialization. A small number of land-owners and government officials ran the economy for the czars, or the royal rulers, until the early 1900s. Then, more capital was invested to build factories and rail-roads. Since the 1920s, the Soviet government has planned the country's industrial development. It has focused on transportation and heavy industry, including steel making, machinery, and armaments.

Today, there are five major industrial centers in the Soviet Union. Leningrad, in the North, has one of the country's best seaports and is a shipbuilding center. The manufacturing region around Moscow, like those surrounding other large capital cities, produces textiles, clothing, and other consumer goods. It also produces vehicles and machinery. Along the lower Volga River Valley are oil refineries and chemical plants that use petroleum from the Caucasus Mountains. Nearby is the Donets Basin, with rich coal deposits and supplies of iron ore that are obtained from nearby sources. It is the major center in the country for the manufacture of iron and steel. Like the heavy industries of the American Midwest, industries that use iron and steel, such as machinery, have located in the Donets Basin. In the southern Ural Mountains, which divide Europe from Asia, is an industrial center that is based on a rich variety of mineral deposits: coal, iron, copper, chromium, zinc, bauxite, and platinum. This industrial center is notable for the manufacture of iron and steel and for plants that use these metals in their products.

There are smaller industrial regions in other countries of Eastern Europe. Poland's major industrial area is centered in Silesia, in the Southwest, where iron and coal are found. Dresden in East Germany is an industrial center that has long been famous for its fine porcelain. Similarly, Czechoslovakia is famous for fine glass.

Industrial Development in Asia

Japan, like Great Britain, is an island nation. Its farmland and its mineral resources are very limited. Yet, trade and the hard work of the Japanese people have made Japan a powerful industrial nation.

After the middle of the 1800s, Japan began to participate in the Industrial

Revolution. It traded with the West, from which it borrowed money and ideas in order to build its industries. It obtained oil and other natural resources from other parts of Asia and sold manufactured goods around the world.

After World War II, Japan developed its steel-making facilities and its shipyards. It also produced small goods such as cameras and electrical equipment. Today, Japan exports small goods of high quality. You have probably seen many Japanese cars on the streets of your community. Your family may well own a Japanese television set, a camera, or a radio.

The most industrialized nation of Asia, Japan is the third-largest industrial producer in the world. It has no oil resources, but it does have hydroelectric power. The Japanese have the largest shipyards in the world, as well as huge installations for making steel, refining oil, processing chemicals, and generating electric power.

Most of Japan's major factories are located along the southern coast of the country's largest island, Honshu. From Tokyo, this industrial center extends westward to the end of the island and beyond it, to the northern tip of Kyushu. There, the iron-and-steel industry uses coal from local mines.

During the 1930s, Japan conquered northern China and developed iron and coal reserves there. This northern region is still the most developed area in the People's Republic of China.

Although rich mineral resources exist throughout the People's Republic of China, the need to feed its huge population—al-

Russian women have long been skilled workers—even in Siberia's huge lumber complexes.

most one-quarter of all the people on Earth—has anchored the economy in agriculture rather than in industry. In recent years, however, there has developed a push toward industrialization.

In the development of light industries, the Chinese have concentrated on the production of textiles. Urban manufacturing centers along the eastern coast of the People's Republic of China ship large quantities of cotton textiles and clothing to world markets. China's few really heavy industries specialize in manufactures to meet the needs of agriculture—farm machinery, irrigation pumps, fertilizers, and other chemicals that are used in agriculture. Most of the industry of the People's Republic of China is still concentrated in Manchuria and in the coastal cities.

Like the People's Republic of China, India has rich mineral resources and a huge population. Many Indians live in farming villages. At one time, India was a colony of Great Britain. During the colonial period, Great Britain built some railroads and educated many Indians. Since independence, Indian leaders have worked to build hydroelectric and other power sources to fuel industrial development.

India has made strenuous efforts to industrialize. The country contains three major industrial areas. One, located north of Calcutta, is an iron-and-steel manufacturing center. Another, located in the region around Bombay, is a center of textile-and-clothing manufacture. A third area, in the south, spreads out from the cities of Bangalore and Madras. Its varied industries include textiles, chemicals, electronics, and aircraft.

To date, the smaller nations of Asia remain largely agricultural. You will learn why in Chapter 22.

Though Japan is modern and industrial, many people still celebrate traditional festivals.

Lesson 2 Review

Recalling Information
1. Which three industries form the backbone of Europe's economy?
2. What is Asia's major economic activity? Explain.

Interpreting Information
3. Why did Europe industrialize before Asia?
4. Why would having to feed a large population inhibit a country's industrial development?

Applying Information
5. What products do you use that come from Europe? From Asia? In what country was each made?
6. If you were a businessperson, in which country or industrial region might you want to establish a company? Why?

Special People

Fusae Ichikawa

Fusae Ichikawa was one of the first leaders of the movement for women's rights in Japan. Japanese women did not have the same rights to vote and to participate in politics as Japanese men. Fusae Ichikawa thought that this was wrong.

In 1918, she organized the New Woman's Association, which sought to change a law that forbade women to participate in politics. Because of her efforts, this law was changed in 1922. Inspired by the American women's suffrage movement, Fusae Ichikawa founded the Woman's Suffrage League of Japan. She and the League worked until Japanese women were granted the right to vote in 1945.

In 1953, Fusae Ichikawa was elected to the Japanese Diet, or parliament. Her election represented the fulfillment of her goal in life. Through her efforts, women in Japan had secured the same right to be elected to political office as men.

Lesson 3

INDUSTRIAL AREAS OF SOUTHERN CONTINENTS

Among the least industrialized areas of the world are the three southern continents of South America, Africa, and Australia. Here are some facts to remember about these continents.

Brazil is the largest country in South America. It covers most of the eastern part of the continent. It is a nation of plateaus, highlands, and tropical rain forests.

The southern part of South America is divided between Argentina east of the Andes and Chile along the West Coast. Find these and the other countries of South America on the map on page 484.

The Andes Mountains and the highlands are rich in such mineral resources as copper, gold, lead, zinc, and bauxite. Iron ore is abundant in the highlands of eastern Venezuela.

The fuel resources of South America consist of a little coal in Chile, a little petroleum in southern Argentina, and rich deposits of oil in western Venezuela.

Though the Amazon Basin is a dense tropical rain forest, its valuable resources for making furniture and other things are scattered throughout it.

Africa can be divided into many geographic and political regions. It consists of the six nations of North Africa—Egypt, Libya, Tunisia, Algeria, Morocco, and Mauritania—and the nations of sub-Saharan Africa—the region south of the Sahara. Sub-Saharan Africa consists of 45 nations, including the nation of South Africa. Look at the map on page 490 to find the names of the other nations of sub-Saharan Africa.

Most of Africa is a giant plateau that is covered by deserts, by forests, or by grasslands. About two-fifths of Africa is desert. The Sahara stretches across most of North Africa. Forests cover less than one-fifth of Africa. Along the western coast of sub-Saharan Africa is a region of tropical rain forest. (Tropical rain forest also covers the valley of the Congo River in Central Africa.)

Africa is a continent of few big rivers, although the Nile is second only to the Amazon in length. Most rivers originate in plateau regions.

Africa has few good natural harbors. The mouths of its rivers lie in swampy, hot lands whose inhabitants are afflicted by many tropical diseases. There are few bays along the coast. Cape Town, South Africa, is situated on one of the few bays.

Africa has many mineral resources, including gold, diamonds, copper, uranium, iron ore, and tin. Only South Africa has coal; petroleum is found in the North African countries of Morocco, Algeria, Libya, and Egypt. Like South America, Africa is still being explored for minerals.

Australia is the smallest continent and the only continent that is also a country. It has a high elevation and a dry climate. Most of the country consists of a plateau and of a chain of mountains that stretches along the east coast. Most of the land consists of desert or steppe.

Only along the mountains and the north coast does much rain fall, and in the north, the rain falls only in summer. Australia has only one major river, the Murray, which starts in the mountains and flows westward before emptying into the southern Indian Ocean near Adelaide.

Australia is one southern continent that does have large coal deposits, especially in its mountains. It also has some petroleum, uranium, and many other minerals, including iron ore, gold, copper, manganese, and bauxite.

History of Industrialization

All of the lands of the southern continents used to be colonies of European countries. Ethiopia in East Africa was a colony for only a few years, but the other countries were ruled by Europeans for a much longer time.

In the 1500s, Spain and Portugal conquered South America. From their base in Peru, the Spanish directed the mining of gold and silver in the Andes. In northern Argentina, they raised mules to work in the mines. They established sugar **plantations** in some of the coastal areas. A plantation is a large farm on which only a single cash crop is grown. They sent the products of the mines and of the plantations to Spain and imported goods that were manufactured in Spain. The colonists were forbidden to establish industries. Money that was earned from the products of South American mines and of plantations was not invested to develop South America.

In northeastern Brazil, the Portuguese established sugar plantations. For the most part, the Portuguese colonists failed to extract the country's great mineral resources.

Farmers in the highlands of Peru still use oxen for plowing.

A few families owned most of the land; the majority of the people remained poor.

In the 1800s, the countries of South America won their independence but continued to send raw materials to Europe and to import goods that were manufactured in Europe. Later, as the United States became more industrialized, the countries of South America exported raw materials in exchange for goods that were manufactured in the United States.

European and American businesses eventually discovered the untapped resources of South America. They provided the capital to develop these resources and built railroads to ship them to markets. Despite the establishment of these enterprises, the patterns of South American trade with Europe and with the United States did not change. The raw materials of South America were still exported to Europe and to the United States for manufactured goods.

British traders developed the pampas of Argentina into a great cattle-growing region. In order to supply meat to the growing cities of England, they brought to Argentina new kinds of cattle and new kinds of grass that could be grown to feed the cattle. They built railroads from the cattle farms to the port of Buenos Aires. The only industries that they built were packing plants to prepare the meat to be shipped to England.

The story in Africa unfolded in much the same way. Europeans developed mines to supply raw materials for their industries. They built railroads to carry the minerals to the coast and ports where the raw materials of Africa were loaded onto ships that were destined for Europe.

European companies built plantations to produce rubber, cotton, coffee, tea, bananas, and cacao (the raw material for chocolate). After these raw materials were made into manufactured goods in Europe, some were shipped to Africa.

Even after the countries of Africa became independent in the 1960s, this kind of trade continued. Most of the people of these countries were poor, and so there was little money to invest in manufacturing. Furthermore, there were few skilled workers to operate machines.

Only in South Africa, which became an independent member of what was called the British Commonwealth in 1910, did industry develop. As you know, South Africa contains many valuable minerals and the only sizable deposits of coal that are found on the continent.

Australia was settled by the English, who established individual colonies along the coast. In 1901, all of these colonies were united into one country. Even after unification, industrial development was confined to the capital cities of the states that were located along the coast. Find the states and their capitals on the map on page 30.

New Zealand has even less industry than Australia. The country still exports food and raw materials to Europe and to North America and imports manufactured goods.

Southern Continents—Industry

Today, the countries of South America and Africa are trying to expand their industries. Their people have learned that producing manufactured goods can increase their standards of living. They have also learned that developing their own industries can make their countries richer. Industrial development provides jobs and profits that can be invested in education, in health services, in transportation, in communications, and in other services.

Each of these continents has some centers of industrial development. Brazil's main industrial center is in the southern part of the country, around the cities of Rio de Janeiro and Sao Paulo. Between them, at Volta Redonda, is a steel mill. Sao Paulo is becoming a big industrial center. Its factories produce textiles, shoes, motor vehicles, chemicals, rubber products, and metal products. Brazil and other industrializing countries are discussed in Chapter 22.

Buenos Aires, the capital of Argentina, is the major industrial center of the country. In addition to its meat-packing plants, Buenos Aires has factories that produce automobiles, textiles, and metal products. Its refineries process oil from the southern part of the country.

One of South America's oldest manufacturing centers is located in Antioquia in central Colombia. Using both the transportation network of good river routes to cotton-growing areas and the skills of settlers who were interested in developing industry, it became one of the first textile centers in South America.

The only major industrial center in Africa today is South Africa. Its industry is located near the mineral deposits around Johannesburg and Pretoria in the north. Other factories have been built in Cape Town. South Africa sells manufactured goods to some of the other countries of Africa. It makes automobiles, iron, steel and other metal products, as well as chemicals and other goods.

Minor industrial centers in Africa supply consumer goods to local customers. These areas in Africa are repeating the historic pattern of industrialization in England and America. The textile industry, which was one of the first industries to be developed in England and in the United States, is one of the first industries to be developed in Africa. You will read about the African country of Nigeria in Chapter 22.

Australia has built iron and steel mills near Newcastle, where coal is situated. Most of the rest of Australia's industry is located in Brisbane and Melbourne. These industries make automobiles, textiles, and other consumer goods for Australians. In the countryside, there are some manufacturing plants that process food that is produced from sheep and cattle and from the wheat that is raised on the farms.

Lesson 3 Review

Recalling Information

1. Give three reasons why the southern continents are among the least industrialized areas of the world.
2. How did colonialism affect the industrialization of the southern continents?

Interpreting Information

3. How might industrialization improve the lives of the people who live in the southern continents?
4. How does the natural environment of the southern continents affect industrialization?

Applying Information

5. If you were in charge, which resources do you think you would try to develop in the southern continents?
6. If you were a businessperson, in which southern continent would you want to establish a company? Why?

Skills for Thinking

READING AN ORGANIZATION CHART

You have learned several ways in which to organize information. They involve using a diagram, a table, a graph, and a chart. Some charts show how organizations have been set up. A chart of this kind presents a clear picture of the offices, or jobs, the responsibilities, or functions, and the chain of command in an organization.

How Is This Organized?

The chart on this page shows how the government of Japan is organized. Each block shows a major institution of the government. The arrows are used to show the *source* of authority, or power, and the *ob-*

ject, or institution, to which that authority is directed.

Study the chart, and then answer these questions.

1. What is the highest authority in Japan? Who must follow the rules set down by this authority?
2. Who has the authority to choose members of the Japanese Diet?
3. What role does the emperor perform? What is the source of his authority?

Make an organization chart to show how your school, your community, or your state is organized. Use arrows to show how the chain of command works.

ORGANIZATION CHART: GOVERNMENT OF JAPAN

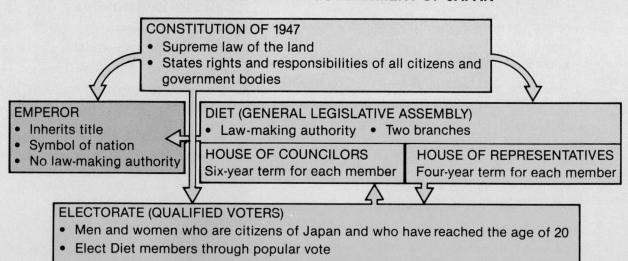

CONSTITUTION OF 1947
- Supreme law of the land
- States rights and responsibilities of all citizens and government bodies

EMPEROR
- Inherits title
- Symbol of nation
- No law-making authority

DIET (GENERAL LEGISLATIVE ASSEMBLY)
- Law-making authority • Two branches

HOUSE OF COUNCILORS
Six-year term for each member

HOUSE OF REPRESENTATIVES
Four-year term for each member

ELECTORATE (QUALIFIED VOTERS)
- Men and women who are citizens of Japan and who have reached the age of 20
- Elect Diet members through popular vote

Chapter 20 Review

Summary of Key Facts

In this chapter, you learned that

- in North America, the United States and Canada are industrialized countries.
- the distribution of people and of industry is uneven in North America.
- industrial growth in the United States is centered in five main industrial regions.
- Western Europe is second only to North America in its industrial output.
- the southern continents are still undergoing industrialization.
- industrial centers develop where there are resources and a competent labor force.
- in part, the southern continents have not developed because they lack two important resources, coal and oil.

Using Vocabulary

On a separate sheet of paper, write the term that will correctly complete each sentence.

consumer goods   anthracite
bituminous coal   Sun Belt

1. Eastern Pennsylvania has deposits of ____ coal.
2. People like to work in the ____ because of its warm climate.

3. ____ are those that are produced for people's use.
4. After the Civil War, ____ was used to make steel.

Discussing the Chapter

1. Discuss the distribution of industrial centers in North America. What are some of the reasons for the uneven distribution of industry?
2. How does the environment affect industrial development?
3. What resources are needed for industrial development?
4. Compare the industrial development of North America and Eurasia to the industrial development of the southern continents. How are they different? Why?

Reviewing Skills

Use the chart on page 408 to answer the questions.

1. Name the two houses, or branches, of the Diet. What does the Diet do?
2. Which is a higher authority, the Diet or the emperor?

Four Industrial Centers Compared

Chapter 21

Introduction

Skyscrapers line the avenues. The sounds of industry—people, traffic, machinery, and construction—greet you as you walk down the street. Crowded sidewalks pulse with the movements of people hurrying to reach their destinations. In towering office buildings business people work hard to help meet the needs of their society.

Whether you live in an industrial center in the United States, in Canada, in Europe, or in Asia, much of your surroundings are similar to those of people who live throughout the industrial world. Large buildings, traffic jams, the hum of huge machines, and crowds of people are part of your everyday life. Despite these similarities, each of the world's industrial centers is unique. Different natural environments, resources, cultures, and histories have produced different industrial environments in each geographical region.

In this chapter, you will learn about four industrial centers—one in Canada, one in the United States, one in Europe, and one in Asia. As you read about these centers, think about how they are different from each other and about how they are alike. Think about how they compare to the New York City area that we just studied. Consider how they match or refine your picture of the industrial world as a distinct environment.

Sunday strollers on the Ginza, Tokyo. Why do you think that no vehicles are allowed here on certain days?

Lesson 1

TORONTO, CANADA

In 1792, John Graves Simcoe was lieutenant governor of Upper Canada. His first job was to attract settlers to this wilderness, and he had to make sure that they would be safe and well provided for.

Simcoe thought that the province needed a navy base with a safe harbor. His eye focused on a place that was marked *Toronto* on the maps. Though muddy and full of mosquitoes, it had a good harbor. The more he considered Toronto, the more he liked it. He could see the possibility of building a great navy base and trade center there.

"Muddy Little York"

The place that Simcoe chose was situated on a fertile plain that borders Lake Ontario. Simcoe's plans for a great navy base and a great trade center were not fulfilled at the time. Nevertheless, the new town, which had been named York, was designated the capital of Upper Canada. Roads were built to connect the new capital with all parts of the province. Government officials moved to the town. Farmers settled in the rich countryside around the new town and supplied it with meat, poultry, and produce. Trade began to grow.

Immigrants to the province landed first in the capital, and many stayed there. By

MAP SKILLS: Which geographical features make Ontario's Golden Horseshoe well suited for industrial development?

CANADA'S GOLDEN HORSESHOE

☐ The Golden Horseshoe

0 10 20 30 40 Miles
0 10 20 30 40 Kilometers

N
W—E
S

St. Lawrence River

Oshawa

Toronto
Mississauga

Burlington
Hamilton

St. Catharines
Niagara Falls • Niagara Falls

Lake Ontario

Rochester

Syracuse

Welland Canal

Buffalo

UNITED STATES

1834, "Muddy Little York" was no longer muddy or little. It had become a thriving city, and everyone called it by its original name, Toronto.

In 1855, the first railroad reached the city. Soon, railroads connected Toronto with the rich farmland of southern Ontario, the mineral resources of the Canadian Shield to the north, and western Canada.

Earnings from trade were invested in new railroad lines. Such profits also paid for the opening of mines in the nearby Canadian Shield and for the establishment of industries in Toronto. Some of these industries supplied the railroads with rails, engines, and cars. Other new industries produced both farm and mining machinery. Today, manufacturing is Toronto's most important economic activity. Besides producing heavy machinery, Toronto is a leading producer of electrical equipment and aircraft. It is also a printing and publishing center.

Finance became another important economic activity in Toronto. In the early 1800s, as Toronto began to grow, a healthy banking industry developed to provide not only money for borrowing but also financial services. In addition, companies raised money by selling **stock**. Stock is a share of ownership in a company. Companies sell shares to gain money to expand and to operate. A portion of company profits are then shared with the stock owners to pay them for their investments in the company's future. Canada's biggest **stock exchange** is located in Toronto. A stock exchange is a place where stocks are bought and sold.

Even though it never became a navy

The lofty CN Tower dominates the skyline of Toronto, the center of Canadian industry.

base, Toronto's harbor became a busy port. In 1959, the St. Lawrence Seaway opened. A system of canals along the St. Lawrence River between Montreal and Lake Ontario, it enables products from all parts of Ontario to be shipped first to Toronto and then to locations throughout the world.

Toronto's network of railroads, highways, and shipping routes has helped to create a trade center that is greater than Simcoe had dreamed. Development eventually spread far beyond Toronto. Today, Toronto is the center of a large industrial area, sometimes called Canada's Golden Horseshoe, that rings Lake Ontario.

Dominating downtown Toronto is the Canadian National (CN) Tower, a communications center for radio and television. It rises more than 1,800 feet (548.6 m) and is the tallest self-supporting structure in the world.

Clustered around it are the skyscrapers of the central business district. Many of these tall buildings are the headquarters of banks. Farther north, on a hill that is surrounded by Queen's Park, stands the Parliament Building for the Province of Ontario, as Upper Canada is called now.

To the east are the lakefront and the harbor. Along the lakefront are miles of parkland and beach. In winter, the parks provide skating ponds. In summer, beautiful flower gardens dot the parks. Next to the harbor are many rail lines and some of the city's oldest factories. Old factories also line the lakefront to the west, especially near the railroad lines.

The development of cars and trucks enabled Toronto's industries to be situated away from its harbor and its rail lines. Radiating outward from the central city are roads and highways that are lined with factories.

Toronto is more than a center for business and government, however. It is home to more than 2,500,000 people. Almost all of the first settlers in Toronto came from Great Britain and from the United States. Emigrants from Ireland, Germany, Italy,

Each year, millions of tons of cargo pass through Toronto's busy port.

Below, a Toronto grocery store serves the Portuguese-speaking immigrant community.

The Canadian Opera Company performs for appreciative audiences throughout Canada. Why is *Joan of Arc* a popular production there?

China, and other countries soon followed. Today, Toronto has more Italians than some cities in Italy and more Germans than some cities in West Germany. Portuguese, Japanese, Koreans, Chinese, Indians, Pakistanis, and West Indians also live in Toronto. In fact, more than half of the city's people were born outside Canada.

Living in Toronto

Many of Toronto's immigrants settled in downtown areas where they opened churches and synagogues, stores, restaurants, and clubs to carry on the cultures of their homelands. Some of these neighborhoods still exist. Immigrants to these neighborhoods continue to use their own languages. Wearing folk costumes, they celebrate special national holidays by playing their own music, performing folk dances, and preparing and eating special foods. The restaurants and festivals of the immigrant groups have helped to make Toronto a lively and an interesting city.

Many of Toronto's older neighborhoods are changing, however. With the fast growth of the city, houses became very expensive. Like the skyscrapers that changed the downtown skyline, high-rise apartment buildings have sprung up as a quick answer to the problem of housing Toronto's residents. Single-family houses exist in the new suburbs around Toronto, but old houses downtown are being torn down so that large apartment buildings can be built. Some of the original families have been displaced, and their neighborhoods have lost some of their ethnic character.

Like many other large cities, Toronto has problems and challenges. Transportation is one challenge that faces Toronto. Moving workers to and from their jobs every day is a huge task. In 1954, the first subway line opened; it has since been greatly expanded. Feeding into the subway system is a vast network of bus, trolley, and trolley-bus lines that bring workers into the suburbs around Toronto.

415

How is the city hall in Toronto an example of urban planning? Which arts, sports, and businesses are centered here?

In many rapidly growing cities, water is often a problem. The increasing population of Toronto soon overtaxed its water supply and its sewage-treatment facilities. Bold steps were needed and eventually were taken to solve these problems.

Toronto's leaders proposed that the city of Toronto and its five suburban boroughs be unified under one metropolitan government in order to provide water, sewage disposal, and other services for the entire area. The new Toronto metropolitan area has been so successful that similar metropolitan systems have been created throughout Ontario to handle the problems of rapid growth and of industrialization.

Lesson 1 Review

Recalling Information

1. What features led to the selection of Toronto as a place for a new town?
2. What two events led to Toronto's early industrial growth?

Interpreting Information

3. You have read about some of the problems that were created by Toronto's rapid growth. What other problems might you expect to find?
4. Why does Toronto continue to attract so many immigrants?

Applying Information

5. You have read a description of Toronto and seen pictures of it as well. Does it seem to be a good place to live? Think about the layout of the city, the natural surroundings, the people who live there, and the kinds of work that they do. Do you think that you would like to live in Toronto? Why or why not?
6. The metropolitan government is in charge of planning in Toronto. Find out who is in charge of planning in your community.

Lesson 2

SILICON VALLEY, U.S.A.

You will not find the name *Silicon Valley* in any atlas index or on most maps. The area is not particularly rich in the crystalline element known as **silicon**. In fact, Silicon Valley is not even a valley. (There are hills along only one side of it.)

The name is still a good one. Silicon, which can be used as a semiconductor of electricity, is an important ingredient in electronic technology. Silicon Valley, a region of California, south of San Francisco, boasts what is probably the greatest concentration of electronics firms in the world. In recent years, it has gained worldwide fame as one of the newest and the fastest-growing industrial centers in the world.

It is an industrial center, however, that is quite different from Toronto, London, and New York City.

From Cherries to Chips

Silicon Valley is a small spur of California's Central Valley. It is about 30 miles (48.3 km) long and extends south from Palo Alto to San Jose. Its 10-mile (16.1-km) width is bounded by low hills and by the Diablo Mountains on the west. On the east are the waters of San Francisco Bay. The area includes about 13 towns that contain a total population of more than 1 million.

The climate in Silicon Valley is like that of the Mediterranean region. Temperatures are mild almost all the time. There are basically two seasons—a rainy one during the

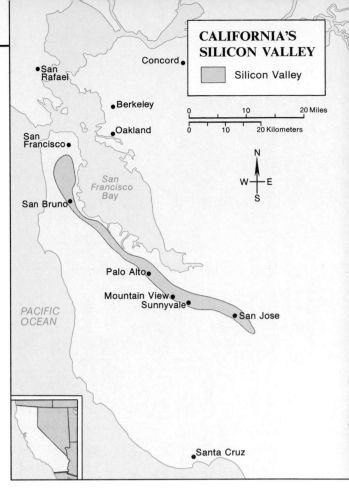

MAP SKILLS: From California's Silicon Valley, in which direction would you travel to reach San Francisco? Santa Cruz? The Pacific Ocean?

winter and a dry one during the rest of the year. The original vegetation there was oak forest.

For decades, the region was a quiet land of fruit farms. About 100,000 acres (40,470 ha) of orchards produced cherries, pears, apricots, and plums. Then, high tech came to the valley.

If you were to ride through Silicon Valley today, you might be surprised to see no smokestacks or railroad sidings. There would be none of the noise and the clutter that used to be associated with manufacturing. Instead, you would see neat collections

417

**Clusters of low, tidy buildings sprawl over Silicon Valley.
Dozens of high-technology firms have their headquarters here.
Can you explain how this valley received its modern name?**

of low buildings set in well-landscaped areas that look a little like college campuses.

Because high-technology industries tend to produce smaller products from already processed materials, they can be supported by trucking and air-transport systems. Thus, the mines, the ships, the railroads, the huge mills, and the factories that are associated with traditional heavy industry are not needed in the new high-technology businesses. High tech sought new locations.

Many electronics firms are located in industrial parks that have tennis courts, swimming pools, and jogging trails.

High tech requires a highly skilled work force and the continual introduction of ideas and products. Silicon Valley has no trouble attracting skilled personnel. As part of the Sun Belt, Silicon Valley is an appealing place to live, and the concentration of electronics firms attracts scientists and technicians. An unusually large number of its residents have earned doctoral degrees (the highest degrees that can be earned upon graduation from universities).

Silicon Valley has a history of attracting adventurous and ambitious business leaders. The most successful firms are not branches of old, established corporations. Instead, they are new companies that are managed by eager, young entrepreneurs (business adventurers).

Do you remember how Samuel Slater transformed the young United States by introducing the cotton mill into the Northeast? Silicon Valley people tell success stories that rival Slater's.

One successful person was William Shockley. Along with two other Bell Telephone researchers, he won the Nobel Prize in physics for inventing the **transistor**, an electronic device containing a semiconductor material that regulates the flow of electric current much as a spigot controls the flow of water in pipes.

Before Shockley's invention, electric currents were regulated by the vacuum tube, a type of modified light bulb which is bulky, relatively expensive, easily broken, and which tends to overheat. The transistor, on the other hand, is much smaller, cheap to make, durable, and produces hardly any heat. Thus, since the mid-1960s, most electronic devices, such as radio or television, have used transistors.

In 1955, Shockley moved west and set up his own firm in Palo Alto. Shockley gathered around him a number of other scientists. The focus of their research was semiconductors. They wanted to improve transistors by using material such as silicon to conduct electricity. Their work eventually led to the integrated circuit, an electronic circuit that is composed of two or more transistors and is produced on a single, thin silicon wafer, or **chip**.

Today, the economical and reliable chip has become the basic component of almost every electronic device. Through miniatur-

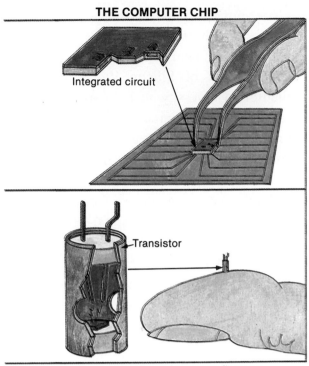

THE COMPUTER CHIP

Integrated circuit

Transistor

Many thousands of transistors can fit on an integrated circuit, nicknamed the "chip."

Integrated circuits (top) are the building blocks of modern computers and of electronic equipment. One may contain as many as 30,000 tiny transistors (bottom).

ization, one chip may easily contain thousands of transistors in a space the size of a dime. They can be made to store information, or they can be designed to control the operation of machines or even of other chips, as in a computer.

Shockley's company eventually failed. He could produce the chip, but he could not yet produce it at a price that would enable it to be commercially marketed with success. Soon thereafter, though, scientists who were associated with Shockley formed successful firms of their own. These "spin-offs"—together with new companies ("start-ups")—sparked the change from cherries to chips.

Two other vital factors contributed to the development of Silicon Valley. One was Stanford University in Palo Alto. Eager to strengthen its resources in science, Stanford provided its students and its faculty with an encouraging environment in which to research computer chips and related technologies. The other factor was the availability of venture capital—money that is invested in new and as yet unproven enterprises. The semiconductor industry was lucky to have had many people who were eager to provide capital for new businesses.

Beginning in the late 1950s, valley orchards dwindled as the number of semiconductor firms grew by leaps and bounds. These firms were joined by businesses in a host of related fields: computers, computer software, lasers, pocket calculators, video games, digital watches, and cordless telephones. According to one estimate, the area had about 3,000 electronics firms by 1984. The population of San Jose alone zoomed from 95,000 in 1950 to 660,000 in 1980, which made it the fastest-growing city in the United States. The valley creates about 40,000 jobs a year.

Strange as it may seem, much of the actual manufacture of computer chips now takes place elsewhere. Silicon Valley, however, is still remarkable for its concentration of computer and information technology. Even for those firms that have many overseas operations, Silicon Valley remains the heart of research and development. By the 1980s, the region was the ninth-largest manufacturing center in the United States.

Living in Silicon Valley

When Tom has some free time, he enjoys assembling his own computer. Tom's hobby is a continuation of his work in computer engineering. In Silicon Valley, where he lives, it is not uncommon for people's entire lives—work, recreation, family get-togethers—to revolve around electronics. As one executive said: "Our credo [motto] is work hard, play hard, and don't worry about the difference between work and play. There isn't any."

Another characteristic of life in Silicon Valley is informality. Shirtsleeves and first names are the rule in many companies. The relaxed atmosphere, however, does not prevent a serious commitment to work. Competition is intense, and individuals feel a tremendous pressure to excel. Those who do excel are much in demand. They are offered and can take advantage of better opportunities. They may change jobs as often as once a year. (About one-half of the workers in Silicon Valley do so.)

Although the stress is great, so are the rewards. Salaries for high-level personnel are good. Bonuses are paid in the form of vacations to faraway places or expensive cars. Luxurious homes dot the hillsides throughout the valley, especially in the north.

This luxurious kind of living is not enjoyed by all of the population of the valley, however. About half of Silicon Valley's 200,000 employees work on production lines. Many of them belong to such minorities as Mexicans, Filipinos, Southeast Asians. Most do not have much education. Their work tends to be monotonous, and their pay is low. Those who work in **wafer**

fab, or the manufacture of chips, cannot afford the higher-priced houses of the valley. Most of these workers live in modest housing in or near San Jose. Many spend hours on crowded freeways while driving to and from work because there is practically no public transportation. Yet, even for these workers, there is unusual opportunity for improvement.

Lesson 2 Review

Recalling Information
1. Where and what is Silicon Valley?
2. How is Silicon Valley unique as a center of industry?

Interpreting Information
3. Why did Silicon Valley change from an agricultural to a manufacturing center?
4. Compare Silicon Valley to Toronto in terms of natural setting, industrial base, and life-style.

Applying Information
5. Make a list of all the electronic devices that you use almost everyday. What services do these devices perform for you? How would your life differ if you did not have them?
6. Have you had any experiences with computers? Why do you think many people enjoy using them?

Computers can be both educational and entertaining (shown above). Below, workers assemble computer parts in a California plant.

Lesson 3

RUHR REGION, WEST GERMANY

Most of West Germany is known for its picturesque landscape. It is a country of rich farmland, spectacular forests, snowcapped mountains, and broad rivers. One of its rivers, the Ruhr, gives its name to one of the leading industrial regions in the world.

About 12 million people live in the Ruhr region, making it one of the most densely populated areas in Europe. You can see on the map that the Ruhr region is a megalopolis which stretches about 35 to 50 miles (56.1 to 80.5 km) along the Ruhr River and runs southward along the Rhine to the cities of Dusseldorf and Wuppertal.

The region includes large coal reserves, which helped in its development as an industrial center. Its many heavy industries produce, among other things, chemicals and steel. West Germany is the third-largest producer of steel in the world (after the United States and Japan), and about 75 percent of its steel is produced in the Ruhr region. Ruhr steel is used in the manufacture of heavy machinery, automobiles, ships, tools, and other products of the region. The region also has light industries that produce textiles and precision instruments, among other things.

MAP SKILLS: How was Ruhr Valley pollution carried to other parts of West Germany?

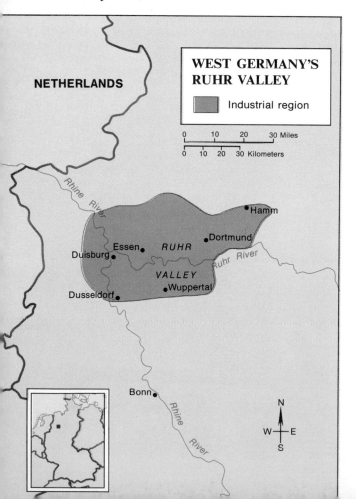

WEST GERMANY'S RUHR VALLEY

Industrial region

0   10   20   30 Miles

0   10   20   30 Kilometers

NETHERLANDS

Rhine River

Hamm

Dortmund

Essen RUHR

Duisburg

VALLEY

Dusseldorf Wuppertal

Ruhr River

Bonn

Rhine River

N
W—E
S

A Seesaw History

Many of the world's giant industrial centers have serious air-pollution problems. In contrast, the air in Dusseldorf and in other cities of the Ruhr region is amazingly clear. The region contains hundreds of beautiful parks and scenic lakes. This, however, was not always true.

A few years ago, the Ruhr region was one of the ugliest and the most polluted industrial areas in the world. Coal was used to run the area's huge factories, and giant smokestacks belched chemicals and smoke into the air day and night. People who breathed this polluted air developed lung diseases, and their homes were covered with black soot.

Water pollution was also a problem in the region. Factories pumped chemical wastes

A steel company's offices rise behind old town houses in West Germany's Dusseldorf, main city of the Ruhr industrial region.

into the Ruhr and other tributaries of the Rhine, killing fish and other life forms. It was unhealthy for people to swim or to boat on the waterways.

The situation became so serious that the people of the Ruhr region pressured the government to correct the situation. The West German government passed laws that required factories to use machines that released less smoke into the air. The Ruhr Association was formed to battle pollution in the Ruhr River. Today, more than 100 sewage plants clean the water that drains into the river. Every business or city that uses the river must pay money to the association to help with the continuing cleanup.

People can now fish, swim, and boat on the Ruhr River. In cities such as Duisberg, you can still see red-and-purple smoke billowing from the smokestacks of factories, but, on the whole, the Ruhr environment has improved. It has become a healthier place in which to live.

Dusseldorf—Commercial Center

Dusseldorf, now the business and banking center of the Ruhr region, began as a small fishing village and farm community more than 1,000 years ago. As early as the 1820s, however, people discovered that the fertile land around the town contained some of Europe's richest coal deposits. A small,

The Ruhr River, a lifeline of German industry, is well guarded against pollution.

coal-burning steel mill was built in the region, but because the iron ore to make the steel had to be imported from other areas and because the means of transportation were poor, large-scale steel production was impossible.

Then, around 1869, the government began to build railroads and canals in the area. After these were completed, iron could be easily transported to the area from mines near the Mosel River Valley, and a thriving steel business developed. Machinery was also manufactured. Industrial development continued into the twentieth century.

Like much of the Ruhr region, Dussel-

dorf was almost destroyed during World War II. Most of its industry was bombed out. In 1948, the United States helped West Germany to rebuild its towns and its industries. By the 1950s, Dusseldorf was producing more goods than it had before the war.

Living in Dusseldorf

Imagine that your family is vacationing in Dusseldorf. It is summer. People stroll through the lush green parks and the flower gardens. They swim, sunbathe on lawns, and go boating on the waterways.

You have been invited to spend a couple of days with a steelworker named Heinz and his family. Heinz works in a steel mill that has employed his father for the past 30 years. Many fathers and sons in the Ruhr Valley work for the same company.

At noon, you share the main meal of the day with Heinz and his family. On the table is an array of delicious food. You especially like the sauerbraten, which is roast beef that has been soaked in wine vinegar before cooking, the spicy sauerkraut, which is pickled cabbage, and the potato cakes. The adults drink beer with the meal.

Later in the afternoon, you go to a café for hot chocolate and pastries. In the evening, you eat a light meal of bread, sausage, and cheese.

While you are in Dusseldorf, you attend a soccer match in the Rhine Stadium. Soccer is West Germany's national sport.

Heinz says that if you were to stay all year, you would find other exciting things to do. In the fall, the children of Dusseldorf participate in the Festival of St. Martin, which has been celebrated on November 10 since 1586. About 50,000 boys and girls sing and dance as they wind through the streets. In the winter, many people attend the famous Christmas festival in Essen. People in the Ruhr Valley also love to ice-skate in the winter.

Lesson 3 Review

Recalling Information

1. Name three ways in which the Ruhr River is used. Who supervises the cleanliness of the Ruhr River?
2. Which resources have made industrialization possible in the Ruhr region?

Interpreting Information

3. Why are industrial centers generally not considered picturesque? Why is the Ruhr region picturesque in spite of industrialization?
4. Why is the Dusseldorf-Duisburg area a megalopolis?

Applying Information

5. Are there any areas near you that could benefit by following a cleanup plan similar to that used in the Ruhr region? Explain. How might such a plan be good for a nation's economy?
6. What might you find attractive about living in Dusseldorf?

Ruhr Valley children (above) turn out by the thousands for the annual costume festivals. Soccer (below) attracts huge crowds to Rhine Stadium in Dusseldorf.

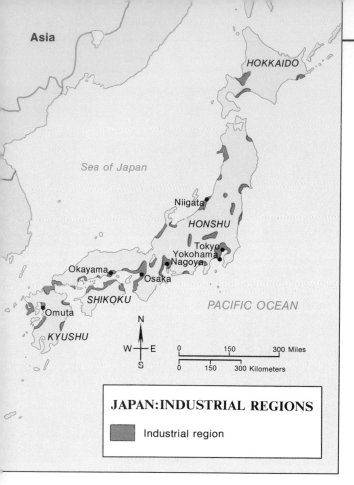

Sea of Japan

HOKKAIDO

Niigata
HONSHU
Tokyo
Yokohama
Nagoya
Okayama
Osaka
SHIKOKU
PACIFIC OCEAN
Omuta
KYUSHU

N
W—E
S
0   150   300 Miles
0   150   300 Kilometers

JAPAN:INDUSTRIAL REGIONS

Industrial region

MAP SKILLS: Which of Japan's four islands is the most heavily industrialized?

Lesson 4

TOKYO, JAPAN

Tokyo is Japan's capital and its financial, transportation, commercial, and industrial center. More than 11 million residents make Tokyo the largest city in Japan and one of the largest cities in the world. One of every ten people in Japan lives in Tokyo.

A City of the Old and the New

Like large cities everywhere, Tokyo is a city of tall office buildings, large and small shops, restaurants, markets, traffic jams, and crowded sidewalks. It is also a city in which the old and the new exist side by side. If you were to take a walking tour through Tokyo, you would see low buildings in the traditional Japanese style intermingled with tall, modern buildings. You would also see Buddhist and Shinto temples and shrines where most Japanese worship. Some, such as Tokyo's Kannon temple, date back to A.D. 600. You might stop to rest in one of the beautiful parks that surround most of the older temples and shrines of the city.

Tokyo is bordered by the Edo (EH*doh) River on the southeast, and the Tama (TAH*mah) River on the south. Western Tokyo, an area of uplands, is the location of embassies, universities, schools, and residential areas. The eastern part of Tokyo is a lowlands region that reaches down to Tokyo Bay. Much of this area is built on landfill that has been reclaimed from Tokyo Bay. As a result, it is an area in danger of flooding during the heavy rains of the monsoon season.

After some time in Tokyo, it might become clear to you that the city is actually a collection of villages. Tokyo's 223 square miles (578 sq km) are divided into 23 smaller units, called wards. These small neighborhoods are connected to one another by wide streets and highways.

Tokyo was founded in the twelfth century as the village of Edo. As early as 1590, it became one of the important military and economic centers in Japan. In 1868, Edo became Japan's capital. It was renamed *Tokyo*, which means "eastern capital."

The Work-a-Day-World

Tokyo has more than 80,000 factories. Many of them are small and employ fewer than 20 workers. There are also huge, modern industrial plants that employ between 10,000 and 20,000 workers.

Tokyo's leading industries now include electronics, machine-tool manufacturing, publishing, and printing. Small companies produce computers, typewriters, televisions, and other electronic products. Large numbers of these and other products are exported to the United States, Japan's leading trade partner, and to other countries.

The manufacture of automobiles is also one of Tokyo's important industries. Cars are a major Japanese export. There is also a large market for Japanese automobiles at home. In the nearby port city of Yokohama, large tankers, containerships, and other kinds of cargo ships unload raw materials that are used by the automobile industry and take on finished automobiles to be shipped abroad.

In a city of more than 11 million people, the large number of cars causes problems. In spite of modern freeways, Tokyo's two million cars create more traffic than the roads can handle. Severe traffic jams and air pollution have become a part of everyday life in the city. To help to solve the problem, the Japanese government has built a public transportation system that consists of a complicated system of subways, bus lines, and commuter trains that are among the fastest and the most efficient in the world. The system carries almost 10 million riders a day; yet Tokyo's highways remain jammed.

Serene, snowcapped Mount Fuji is 60 miles (96.6 km) from Tokyo's congested streets.

Living in Tokyo

The Japanese place great emphasis on education. As a nation, Japan has the highest literacy rate in the world. With 2,300 schools and more than 190 colleges and universities, Tokyo has become the nation's educational center.

Many Koreans and other foreign **ethnic groups** live in Tokyo. An ethnic group is a number of people who are united by race or by national background and who share the same language and customs. The overwhelming majority of the city's population, however, is Japanese. A common heritage may help to explain why the people of

427

Along with industrialization, the Japanese have adopted some Western pastimes, too—including baseball. Here, the Tokyo Giants and the Nagoya Dragons play before a sellout crowd.

Tokyo continue to support their traditional values and customs. Although industrialization and contact with the Western world have brought changes to the city, old traditions have not been lost. The home, in particular, is a place where traditional ways are maintained.

A typical Japanese family lives in a one-story house a few miles outside the city. The house contains four rooms. The walls that separate the rooms are made of paper screens. Sliding doors between the rooms are made of wooden frames that are covered with paper. According to custom, you take off your shoes before you enter the house so that outdoor dust will not soil the thin straw mats, which are called *tatami* (*tah*TAH*mee*), that cover the floors.

All furniture in the house is low. Mats, which can be rolled up, are used for sleeping. At dinner, the family sits on cushions on the floor around a low table. The meal consists of rice, sliced raw fish, deep-fried vegetables, soybean curd, pickled ginger, and green tea. The meal is eaten with chopsticks, not forks, spoons, and knives.

Traditions are also upheld in the workplace. Imagine that you are visiting a Japanese family. Your host is a sales engineer for a large electrical company. You

A Japanese mother and her daughter share the traditional tea ceremony. What does their clothing tell you about modern Japan?

accompany him in the morning to his job to find out what it is like to work for a big Japanese corporation.

On a typical morning, your host leaves his house promptly at 6:40 A.M. By eight o'clock, he is at work. He and his co-workers begin the day by singing the company song. Singing the company song makes employees feel that they are part of a corporate "family."

This day, the morning's work consists of answering telegrams from the United States about company products. After a 45-minute lunch break, the afternoon's work consists of revising an English-language manual for

a new stereo system. At 4:45 P.M., the workday ends, and employees again sing the company song. Your host then invites you to have dinner with him at the office cafeteria. After a light dinner of grilled fish or chicken, he must attend a company-sponsored English class. He doesn't return home until 9:00 P.M. It is clear to you that both workers and managers in Japanese industry spend long days working hard at their jobs.

Lesson 4 Review

Recalling Information

1. In what way is Tokyo a blend of the new and the old?
2. What are Tokyo's main industries?

Interpreting Information

3. What traditions do the Japanese value? What evidence do you have to support your answer?
4. How do employees in Japan feel about their companies? Why? What effects do their attitudes have upon their work? Explain.

Applying Information

5. Is Tokyo a city in which you might want to live? Why? Are there other cities you have read about that you would prefer to Tokyo? Explain.
6. Are there any systems that you have read about that you think Japan should adopt? Which ones, and why?

UNDERSTANDING COMPUTERS

Computers are both tools and products of high-tech industry. They have even introduced into our language various terms that have special meanings.

Mainframe computers are the largest and the most powerful computers. Large businesses, government agencies, and even universities use mainframes to store and to process information. **Minicomputers** are smaller than mainframes but are still very powerful. They are used by medium-sized and small businesses and by some school systems. Home computers, which are called **microcomputers**, are the smallest and the least powerful of information systems.

Within every computer is placed a central processing unit that carries out the instructions that are given to the computer. The memory stores the instructions, or the programs, and the information that is being processed.

A computer uses two kinds of memory—RAM and ROM. RAM stands for Random Access Memory. RAM is the place where the operator writes programs and stores data, or information. Since RAM is temporary, all the stored data is erased when the computer is turned off, unless the in-formation has been saved on a disk.

ROM, or Read Only Memory, contains the programs that the computer needs to operate. It is a permanent part of the computer, and so, it is not erased when the computer is shut off. The operator usually cannot change or add to ROM.

How Do I Use What I Know?

Using what you just read, answer these questions.

1. At the headquarters of the National Aeronautics and Space Administration (NASA), what kind of computer would be used to monitor hundreds of satellites?

2. An operator at a hospital clinic inserts a disk into a computer and enters data to update patients' bills. The disk is then removed, and the computer is turned off. What has happened to the data?

3. A person is updating a checking account on a microcomputer. Suddenly, the electricity goes off. What has happened to the data just entered?

4. What kind of computer would a chain of hardware stores use to keep track of their accounts?

Chapter 21 Review

Summary of Key Facts

In this chapter, you learned that

- Toronto is a great industrial center that has a diversified economy.
- Silicon Valley changed from a fruit-growing area to one of the fastest-growing industrial centers in the world.
- semiconductor technology was developed in the valley, which is still a center of high technology.
- West Germany's Ruhr region is one of the major producers of iron, steel, cars, and heavy machinery in the world.
- the environment of the Ruhr region, once heavily polluted, has been cleaned up through government action.
- Tokyo, a modern city of 11 million, is the center of Japanese trade and industry.
- traditional values and customs have been preserved in modern Japan.

Using Vocabulary

On a separate sheet of paper, write the term that will correctly complete each sentence.

venture capital   silicon
chip   stock

1. _____ is a crystalline element that is used in electronic technology.
2. _____ is money that is invested in a new and unproved enterprise.
3. To own _____ in a company is to own a part of that company.
4. A computer _____ , or silicon wafer, holds two or more transistors.

Discussing the Chapter

1. How did Toronto grow to become a large city?
2. Why is Toronto considered to be a very desirable place in which to live?
3. How has Silicon Valley changed since the late 1950s?
4. Why is Silicon Valley considered to be a large center for industry, although not much manufacturing of raw material goes on there?
5. How did environmental pollution become a severe problem in the Ruhr region?
6. What part does Tokyo play in the economy of Japan?
7. How do the Japanese maintain their traditional ways? Give examples.

Reviewing Skills

Use the information on page 430 to answer the questions.

1. What is the difference between RAM and ROM?
2. What are the kinds of information that a computer needs in order to operate?

Unit 6 Review

Summary of Key Facts

In this unit, you learned that

- an industrial environment is largely an artificial or human-made environment.
- Western Europe, North America, and Japan are highly industrialized; the rest of Asia, Africa, and Latin America are developing their industries.
- nations of the world are linked by an interdependent global economy.
- industrialization brings urbanization and higher standards of living, but it creates other problems.
- advances in technology and in automation have led to a shift in the labor force toward more nonmanufacturing jobs in service industries.
- California's Silicon Valley is a center for the invention and the manufacture of computer technology.
- both Toronto, Canada, and Tokyo, Japan, have diversified industrial economies.
- Germany's Ruhr region is a leading center of heavy industry.

Discussing the Unit

1. Why has industrialization occurred more rapidly in some parts of the world than in others? Why have Africa and Latin America remained mostly unindustrialized?
2. Use examples to explain how the global economy of interdependent nations works.
3. How does technology contribute to the development of industrial economies?
4. How has the economic development of Toronto been different from that of California's Silicon Valley?
5. Discuss the problems that have been caused by industrialization in Tokyo and in the Ruhr region.

Activities

1. Use your school library to find old photographs and maps of the region where you live. Prepare a report to show how industrialization has changed your area.
2. Make a list of objects in your home that were made in other countries. Write the name of the country in which each object was made. Identify as many different places as possible.

Test

Using Vocabulary

On a separate sheet of paper, write the sentence in each pair that uses the underlined term correctly.

1. The <u>labor force</u> is made up of farmers and agricultural workers, miners, loggers, fishers, industrial workers, and workers who are employed by service industries.

   Retired workers form the <u>labor force</u>.

2. Modern conveniences help to create a high <u>standard of living</u>.

   Today, a woman's <u>standard of living</u> is about 73 years.

3. <u>Mass production</u> is an advanced transportation system.

   The making of large numbers of goods using lines of workers or machines is called <u>mass production</u>.

4. <u>Venture capital</u> is invested in new, unproved enterprises.

   A <u>venture capital</u> was a colonial trading outpost.

5. An <u>export</u> is an unused harbor.

   A manufactured item that is sold to another country is an <u>export</u>.

6. An industrial country relies on <u>imports</u> from around the world.

   <u>Imports</u> are important exports.

The Big Question

How has industrialization changed the world and the ways in which people live?

Write your answer in complete sentences. Draw upon the information in this unit to write a good answer.

Using Map Skills

Use the map on page 426 to complete this exercise.

1. Which of Japan's islands is the farthest north?
2. On which island is the city of Okayama located?
3. Which of Shikoku's coasts has become heavily industrialized?

Identifying a Geographic Theme

Think about the geographic theme of **movement** as you complete this exercise.

List some goods that people in your state produce and send to people in other states. List some goods received from other states.

Unit 7

A Changing World

The world has always been changing and will continue to change. A hallmark of the modern world is the *acceleration*, or "increase in the rate," of change. Things change quickly today because of technology. Technology has made communication and transportation more efficient. This has, in turn, caused other changes.

Nonindustrialized areas are being industrialized. Most areas of the world, even those inhabited by traditional societies, are affected by this. Both the industrial world and the industrializing world face a future of opportunities and of challenges.

Concepts

developed nation
developing nation
trade-off

gross national
product

The Big Question

What are the main global issues that face our world today?

Focus on a Geographic Theme

In this unit you will study the geographic theme of **human-environment interactions**. As you know, people try to change their environment to create a better life. Consider some ways that your environment has been changed by technology. How does technology affect the way you live?

A Yosemite National Park ranger works with a biologist. How is cooperation important in a changing world?

Developing Nations

Chapter 22

Introduction

Think about the families you know, the homes in which they live, the food that they eat, and the entertainment that they enjoy.

Although poverty exists in the United States, most Americans enjoy a high standard of living in comparison to most of the rest of the world's population. The latest figures show that the average American household has two rooms per person. More than 80 percent of American households have central heating. More than 90 percent have at least 1 telephone, and almost 100 percent have 1 television set.

Most Americans eat well, dress well, and have adequate housing. Like children in most industrial countries, most American children live more comfortably than their parents did.

In many parts of the world, however, millions of people go to bed hungry. Many are starving. Most of these families live in one-room dwellings without running water. Children who are younger than you work 10, 12, or even more hours each day. Things that seem ordinary to the average American would be great luxuries to three-quarters of Earth's population.

Why are there such extremes in the world? Why are there "have" and "have-not" nations? You will find out in this chapter.

◀ **Many West Africans work at new computer centers. What economic and social problems can computers help us to solve?**

WHAT IS A DEVELOPING NATION?

You can compare nations as you can compare people. Some nations are rich. Others are poor. Still others fall between rich and poor. Just as people perform different kinds of work, nations depend on different kinds of economic activity. Some nations, such as the United States and Japan, have advanced technology that helps them to produce many goods to sell. The sale of goods gives these nations money to buy goods that they cannot produce economically. In such countries, many people work in factories. Nations that fit this description are called **developed nations**.

Other countries with much simpler technologies produce, sell, and earn less, and, therefore, have much less than developed nations. Such nations are called less developed countries, LDCs, or **developing nations**.

The map on the facing page shows how the nations of the world can be classified as *developed* or *developing*. Identify the developed nations. Then, find the developing nations. In which category are there more nations? On which continents are most of the developing nations situated? Which of them is the largest?

The developing nations of the world are by no means alike. Some have practically no industry. Others are in the early stages of building industries. Still others are advancing rapidly toward becoming developed nations. No matter how much industry they have, all developing nations have certain characteristics.

Characteristics of Developing Nations

One characteristic derives from the fact that most people in developing nations work in agriculture. In those countries that are the least developed, as many as 75 of every 100 workers are involved in farming of some kind. (Compare this to the United States, in which the labor force that works in agriculture is about 3 of 100.)

Furthermore, the technology of farming in developing countries is simple and non-mechanized. Farmers in the least developed countries have only simple tools with which to work. Such agricultural tools cannot be used to plant, to cultivate, and to harvest large amounts of crops. Often, farmers produce barely enough to feed themselves. This kind of farming, as you have learned, is called subsistence farming.

Also common in developing nations is plantation farming. Plantations are usually owned by rich landowners or corporations. They rely on large teams of workers to do the farming by hand. Plantation owners do not need to invest in expensive labor-saving farm machinery because the labor supply is large and inexpensive to employ. Workers in developing nations exceed the number of jobs available, and those who get jobs are hired at very low wages.

A second characteristic of developing nations derives from the fact that they often lack well-balanced economies. Since they need money to finance economic growth,

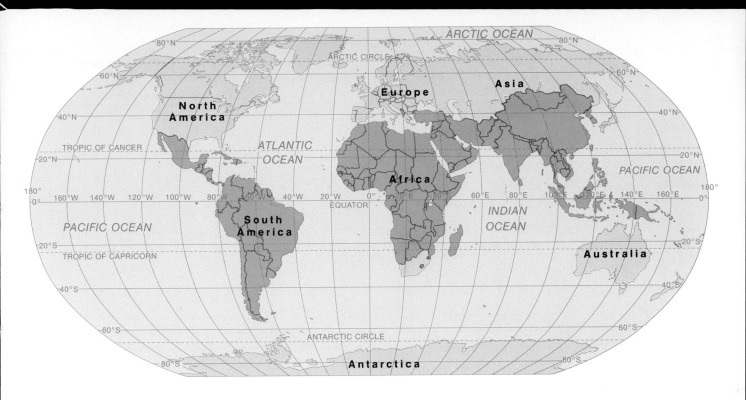

WORLD: DEVELOPING NATIONS

Developing nation

MAP SKILLS: Use the map on pages 32 and 33 to help you to name 10 developing nations in the Northern Hemisphere and 10 in the Southern Hemisphere.

they tend to concentrate on those goods that bring the largest profits in the shortest time. For example, several Caribbean countries produce only one crop, usually sugarcane or bananas. Such cash crops grow well there and are sold in parts of the world where they are not grown. Other developing nations mine only one or two minerals, which serve as the bases for their economies.

What happens when bad weather destroys a cash crop? What happens when minerals— nonrenewable resources—begin to run out? When this kind of calamity happens, a developing nation loses its only source of income. Disaster threatens its economy.

A third characteristic that many develop-

ing nations share is a rapidly growing population. The populations of developing nations are growing two-and-one-half times faster than the populations of developed countries. This means that each year, there are many more people to feed in the developing nations. There are also many more people to clothe and to house.

What happens when a country produces and sells only a few kinds of goods while its population is growing rapidly? The population growth outstrips the capacity of the economy to support it. This condition helps to produce a fourth characteristic of developing nations—widespread poverty.

In most of the developed nations, the

COMPARING COUNTRIES

	Country	Infant deaths per 1,000 live births	Male life expectancy in years	Female life expectancy in years	Male literacy % of population	Female literacy % of population
Some least developed countries	Chad	160	29	35	12	1
	South Yemen	114	41	42	48	8
	Haiti	110	47	50	29	18
Some developing countries	Chile	33	64	70	89	87
	Syria	15	54	59	60	20
	Mexico	77	63	67	78	70
Some developed countries	United States	11	70	78	99	99
	Japan	7	73	79	99	97
	Greece	17	71	75	93	76

What is the difference in years between the average life expectancy of men in Chad and of men in the United States?

majority of people are fairly comfortable. Although there usually are small groups of both very rich and very poor people, most people are middle class, that is, in between. In countries that are primarily agricultural, the poorest are either subsistence farmers, who scratch out a living on usually infertile land, or low-paid plantation workers.

Many of the poor in the developing countries are those who have neither land to work nor jobs from which to earn wages. Each year, thousands of the rural poor flock to the cities in the hope of finding work. Their hopes die quickly when they discover that there are not enough jobs in the cities for them. Often, life in the city is even more desperate than rural life.

The chart on this page shows another set of characteristics of developing nations. To develop economically, a nation needs people who are healthy and strong. It also needs educated people who have been trained to develop the skills that are needed to maintain an industrialized economy.

First, the chart deals with measures of national health such as the infant mortality rate and the average life expectancy. The infant mortality rate, as you know, is the number of infants per thousand who die in the first year of life. Life expectancy is the number of years that the average man or woman lives.

The chart deals also with **literacy** rates, the percentages of adults who can read and write. Literacy depends on education, and many developing nations do not have the money to build enough schools or to hire enough teachers. Moreover, many children cannot attend the schools that do exist because they must work to help to support their families. How do the literacy rates of the less developed countries compare to those of the developed countries?

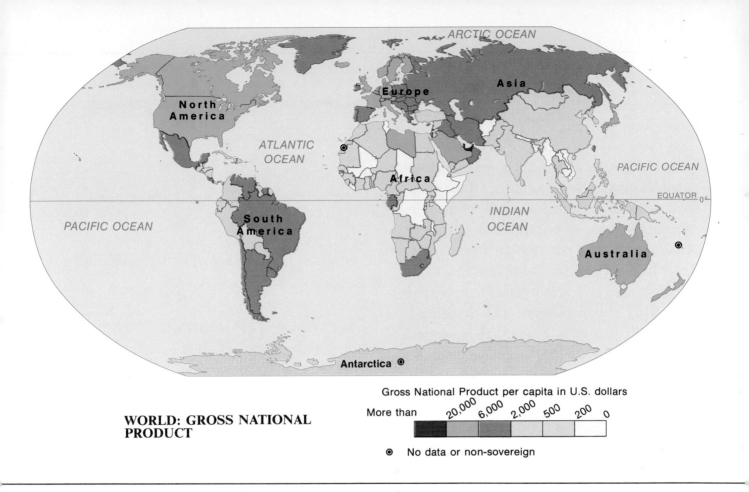

WORLD: GROSS NATIONAL PRODUCT

Gross National Product per capita in U.S. dollars

More than 20,000 6,000 2,000 500 200 0

◉ No data or non-sovereign

MAP SKILLS: Compare this map with the map on page 439.
Which developing nations have the highest per capita GNP?

Compare both sets of figures. How do the infant mortality rates of developing nations compare to the rates in developed countries?

Infant mortality rates and life expectancy rates are often the result of unsanitary living conditions and of the lack of adequate nutrition and health care. Poor nations cannot afford to clean up their crowded cities, to provide safe drinking water for everyone, and to eliminate the conditions that favor the spread of diseases. They have fewer doctors and hospitals than developed nations have.

Are developing nations poor in resources? Many are. However, it would be a mistake to conclude that all developing nations are poor in resources. In fact, a handful of them are among the richest nations in the world. Examples are the oil-rich countries of the Middle East. Countries such as Saudi Arabia and Kuwait have vast oil reserves.

Measuring the Wealth of Nations

Economists estimate that three-fourths of the world's people live in developing nations and that one-fourth live in developed nations. How have economists come to this judgment? In part, they have ascertained which nations have the characteristics of less developed countries and which do not. They have also compared the wealth of the world's nations. In general, nations with the least wealth are judged to be developing, and those with the most are developed.

One measure of wealth is gross national product, or GNP—the value of all the goods and services that a nation produces, both inside and outside its borders, in a year. Yet, GNP alone does not show a nation's true wealth. Compare, for example, India to the Netherlands. In a recent year, India's GNP was $167 billion, whereas the Netherlands had a GNP of $139 billion. Those figures suggest that India is wealthier than the Netherlands, but that is not true. In the same year, India's population was 684 million, and the Netherlands had 14 million people.

To get an accurate picture of a nation's wealth, economists divide GNP by the number of people who live in that country. This calculation results in a country's **per capita** GNP. (*Per capita* is the Latin expression for *per head*, meaning "per person.") Dividing $167 billion by 684 million people results in a per capita GNP of about $245. If the value of all of India's goods and services had been distributed equally to every man, woman, and child in the nation, each person would have received $245. The per capita GNP for the Netherlands in that year was $9,930. Which nation was wealthier?

A nation's wealth can be figured as gross domestic product (GDP), or wealth produced only within a nation's borders, not outside its borders.

The map on page 441 shows the range of figures for per capita GNP in the world. The charts on pages 493 to 499 give information on GDP.

Lesson 1 Review

Recalling Information
1. Name five characteristics of the developing nations of the world.
2. Is *gross national product* or *per capita GNP* better for comparing the wealth of nations? Why?

Interpreting Information
3. Use the map on page 441 to find the per capita GNP in the United States. Name the nations that have similar per capita GNPs. Which are the poorest nations of the world? (Use the world map on pages 32 and 33 if you need help in naming the nations.) Which are the wealthiest nations in terms of per capita GNPs?
4. Compare the maps on pages 439 and 441. Which developing nations are *not* poor?

Applying Information
5. Suppose that you lived in one of the poorest developing nations. How might your life be different from what it is now? What could you do to try to make it better? What could your government do to improve conditions?
6. Many people of traditional societies are poor according to the standards that have been set by developed nations. Yet, some choose to hold on to old ways and do not want to change. In your view, what might be a good reason to retain old ways?

Lesson 2

THE ROAD TO DEVELOPMENT

Although some groups within a nation may disagree, most, if not all, of the developing nations want to join the ranks of the developed nations. They see the building of factories and the improvements that are made in transportation and in communication as ways to raise standards of living. They expect that development will create jobs for their people and will improve living conditions. They hope that industrialization will create the wealth that is needed to provide education and health-care services for their people.

Unfortunately, the road from developing nation to developed nation is a very difficult one to travel. The condition of the road itself is poor to begin with and only very gradually improves. There are many roadblocks and interruptions from outside along the way. Progress is often very slow, especially at first.

Roadblocks to Progress

A nation's geographical features can be helpful or not helpful to its development. Compare the map on page 439 to the climate map on pages 138 and 139. As you can see, a large number of the developing nations are located in the low latitudes, in or near tropical or subtropical regions, where climate conditions make work and development more difficult.

Deserts and dry grasslands receive little rain. Regions that are subject to monsoons receive too much or too little rain, depend-

Indians of Dehli shared hospitality but few customs with their British rulers.

ing on the season. The soil of tropical forests is often too fragile for wide-scale farming. In large parts of the tropics and the subtropics, so much effort must go into farming that little progress can be made in industrial development.

The world's resources are not equally distributed. Many developing nations lack minerals, such as iron ore and coal, that other nations have used to industrialize.

Historical factors have also hindered development. Almost all of the developing nations were once colonies of European countries, of the United States, or of Japan. Colonial authorities in foreign countries decided which crops to grow (those that were expected to produce the most profit with the least investment). They also decided which minerals to mine. The colonizers did not want their colonies to develop industries. Instead, they wanted them to provide raw materials and to serve as markets for manufactured goods that were made in the controlling nations.

Not until after World War II did most of the developing nations become independent. Only then could they begin to industrialize.

Internal political situations, too, can interfere with development. Because living conditions are not comfortable and circumstances are not stable, many developing nations have had frequent changes of government. Some are under the control of military leaders who overthrew elected governments. Others face the continuous threat of political uprisings. This political unrest further impedes economic development. It is hard to borrow money, to make investments, or to develop industry in a nation whose government might change overnight or whose people are rioting or waging guerrilla warfare against the government.

In some developing nations, political unrest has resulted from corruption within governments. The combination of great poverty and large opportunities for investment causes some government officials to steal vast amounts of money. Money that might have been spent for education or for health care has instead enriched officials and their friends, who take unfair advantage of their privileged access to money.

Conflicts among groups of people within a developing nation have sometimes impeded development. For example, one group may support industrial growth. Another group may resist such efforts because its members believe that traditional ways are simpler and better than modern ways.

During the 1970s, this kind of clash occurred in Iran in the Middle East. There, the *shah*, or emperor, was working for rapid development. Some groups within the country, however, believed that development threatened traditional values. They rose up and made the shah leave the country.

Religious or ethnic conflict can also hinder development. In the developing countries, there are many ethnic groups, or groups that are united by race, nationality, language, and customs. In Africa, for example, the country of Uganda is made up of the peoples of four major ethnic groups. In Asia, the country of India is sharply divided along religious lines: part Hindu and part Muslim. Ethnic or religious differences can stand in the way of the cooperative efforts that are required for economic development.

Another important factor is size. More than 25 of the developing countries are smaller than Connecticut. More than 55 have fewer people than Chicago. A small territory and a small population can work against economic development. Little land means little fertile soil and possibly few natural resources. A small population limits the pool of labor available for development.

Sources of Money for Development

As you have learned, development requires vast sums of money. Advanced technology, including machinery, is very expensive. So are roads, schools, and hospitals. From what sources are the developing nations to get such large sums of money? One source is a favorable **balance of trade**. The term *balance of trade* describes the difference in value between a country's sales of goods to outsiders (exports) and its purchases of goods from outsiders (imports). A *favorable* balance of trade occurs when a nation exports more goods than it imports. When imports are greater than exports, however, a nation is spending more than it is earning in international trade; money is leaving a country faster than it is coming in, and so, its balance of trade is *unfavorable*.

Unfortunately, many developing nations have unfavorable balances of trade. Money that flows out of countries that buy more than they sell drains off funds that could otherwise be invested in development.

To improve their balances of trade, developing nations often must sell raw materials—their natural resources. If they get good prices and if their supplies are ample and are marketed wisely, this method of solving the problem will work. If not, the sale of nonrenewable natural resources can be disastrous.

About 25 years ago, a group of developing nations formulated a plan that was designed to improve their balances of trade. They were all rich in a natural resource that was much in demand—oil. Yet, they were

Chile has developed its industrial strength by exporting large amounts of copper to other nations.

not satisfied with the prices that they received for oil that was sold on the world market. They also were concerned that they would run out of this resource one day—oil is a nonrenewable resource.

They therefore wanted to obtain the highest possible price for their oil as long as the oil lasted. They wanted to use this wealth to develop their economies. They hoped that by the time the oil ran out, they would have better-balanced, healthier economies.

In 1960, these nations joined together to form the Organization of Petroleum Exporting Countries (OPEC). OPEC controls a major part of the world's oil production. By forging agreements among member states, the organization decides how much oil to produce each year and how much to charge for it. During the 1970s, OPEC raised the price of oil. From $2.30 a barrel in 1972, the price rose to $32 in 1981.

OPEC has proved to be a mixed blessing for its members. The industrialized nations were distressed by having to pay such high prices for oil. Thus, they encouraged non-OPEC oil companies to explore for other sources of oil. They also tried to develop alternative energy sources, such as solar power. Finally, they tried to reduce significantly the amount of oil that they used. The sale of small, fuel-efficient cars boomed throughout the industrialized world.

As a result of measures that were taken to reduce the use of oil, the demand for OPEC oil decreased. Oil prices dropped, causing problems for some member states that had spent or borrowed too much money when things were going more easily. When the price of oil was high, OPEC nations had

begun expensive development programs. When the price was cut, they had to give up some of their programs because they could no longer pay for them or for the interest charges on their development loans.

Foreign Money

Developing nations need, and usually welcome, foreign investment to help finance development. Large corporations with headquarters in developed countries invest in developing nations. Because they operate in many nations, they are called **multinational corporations**. Such corporations build factories and roads, and open mines. They do so to use the cheap labor and raw materials in developing countries.

Investments made by multinational corporations provide jobs in a developing nation and can also speed industrial development. Multinational corporations, however, take profits from their businesses in developing countries. Profits go to their headquarters in developed countries, and thus do not contribute as much to national development as they might if the developing country owned the business.

Multinational banks will lend money to companies and to governments in the developing nations. Anyone who borrows pays for the use of the money in the form of **interest** charges. Both the borrower and the lender expect a firm that borrows to start or to enlarge a business to produce profits, and part of the profits will go to pay the interest charges and to repay the loan. Once the loan is repaid, the rest of the profit is kept by the borrower.

What would happen, however, if profits

were not made, or if they were too low to repay the loan? What would happen if the borrowed money ended up in the bank accounts of dishonest politicians or were wasted by incompetent managers who did not know how to run businesses? What would happen if worldwide interest rates rose so high that borrowers found it difficult to pay the interest and impossible to repay the loans themselves? These possible situations have become actual problems for both the developing nations and the banks that lent the money to them.

Mortgaging the Future

Faced with a desperate need for money, some tropical and semitropical developing countries have felt forced to sell renewable natural resources faster than such resources can be renewed. In these countries, the sale of rain-forest trees for lumber is a practice that has had such negative results.

Cutting down rain forests is harmful in both the short run and the long run. In the short run, it ruins the soil because the cleared soil does not remain fertile for very long. Heavy rains leach out its nutrients. In addition, without trees to hold the soil in place, the soil soon erodes under the force of the rains. After only a few seasons, the soil can no longer be used productively.

In the long run, the clearing of trees destroys the entire biome. With the loss of soil, the natural vegetation cannot grow back. Animals lose their homes and food sources. Even the climate changes when trees are cut down. When no trees shade the ground, temperatures rise. Moisture evaporates under the hot sun, so, humidity de-

clines and there is less rainfall. A nation that cuts down its rain forest is made poorer rather than richer. You will read more about this problem in the next chapter.

In this lesson and in Lesson 1, you have learned the characteristics of developing nations and have read about some of the difficult problems that they face in their development. In the next three lessons, you will look at three developing countries—Nigeria, Indonesia, and Brazil. You will read about the problems of development that each country faces and about how each country is trying to solve them.

Lesson 2 Review

Recalling Information

1. Give examples of three factors that have prevented some of the countries from developing.
2. Describe three ways in which a nation might speed its development. Give the drawbacks of each way.

Interpreting Information

3. Do you think that it is possible for every nation of the world to become a developed country? Why or why not?
4. What effect do you think that foreign investment has on a developing nation?

Applying Information

5. Which geographical factors in your area were advantageous to development?
6. Could our nation have become highly industrialized if it lacked raw materials? Explain.

Special Feature
Citizenship: The Peace Corps

Botswana needs medical technicians. Rice farmers in Nepal need to improve the yield of their crops. Kenya needs carpenters and machinists. How can people in developing nations obtain the skills and the practical know-how that are needed to raise their standards of living?

One thing that they can do is to use the resources of the Peace Corps. The Peace Corps is a foreign-aid program that was created in 1961 by President John F. Kennedy. The Peace Corps sends American volunteers to developing nations throughout the world. Some volunteers teach subjects such as English and mathematics; others train workers in useful skills. Others help to supervise community projects that are designed to improve health care, transportation, and food production. The Peace Corps is dedicated to achieving one goal: helping developing nations to help themselves.

Lesson 3

NIGERIA

Look at the map of Nigeria on this page. Which nations border it? Is it above or below the equator? Does it have any coastline, or is it landlocked?

This West African country is about the size of California, Arizona, and Nevada combined. It is neither a huge nation nor a small one; yet, it is the most populous nation in Africa. With about 90 million people, Nigeria has more than one-third the population of the United States. Rich in natural resources, especially oil, Nigeria is considered to have a good chance to become a developed country by the year 2000.

The Land and Its People

Nigeria includes parts of two biomes—savanna in the north and tropical rain forest in the south. It can also be divided into four climate and geographic zones. Along its coast is a belt of low, hot, humid, swampy land. This is poor farmland, but the area is rich in oil deposits and has several fine ports, including Lagos, the capital city.

Farther inland is an area of tropical forest, much of which has been cleared for farming. North of this forest, the land rises to a dry central plateau that is primarily savanna. Much of this region—most of northern Nigeria—is used for farming and for grazing. It also contains rich deposits of coal, iron, tin, and other minerals. A number of industries are being developed in the plateau region.

The far north consists of a very dry, de-

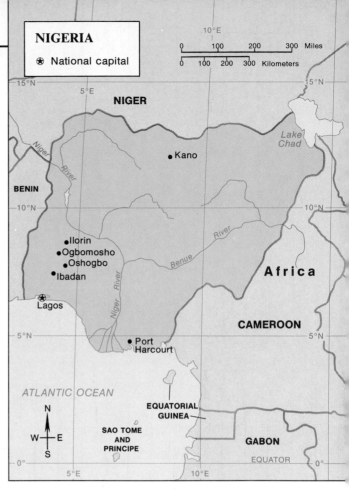

MAP SKILLS: How might Nigeria's two great rivers serve the country's development?

sertlike region that borders the Sahara. This inhospitable land is the least populated part of Nigeria.

Nigeria's boundaries are the result of its history as a colony. Starting in the mid-1800s, the British took control, bit by bit, of what is now Nigeria. In 1914, the British government merged the areas that it controlled into a single colony. When Nigeria became independent in 1960, it kept these boundaries. In doing so, it became a nation of many different ethnic groups. It faced the problems of trying to achieve a working government out of the diverse groups.

Nigeria includes about 250 ethnic groups

Nigeria uses its oil revenues to finance new factories, schools, and hospitals.

who speak more than 200 languages. The largest groups are the Hausa and the Fulani in the north, the Ibo in the southeast, and the Yoruba in the southwest. In addition to speaking different languages, each group has its own culture. Traditional suspicions and even hatreds that were felt by some groups toward other groups have made political unification a major problem for Nigeria.

Other Problems and Prospects

Literacy remains low in Nigeria. Only about one-third of the people can read and write. How does illiteracy make development more difficult?

Infant mortality in Nigeria is high. One infant in eight dies before reaching his or her first birthday. Life expectancy is only 41 years. Yet, the population is growing at a rapid rate. As farmland becomes more crowded, people from rural areas pour into the capital city of Lagos and into other cities. City governments are finding it almost impossible to cope with problems of housing, sanitation, and health care. If the population continues to grow at such a rapid rate, Nigeria will have to double its food production by the year 2000 to avoid famine.

Like many other developing countries, Nigeria considers industrialization to be a way of obtaining money to expand education and health services, to increase agricultural production, and to provide jobs for its rapidly growing population. Since independence, it has made considerable progress toward industrial development. It has begun to take advantage of its rich mineral resources. Manufacturing—including steel production, auto assembly, textiles, and food processing—has grown in importance. Today, manufacturing accounts for about 10 percent of Nigeria's GNP.

Much of the industrialization that Nigeria has accomplished has been financed by oil exports. Oil alone accounts for one-fourth of Nigeria's GNP and for 90 percent of its exports. In other words, oil brings in almost all of the revenue that Nigeria receives from world trade. Unfortunately, the demand for oil has fluctuated in recent years. In the 4-year period from 1980 through 1983, Nigeria's oil revenue decreased from a peak of $24 billion to $10 billion. By 1984, the government had to reduce its spending and to raise taxes to make up for the huge loss of oil revenue. As a result, programs to support new manufacturing and to improve health and education had to be curtailed, and development was slowed.

Even during times of high oil income, much money was lost to political corruption. In the early 1980s, dishonest government officials siphoned billions of dollars of oil revenue from the treasury.

Nigeria has also suffered from political instability. The extent of the problem can be appreciated from the following summary of major political events that have occurred since independence.

Major Political Events

1966: A group of military officers, mostly Ibo, overthrew the government and established military rule. Seven months later, non-Ibo officers overthrew that government.

1967: The Ibo declared their region in the Southeast to be independent of Nigeria. They set up the Republic of Biafra. Three years of civil war followed. A million people, mostly Ibo, died in the fighting or from starvation.

1975: Still another military rebellion took place. A government was established that promised to restore civilian rule.

1978-1983: Political unrest, assassinations, and corruption wracked the country.

1984: The military took over the government again. About 500 politicians, including the elected president and the vice president, were jailed. Later, they were tried for corruption.

Nigeria has many resources, including oil, enough farmland to feed its people if the land is well managed, and a large enough population to support an industrial economy. Nevertheless, grave political and economic problems have held back development.

Lesson 3 Review

Recalling Information

1. What are Nigeria's greatest resources that can be used to promote industrial development?
2. Name three of Nigeria's most serious problems.

Interpreting Information

3. How can technology help a developing nation such as Nigeria?
4. In what ways did British colonialism lead to problems for Nigeria after independence?

Applying Information

5. Suppose that you were the president of Nigeria and had to deal with all its complex problems. What would you do to help your country?
6. Should the United States and other developed countries help Nigeria on its road to development? If so, how? If not, why not?

INDONESIA

Look at the map of Indonesia on the facing page. As you can see, it is composed of many islands. The 13,600 islands stretch along the equator for 3,000 miles (4,829.9 km). The distance between the ends of the Indonesian island chain is greater than the distance between New York City and Los Angeles. In land area, Indonesia is a bit more than twice the size of Nigeria.

Like Nigeria, Indonesia is a country of many different peoples. More than 300 ethnic groups make up this far-flung island nation.

Its population of about 157 million makes Indonesia the fifth-largest country in the world. This figure may well reach more than 200 million by the year 2000.

The Land and Its People

All of the islands of Indonesia are in the equatorial zone, the hottest part of the tropics. All of Indonesia lies in a tropical rain-forest biome. Its climate zone is wet tropical, and most of the country receives very heavy rainfall from monsoons. Monsoon rains can make farming difficult. Many of the areas that have been cleared of their natural rain-forest cover suffer greatly. The heavy rains leach minerals from the soil and even wash the soil away. Sometimes, the wet season brings too much rain, and the dry season brings too little, and agricultural production is disturbed.

Even so, agriculture is Indonesia's major economic activity. About 65 percent of the nation's workers are engaged in agriculture. Many work in plantation farming, raising crops—rubber, coffee, sugarcane, and tea—for export. Many others are subsistence farmers who often grow rice as their major crop. Their farms are very small, usually no more than 1.5 acres (0.6 ha).

Indonesia's most heavily farmed island is Java. Find it on the map. Java is also the most heavily populated island in the country. Although it covers only 7 percent of Indonesia's land, Java contains nearly three-fifths of the population. With 91 million people living in an area that is the size of New York State, Java is one of the most crowded places on Earth.

Progress and Problems

Indonesia was a European colony—the Netherlands East Indies—until 1949. Since then, the nation has made enough economic progress for it to be considered a middle-income nation. It has a per capita GNP of about $600. That may not sound like much, but it would be enough for Indonesians to live fairly comfortably if the nation's wealth were more evenly distributed. That, however, is not the case. As is the case in almost all developing nations, Indonesia suffers from having much of its wealth concentrated in the hands of a few very rich people. This rests the burden of poverty on almost 40 percent of the population.

The progress that Indonesia has made can be traced to the export of its extensive mineral resources, including tin, nickel,

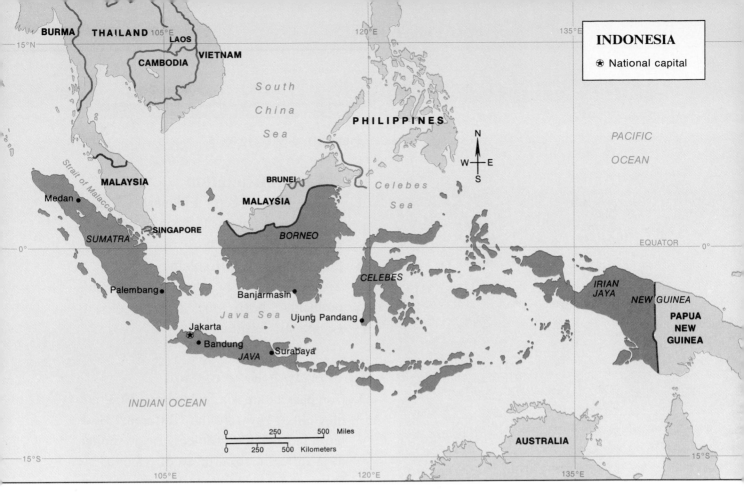

MAP SKILLS: Indonesia consists of a chain of 13,600 islands. What are the names of the oceans and seas which surround them?

bauxite, copper, oil, and natural gas. The sale of oil and natural gas alone provides 80 percent of Indonesia's income from exports.

Although it yields profits, the sale of raw materials does not create large numbers of jobs. Indonesia is trying to develop a balanced economy and to create jobs by promoting growth in other industries, such as tobacco processing, textiles, food processing, clothing, and chemicals.

In the early 1970s, when profits from the sale of oil were increasing, the Indonesian government was able to put considerable money into the development of new industries. With the decline in the worldwide demand for oil in the 1980s, however, oil profits fell and industrial growth slowed.

Another problem that the Indonesian government has tried to solve is the great concentration of its rapidly growing population on one island. Java is becoming more and more unmanageable because of overcrowding. The government has attempted to get more people to migrate from Java to other islands, such as Irian Jaya. Locate it on the map on this page. Few people live there, and 90 percent of the land is still covered with rain forest.

Javanese farmers, however, have resisted attempts to be relocated. Even though the

A palm oil plantation in North Sumatra, Indonesia. Which industries use palm oil?

farmers could have more land in Irian Jaya, the soil there is not as fertile as the soil of Java. On Java, they say, you can poke a stick into the ground, and it will sprout and grow.

The government hoped that opening up farmland in Irian Jaya or on other less-used land would help Indonesia with another of its problems—the feeding of its rapidly growing population. Periodically, when crop production has been low, Indonesia has had to import huge amounts of rice. Money that might have been used to support industrial growth had to be spent for foreign-grown rice.

Lesson 4 Review

Recalling Information

1. What have been Indonesia's most pressing problems? How has the government attempted to solve them? Is the plan working? Explain.
2. To what extent have Indonesia's problems been the result of its geographic location?

Interpreting Information

3. Compare Indonesia to Nigeria. How are they alike? How are they different? How have Indonesia's problems been similar to or different from those of Nigeria?
4. What might the Indonesian government do to encourage more farmers to migrate to less-populated areas? What might the effects be on the nation? What effect might the move make on Indonesia's environment? Explain.

Applying Information

5. Suppose that the United States, like Indonesia, consisted of over 13,000 islands. How would that have affected the development of the country? How might the government, the transportation systems, and the economic system be different for the people of the country?
6. If you were a Peace Corps volunteer, would you be more interested in going to Indonesia or to Nigeria? Explain the reasons for your choice.

Lesson 5

BRAZIL

In the early 1970s, Brazil looked as if it would become an industrial giant. Rich in varied natural resources and benefiting from a thriving agricultural system, it had already become the leading industrial nation in Latin America. Its economy was growing rapidly, with no signs of slowing.

Yet, by the early 1980s, Brazil was deeply in debt to other nations. Its miraculous development had faltered. Several setbacks occurred to this promising nation, as you will see. They showed how difficult it can be for a developing nation to sustain development, even after a very promising start.

The Land and Its People

Find Brazil on the map. As you can see, Brazil covers almost half of the South American continent. That makes it larger than the 48 connected states of the continental United States. Like Nigeria, Brazil lies in two biomes. The northern biome consists mainly of tropical rain forest. The southern biome consists of savanna. Most of the country has a warm and wet climate throughout the year.

Brazil has two major landforms. One consists of the lowlands that surround the Amazon River and its tributaries in the north and in the west. The other landform consists of the highlands in the northeast and in the south, which are fairly level plateaus. Locate these areas on the map on this page.

MAP SKILLS: What can Brazil's landowners do to foster both economics and wildlife?

Brazil's lowland area is called the Amazon River Basin or the Amazon region. As you know, it is the largest tropical rain forest in the world, and it may potentially be Brazil's richest single resource. Covering nearly one-half of the country, the Amazon region is a giant greenhouse of both trees and undergrowth. The vast expanse of trees is one of the world's greatest producers of oxygen. Why is this so? What does this mean for the rest of the world? The region is also a valuable timber reserve. Recently, rich mineral deposits have been discovered there as well. This adds to Brazil's already immense wealth in natural resources.

How does the new Brazilian city of Belo Horizonte show its people's love of nature?

The population of Brazil is about 130 million, the largest in Latin America and the sixth-largest in the world. Because Brazil was once a colony of Portugal, Portuguese is its official language. Brazilians are members of a variety of ethnic groups. About 60 percent of Brazil's population comes from Portuguese or other European stock. Blacks, who are descended from slaves, are another important element of the population, as are Indians and Asians.

About 90 percent of the population of Brazil lives along the Atlantic coast, between the city of Fortaleza and the border with Uruguay. Find the southeastern section of Brazil on the map on page 455. Rela-

tively cool temperatures, fertile soil, and rich deposits of minerals have made this plateau region the economic center of Brazil. Half of Brazil's industry—mainly automobile making and steel making—is located there, as are many coffee plantations and cattle ranches.

Progress and Problems

Brazil's development has been built on its rich natural resources. Vast reserves of iron ore feed the nation's growing iron and steel industry. Brazil also has large deposits of bauxite, manganese, copper, gold, and other important minerals.

Agriculture accounts for about 9 percent of Brazil's output. You may know that Brazil is the largest producer of coffee in the world. You may not know, however, that Brazil happens to be the third-largest exporter of frozen chickens and the second-largest exporter of orange juice in the world. Meat products from Brazil's cattle ranches are also important exports to the nations of the world.

Brazil's development reached a peak between 1968 and 1973. During those years, the Brazilian gross national product (GNP) grew at an average rate of 11 percent a year. At that rate, national economic productivity most likely can double in fewer than seven years.

Problems began when OPEC first raised its oil prices. Although Brazil has other abundant natural resources, it produces less than one-fifth of the oil that it uses. It has to import the rest to keep its industries running. Beginning in 1973, Brazil had to pay higher prices for oil. To make matters worse, a winter frost in 1975 killed half of the coffee plants in Brazil. Many farmers were ruined, and Brazil lost half of the revenues that it had expected to receive from its most important agricultural export. These drastic developments reversed Brazil's balance of trade from favorable to unfavorable.

Brazil began to borrow money to finance its unfavorable balance of trade. It invested the borrowed money in income-producing projects. The government expected these projects to earn enough money to pay the interest on the loans and the loans themselves. Unfortunately, the projects did not yield profits, and Brazil had to borrow more money.

The Brazilian government began to tighten the nation's belt. Imports were reduced, and the government tried to increase exports to achieve a favorable balance of trade.

By the mid-1980s, another economic miracle seemed to be developing. Coffee growers had recovered from the big freeze, and production was increasing. Many farmers switched from coffee to another cash crop—soybeans, which are easier to grow. Brazil began to export soybeans.

Increased steel production and growth in manufacturing yielded more revenue from exports. By 1984, Brazil was exporting $10 billion more in goods than it imported. It began to pay its huge debts.

Despite these signs of some economic recovery, Brazil still faces many problems that may plague it for a long time. For example, wealth is unevenly distributed, and poverty is widespread. Millions of poor Brazilians are crowded into the slums of the nation's cities. Because they are uneducated and unskilled, these people either earn low wages or are unemployed.

Brazil also faces problems in the Amazon region. Each year, large areas of the rain forest are logged for timber or cleared for farmland. Mines are opened up, and roads are cut through the rain forest to provide access to the fields. The results have been losses of certain plant and animal species, the rapid loss of soil fertility, and the destruction of habitats.

Lesson 5 Review

Recalling Information
1. What advantages does Brazil have that have helped it to develop? What are its chief disadvantages?
2. What was the economic miracle?

Interpreting Information
3. In what ways is Brazil similar to the United States? How is it different?
4. In what ways will Brazil's development continue to be influenced by developments elsewhere?

Applying Information
5. If you were in charge, how would you reduce Brazil's need for foreign oil?
6. How was your community affected by the increase in OPEC oil prices in the 1970s? What effects did the price increases have on people you know?

Skills for Thinking

RECOGNIZING THE TECHNIQUES OF PROPAGANDA

Most of us value the right to express our opinions. Propaganda is similar to the stating of opinions, but it is different in two important respects.

- Propaganda is organized. It is a campaign that is designed to gain public support for one point of view. The purpose of propaganda is to mold public opinion.
- Propaganda is deliberately designed to appeal to such feelings as hope, fear, love, and patriotism.

Some governments use propaganda to help them to achieve political goals. For example, the government of the People's Republic of China has used propaganda to keep order and to urge citizens to clean up public places. Slogans have urged the Chinese people to "practice hygiene, to observe discipline, and to strive to be a civilized person."

What Is Propaganda's Influence

Different techniques are used to present propaganda. One positive technique is called the testimonial. In the testimonial approach, someone who is well known is shown or is quoted as favoring a program or a policy. An approach that is designed to play on the insecurities of people is called the bandwagon technique. It encourages the public to support a policy because everyone else supports it. It tries to persuade individuals that they will be isolated from everyone else in society if they fail to conform to others' opinions.

The following examples show how propaganda was used by the government of the People's Republic of China in a campaign that was designed to promote good citizenship. Read each example, and then identify the propaganda approach that is used in each appeal. In what ways was it designed to mold public opinion?

1. The Communist party chairman is televised sweeping the streets to launch a cleanup campaign.
2. A newspaper writes about bus drivers who have volunteered to spend their day off scrubbing the capital of the People's Republic of China.
3. People are urged to follow the example of Lei Feng, a soldier who performed many selfless deeds for his country.

Chapter 22 Review

Summary of Key Facts

In this chapter, you learned that

- agriculture is the major economic activity in developing nations.
- much of the farming in developing nations consists of subsistence farming and plantation farming.
- developing nations often lack balanced economies, and most of the population is poor.
- developing nations often have one-crop economies.
- developing nations have low literacy rates, high infant mortality rates, and short life expectancies.
- about three-fourths of the world's people live in developing nations.
- geography, natural and human resources, and history—especially technology, political situations, and cultural values—affect a country's state of development.

Using Vocabulary

On a separate sheet of paper, write the term that will correctly complete each sentence.

developing   developed
literacy   balance of trade
per capita   multinational

1. A _____ nation is one with a high GNP.

2. _____ corporations operate throughout the world.
3. A nation that exports more than it imports has a favorable _____ .
4. To find _____ GNP, you divide GNP by the population.
5. The ability to read and write is called _____ .
6. A _____ nation is one that is characterized by an unbalanced economy, a lack of industry, a rapidly growing population, and, often, widespread poverty.

Discussing the Chapter

1. Why are some nations less developed than others?
2. What are some methods that a country can use to promote development?
3. Why do rich natural resources not guarantee wealth?
4. What has prevented Nigeria from becoming a developed nation? Explain.
5. What problems stand in the way of Indonesia's development? Brazil's?

Reviewing Skills

Write two examples of propaganda that might be used in an advertisement that is designed to persuade people to buy a certain brand of soap. Each example should be based on a different technique.

Future Prospects

Vocabulary

ecologist	gene
trade-offs	annuals
acid rain	perennials
famine	passport
desalination	

Lesson Preview

Lesson 1: Taking Stock in a Changing World

Lesson 2: Choices in a Technological Age

Lesson 3: Some Problem Solvers

Introduction

Knowledge and power meet in one;
For where the cause is not known,
The effect cannot be produced.
Nature, to be commanded,
Must be obeyed.

These lines were written in 1605 by an Englishman, Sir Francis Bacon. During his lifetime, discoverers and inventors made great technological advances that concerned Bacon.

Arguing that knowledge is power, Bacon said that knowing the *causes* of a problem will lead to a solution. The application of Bacon's idea could help us to solve global problems that have been caused by technology.

In earlier chapters, you read how the use of technology increased human power over the environment. This power can destroy land, pollute air and water, and strain valuable resources.

Changes are happening so fast that people have not had time to work out effective ways of coping with them. The challenges are enormous. So, too, are the human and the technological resources that we have to solve global problems. Individuals, groups, and governments throughout the world are searching to find solutions.

High-power microscopes are among the tools used in Libya to help to develop new plant breeds to feed the country.

TAKING STOCK IN A CHANGING WORLD

For as long as anyone remembers, the people of Malaysia have eaten a fruit called the *durian*. It grows on trees in the rain forests there. Lately, durians are becoming hard to find. Malaysians have been chopping down their forests. Yet, that alone does not explain why the remaining durian trees are not yielding much fruit. Changes in the environment have also directly affected the durian crop.

In the past, bats that nested in limestone caves in nearby mountains pollinated the durian trees as they flew from flower to flower to gather nectar. This method of pollination made it possible for the trees to bear fruit. When durian trees were not in bloom, the bats fed on mangrove trees along the coast.

Not long ago, workers from a cement factory began to dig limestone from the bats' caves. At about the same time, people felled large sections of mangroves to make ponds for shrimp farms and for rice paddies. The bats began to disappear when their habitat was disturbed, and the durian trees stopped producing fruit.

Technological Gains and Losses

The situation in Malaysia is just one example of how humans can upset the balance of nature. You have examined the life-support systems of various biomes. You know that all life forms are connected. The removal of one tree will bring about only a small change in the environment. If an entire forest is removed, however, the change would be great. A different environment would be created. The loss of a forest is greater than the loss merely of its trees. It includes the loss of all the animals that depend on the trees and the loss of all the animals that depend on those animals. Thus, a forest ecosystem is destroyed whenever its trees are destroyed.

More than 20 years ago, Paul Sears warned that humans were reshaping Earth. He said that people, through the power of their numbers, their intelligence, their machines, and their command of energy, had "become a geological force."

Paul Sears is an **ecologist**. An ecologist is a scientist who studies ecology, or the relationship between living things and their environments. Ecologists are alarmed because technology is altering the environment of Earth.

Although technology has produced global problems, it has also yielded tools to study, to understand, and to solve them. Until recently, for instance, scientists who study rain forests lacked information about how fast the forests were being cut in the 76 countries where they grow. In the 1970s, orbiting *Landsat* satellites began to make detailed photographs of remote areas of Earth. By studying the photos and other forms of data, scientists were able to analyze the problem. They concluded that every year, 60,617.7 square miles (157,000 sq km) of rain forest are cleared. That means that an area as large as England and Wales together changes from forest to cleared land every year. This is bound to

Redwood trees in a California forest overlook logging roads. How does this landscape symbolize a world situation of today?

have an enormous impact on life on Earth.

Let us review briefly what the nations of the world have gained through technology. Let us also look at the **trade-offs**. A trade-off is a choice that is based on a comparison of benefits and costs.

Environmental Trade-offs

Technology has given the people of developed nations the highest standards of living in history. It has also improved the quality of life for many people. In countries such as the United States, machines do most of the back-breaking work that people once had to perform. Other machines zip through routine tasks such as tallying a day's cash-register receipts. Machines have freed many

people to do more rewarding work.

You read in Chapter 18 that the industrialized nations trade with the rest of the world. Technology made global trade possible. World trade allows people in a country that does not have a resource to buy it from one that does.

Technology has made global communication immediate and more effective. It links people all over the world by letting them hear the same singers and groups, see the same movies, and receive important news bulletins simultaneously.

Technology has improved our ability to do work. Computers have produced a revolution in the organization, the processing, the storage, and the retrieval of information.

They help to design spacecraft, to run machinery, and to forecast weather.

You can probably think of many examples that could be added to this short list of benefits that are obtained from modern technology. Can you also think of examples of costs that have been incurred by the introduction of technology?

Dishwashers, computers, televisions, headphones, stereo systems, and plastic garbage bags all use resources. Industrial nations devour huge amounts of Earth's resources. Many of Earth's resources are limited. We have reached some limits already. We will reach others soon. There is a limited amount of oil, coal, copper, and other minerals that can be used to supply energy and materials to industry. As more countries become industrialized, these non-renewable resources will be used up faster.

Waste and massive air and water pollution are some of the major costs that are incurred by the reckless use of technology. As we use our resources at an ever-increasing rate, at the same time, we pollute and spoil our environment.

When rain and snow fall, they deposit chemicals from polluted air onto trees, grass, buildings, and people. These chemical substances kill fish and eat into trees. **Acid rain** is the popular name for such precipitation. Acid rain is precipitation that is mixed with sulfur dioxide and nitrogen oxides. Most of these pollutants come from the burning of fossil fuels such as oil and

Computers are now commonly found in homes. Libyan students (below) use modern technology.

464

coal. These acids mix with snow, hail, sleet, fog, frost, and rain.

Sweden is downwind of the big industrial centers of Western Europe. Perhaps as many as 20,000 Swedish lakes have no fish because acid rain poisoned their waters.

Trade-offs in Developing Countries

In Chapter 22, you learned about some of the problems and the successes of developing countries. In many of these countries, technology has improved the daily lives of the people. More people in developing countries today live longer lives, are healthier, and are better educated than in the past. In some developing countries, food production has also increased.

In recent years, scientists have developed plant seeds that resist diseases and are more productive than older seed varieties. This "green revolution" has sharply increased the amount of food that was grown in developing lands. Since 1950, the world production of food has doubled.

What are the trade-offs? First, the rapid change to a high-tech world has upset many local cultures. Societies have shifted from traditional, rural ways of life to the lifestyle of the computer age in one generation. In many places, people copied Western ways when they adopted Western technology. Young people turned their backs on their own histories and traditions. Many are now trying to restore their cultural identities

Automobiles are a convenience, but what trade-offs do they require in our lives? How would you change the trade-offs being made between industry and environmental protection?

Landless and poor, many of Calcutta's residents also face problems found in other cities: unemployment, illness, and hunger.

while retaining the material benefits of Western technology.

Rapid population growth is another result of improved technology. Medical advances have added years to human lives. The populations of some of Earth's poorest lands are growing at the fastest rates.

People who are hungry often go elsewhere to look for food and work. Many people in the rural areas of developing countries move to cities every year, even though such cities are far less efficient than cities in developed countries.

Newcomers strain the resources of the cities. They need food and housing but cannot afford to buy them. Their children need schooling. In many developing nations, cities are growing faster than the capacity of their governments to provide needed services.

History is filled with solutions that people devised to overcome enormous problems. In the next lesson, you will learn about how people are facing the challenges of the future.

Lesson 1 Review

Recalling Information

1. Name three environmental problems created by technology.
2. What are trade-offs? Give an example.

Interpreting Information

3. Name some resources that you use regularly. Are they renewable or nonrenewable? What impact does using such resources have on the environment?
4. What actions could the leaders of an overcrowded city such as Bombay or Mexico City take to ease overcrowding? If your proposed program would cost money, suggest where it is to come from.

Applying Information

5. Assume that a large factory is to be built near you. It will create many jobs. What might some of the trade-offs be?
6. What do you consider to be the most important problem in the world today? How does this problem affect you?

Lesson 2

CHOICES IN A TECHNOLOGICAL AGE

When Iroquois leaders had to make an important decision that would affect the governing of their people, they asked a question: How would the decision affect the seventh generation to come? How would it affect any of the great-great-great-great-great-grandchildren of those making the choice?

The Iroquois tried to project themselves into the far future. They tried to conceive of every possible result of their actions. They thought not only of immediate gains but also considered how their actions would affect the future of their people in generations to come.

You have seen how the actions of one group of people can alter the environment and the lives of others. You have also seen how the enormous power of industrial nations has shaped our world. You know that all life is interconnected. Technology and world trade have made all the nations of the world dependent on one another for survival and prosperity.

What can people do to solve their problems in a global age? We have seen that the first step in solving a problem is to understand it. Throughout the world, individuals, groups, and nations are studying Earth's problems. Year after year, some answers are found; some problems are solved or at least reduced. New problems arise which have not been anticipated, and solutions for them have to be found.

Biologist and author Rachel Carson. How has *Silent Spring* helped conservationism?

Individual Efforts

In 1958, a friend invited Rachel Carson, a biologist and a writer, to visit the friend's small bird sanctuary (a protected place). Late one afternoon, a plane flew low over the sanctuary and sprayed DDT to kill mosquitoes. The next morning, Rachel Carson guided a boat through the marshes. She saw dead and dying fish everywhere. Crabs and crayfish lay dead or twitching helplessly, their nervous systems ruined.

Rachel Carson's host urged her to "write about this." She wrote *Silent Spring*, which was published in 1962. This book caused an uproar and alerted people to the unexpected costs of using chemicals to kill weeds and insects.

467

Earth Day, 1970. Why must awareness of the threats to nature often be promoted in cities?

Farmers used chemical sprays to kill insects, to stop fungus, and to control weeds. Poisons such as DDT saved human lives by killing insects that carried malaria, typhus, and other fevers. These poisons had been hailed as miraculous.

Rachel Carson pointed out the unexpected trade-offs. Poisons that were used on land to kill pests washed out of the soil into rivers and lakes. There, they entered the cells of living things that fed in the waters.

Rachel Carson's work shows how much one informed person can do. You will read about some of the work of other individuals in Lesson 3.

Group Efforts

By the start of the 1970s, a great many people around the world realized the dangers that were associated with polluting the environment. At the start of the decade, a group of young Americans had an idea. They said that since there were days that are devoted to mothers, fathers, veterans, and many other people and things, there should be a day reserved to think about and celebrate Earth.

They announced that April 22, 1970, would be Earth Day. They contacted all groups and organizations that worked to protect wildlife and the environment. They encouraged everyone to think of ways in which to celebrate Earth Day.

About 20 million Americans participated in Earth Day. Earth Day helped to make the general public aware of ways to protect Earth and its living and nonliving resources.

Since the first Earth Day, the environmental movement has enlisted millions of people. New groups have been formed throughout the world to find answers to environmental problems. Older conservation and wildlife groups, such as the National Audubon Society, the World Wildlife Fund, and the Sierra Club, gained thousands of members. Young people attended classes in environmental studies and in ecology. Today, a new generation of environmental scientists is working to find more facts and more answers.

Environmental groups sponsor research. They publish newsletters and magazines that spread information about the work that scientists are doing. They send experts to testify before legislative committees. They bring lawsuits to stop polluters.

Environmental groups are leading the worldwide effort to save the endangered species. For many, the rallying symbol of the effort is the whale. These huge mammals have been hunted for centuries. With modern technology, however, they can be tracked by radar in huge factory ships and harpooned by explosive missiles. Today, whales face extinction. By the 1970s, many species of whales were on the verge of dying out.

Treaties that were drawn up to save the remaining whales have been signed by most nations of the world. In addition, many individuals and groups have worked to obtain a ban on whaling, but an organization called Greenpeace has made the most headlines. At risk to their lives, its members travel in small boats to those expanses of the ocean where whaling is done. These dangerous expeditions have not only interfered with whaling operations but have also served to publicize the plight of whales and other endangered species.

Private organizations are also working to solve other global problems such as hunger, poverty, illiteracy, and disease. Several work with international agencies to feed the hungry of the world. Oxfam was started in Oxford, England, to aid victims of **famines** (drastic and widespread food shortages) after World War II. Today, Oxfam workers provide vitamins, food, and medicine to victims of famine. Oxfam has also set up agricultural and educational projects in developing countries.

Engineers at a Virginia waste-treatment plant work above a 10-million-gallon (37,850,000-L) tank.

National Efforts

Throughout the world, individuals have started groups that have joined with larger groups to fight for some cause. Often, they have enlisted enough support to pass laws. Many nations have enacted laws to protect wildlife and the environment.

In the 1960s, the Thames River, which flows through London, was so filthy that it could not support most life forms. The government began a major effort in 1964 to clean the river. Strict laws were passed to stop industries from dumping chemical wastes into the river. The government built advanced sewage-treatment plants.

469

A desalination plant in Saudi Arabia. Notice the solar panels on the roof. Why is solar power a wise investment in this region?

The Thames revived gradually. Fish returned. Even salmon, which can live only in very clean waters, swam upstream. Water birds reappeared to fish for food. In 1984, for the first time in 150 years, a seal was spotted swimming past the houses of Parliament in the heart of the old city.

Environmentalists like to tell the story of the Thames when people say that our problems are too complex to solve. Once the English people understood the sources of pollution and acted to stop it, the river began to revive.

Saudi Arabia and other nations of the Middle East do not have polluted water. Instead, they lack fresh water. They are spending some of their oil income on research to find better ways to desalt, or remove the salt from, seawater. Research into **desalination** may be of great value to many areas that are near oceans but lack fresh water.

Population Growth

Some people believe that soaring population growth is one of the most serious problems of our time. Many nations run educational programs to encourage people to have small families. In many less-developed countries, such programs have not halted runaway population growth. A few, however, have made some progress.

The People's Republic of China has more than one billion people—almost one-fourth of the human race. Historically, China, which is about the size of the United States, has suffered from famines because much of its land is mountainous or too dry to farm. Only one-tenth of its land is arable, or suitable for tilling and growing crops.

The first modern census of the Chinese population was completed in 1982. It showed that there were 100 million more people than the government had realized. The population was growing even faster than had been feared and much faster than the economy could grow. If such population growth continued, the nation would get poorer and poorer.

The government has, therefore, promoted a policy of one child per family. Under the new program, China's population growth has been reduced. Other nations are examining China's success to determine whether to start similar programs. The Chinese program is controversial. China is a communist country that has a totalitarian government which dictates policies that govern every aspect of life. Many people do not think that governments should develop policies about such personal matters as family size.

International Cooperation

Some problems extend beyond national borders. They require international, regional, and even global cooperation. People and nations differ on issues. These differences have led to conflicts, even to war.

At the end of World War II, the United Nations (UN) was formed to promote peace and international cooperation. It tries to settle international conflicts through negotiation rather than war. Other UN agencies

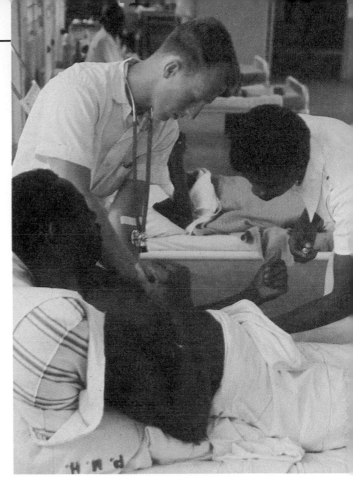

What special education do you think this Peace Corps volunteer brings to his work?

give technical aid to nations. The World Health Organization (WHO) provides medical assistance to developing nations. The Food and Agricultural Organization (FAO) helps these nations to improve farm production. The World Bank lends money at low interest rates to developing nations.

The International Union for the Conservation of Nature (IUCN) is an international organization with environmental concerns. Working together with UNEP, its UN counterpart, it has produced a strategy for world conservation.

Nations are also linked in a variety of regional or special-interest organizations. The Organization of American States (OAS) and the Organization of African Unity (OAU)

471

INTERNATIONAL ORGANIZATIONS

Members of OPEC

Algeria	Iran	Nigeria
Ecuador	Iraq	Qatar
Gabon	Kuwait	Saudi Arabia
Indonesia	Libya	United Arab Emirates
		Venezuela

Members of the OAS

Antigua and	Costa Rica	Haiti	St. Vincent and
Barbuda	Cuba	Honduras	the Grenadines
Argentina	Dominica	Jamaica	Suriname
Bahamas	Dominican	Mexico	Trinidad and
Barbados	Republic	Nicaragua	Tobago
Bolivia	Ecuador	Panama	United States
Brazil	El Salvador	Paraguay	Uruguay
Chile	Grenada	Peru	Venezuela
Colombia	Guatemala	St. Lucia	

Members of the OAU

Algeria	Egypt	Libya	Seychelles
Angola	Equatorial	Madagascar	Sierra
Benin	Guinea	Malawi	Leone
Botswana	Ethiopia	Mali	Somalia
Burkina	Gabon	Mauritania	Sudan
Burundi	Gambia	Mauritius	Swaziland
Cameroon	Ghana	Morocco	Tanzania
Cape Verde	Guinea	Mozambique	Togo
Central African	Guinea-	Niger	Tunisia
Republic	Bissau	Nigeria	Uganda
Chad	Ivory Coast	Rwanda	Zaire
Comoros	Kenya	São Tomé and	Zambia
Congo	Lesotho	Principe	Zimbabwe
Djibouti	Liberia	Senegal	

From which three continents do the members of OPEC come?

are examples of regional organizations that promote the interests of their member states. Many oil-producing nations are members of OPEC.

The people of the world work together in less formal and more limited ways as well. Several years ago, for example, scientists from all nations cooperated during the International Geophysical Year, a year-long study of our planet. What they learned about Earth may help to solve some environmental problems. Scientists share their knowledge across national boundaries. Even the United States and the Soviet Union have cooperated in space-exploration missions.

From a spacecraft, Earth's political barriers are not apparent. As underseas explorer

Jacques Cousteau said:

Space exploration has brought us a most precious gift—global consciousness. However fragmented the world, however intense the national rivalries, it is an inexorable [undeniable] fact that we become more interdependent every day.

Lesson 2 Review

Recalling Information

1. Describe one group effort to help to solve some of the problems of the world.
2. List some of the evidence that proves that the River Thames is no longer polluted. Who cleaned it up?

Interpreting Information

3. Which of the problems that you have been reading about might someone in a developing country think was the most urgent? Why? Would someone in an industrialized country make the same choice? Why or why not?
4. Of all of the world's problems, which is most likely to cause conflicts, even war, between nations? Why?

Applying Information

5. Name organizations in your community or state that are working on environmental problems. What successes have they had?
6. What contributions could you and your friends make to one of the problems discussed in this chapter? Be specific.

Special People

Barbara Ward

Barbara Ward believed that rich nations had the major responsibility of helping poor nations to develop healthy economies if the world was to live in peace. The British economist and author argued that all nations are financially interdependent. She warned that continuing unrest would result if the ever-widening gap between the rich nations and the poor nations was not narrowed in the immediate future.

As an advisor to both the United Nations and the World Bank and as a lecturer, a professor, and an author, Barbara Ward's far-sighted ideas reached millions of people. She is known for her ability to make complex issues understandable to the average person. Many government leaders and scholars were influenced by her advice. United States President Lyndon Johnson acknowledged that he had read her book *The Rich Nations and the Poor Nations* with great interest.

After a lifetime of international influence and honors, Barbara Ward died in 1981. Her ideas live on. Financial and technical assistance that is given by rich countries to poor countries is now commonly accepted world policy.

Temperate but endangered planet, enjoys weather, northern lights, continental drift, seeks caring relationship with intelligent lifeform.

Write to us for a free brochure at
1045 Sansome St., San Francisco, CA 94111.
FRIENDS OF THE EARTH

Environmental-protection groups use modern advertising techniques to aid their cause.

Lesson 3

SOME PROBLEM SOLVERS

The advertisement in the photograph above appeared recently in the newspaper of an environmental group. The ad invited people to join a national organization, the Friends of the Earth, because "you can make a big difference."

In the last lesson, you read that people are beginning to realize that they can do something to tackle environmental problems. Many individuals and groups are working to protect our future. We shall look more closely at how some "intelligent life forms" are making a difference.

Preserving Plants and Habitats

At the dawn of the agricultural age in the Americas, the people in Mexican valleys learned to save and to plant the seeds of wild maize, or corn. Over many centuries, Native Americans cultivated corn. They shared their knowledge with European settlers. From these beginnings came all the corn that is grown in the world today.

In the last few decades, plant scientists have crossbred many strains of corn. To *crossbreed* means "to breed two varieties of the same species." The resulting plant is called a hybrid. Today, American farmers use these hybrids to grow three times as much corn as their grandfathers did.

Some trade-offs are involved in developing new varieties of plants, however. The new varieties do not always have the same defenses against insects and diseases as older varieties. Botanists (plant scientists) believe that it is important to save original wild strains of plants in order to preserve their **genes**. Genes are elements that control the passing along of characteristics from one generation of living things to another. If a strain of plant dies out, the characteristics controlled by its genes cannot be passed on. Grain banks have been started to preserve samples of the genes of all known grains.

Concern over the extinction of plants has led to the search for original strains of the grains that we eat. A few years ago, Mexican and American botanists were studying plants in a remote forest in southwestern Mexico. Rafael Guzman of the University of Guadalajara in Mexico and Hugh Iltis of the University of Wisconsin led the team. They found a surprising kind of wild corn, which they named *Zea diploperennis*.

This corn turned out to be not only the most primitive relative of modern corn ever discovered but also proved to be unique in its growing habits. Modern hybrid corn is an **annual** plant. Annuals grow from seeds that are planted each year. After they are harvested, such plants die. New seeds must be planted every year if crops are to grow. The maize found high in the Mexican hills is a **perennial** plant. Perennials continue to live year after year. They do not die in winter, though they may lose their leaves.

Tests of the wild corn indicated several

Another ear of Mexico's wild maize is being selected for agricultural tests.

Past and Present

Consider these facts:

● **Roughly 250,000 species of higher plants exist on Earth.**

● **Some 70% of these plants exist in the tropics, mainly in rain forests. (For instance, a mature rain forest may contain as many as 2,300 species of trees alone. A temperate forest, by comparison, may have no more than seven to 15 species.)**

● **About 80,000 species of plants are known to be edible, and most come from rain forests.**

● **Yet fewer than 200 of these are used commercially, and of these 200, 16 provide 90% of the world's food.**

It is obvious that rain forests are treasure chests of genetic material. Yet how are they being used today? Vast acres are being cut down and replaced by farms. The genetic material that they hold gets discarded or burned for fuel.

other benefits. Wild maize resists disease much better than modern hybrid corn. Also, wild corn grows naturally at unusually high elevations—7,000 to 10,000 feet (2,133.6 to 3,048 m). It may be possible to develop a new disease-resistant hybrid that could grow at higher altitudes than modern hybrids. Perhaps, it may even be possible to obtain a breed of corn that will not have to be replanted each year.

So far, botanists have found only a few thousand stalks of *Zea diploperennis* that were growing. Settlers, loggers, and grazing animals all threatened to destroy the corn. Doctor Maria Luz Puga of the University of Guadalajara succeeded in getting some of the habitat of the wild maize set aside as a scientific preserve.

These birds are thick-billed murres that are nesting to raise their young on Digges Island, Canada. How does the study of their migrations and habits help us to protect them for the future?

Preserving Animals

Seventeen teams of American volunteers traveled to northeastern China in 1983 and 1984. Their job was to count species of birds at the vast Zha Lung marsh.

Zha Lung is bounded by the Heilong and the Ussuri rivers that flow along China's border with the Soviet Union. The marsh is one of the largest freshwater wetlands on Earth. Located just east of the dry Mongolian plains, Zha Lung's 560,000 acres (226,632 ha) have been reserved for wildlife. Every year, thousands of migrating water birds pause at Zha Lung. Among them are Siberian cranes, a species that consists of no more than 300 survivors.

Doctor George Archibald has devoted his life to protecting endangered cranes and their habitat. To him, working at Zha Lung is a dream come true.

From the late 1960s to the mid-1970s, the Chinese government ordered people to kill birds. Chairman Mao Zedong said that birds ate food needed by humans. Since he could not then get into China, Doctor Archibald went to South Korea, where he spent each winter of the 1970s studying the migrating flocks of cranes. He noticed fewer and fewer young cranes. He and his co-workers feared that the Zha Lung marsh was being drained for farmland.

In 1977, policies in China changed

abruptly, and the government began to set up nature preserves. In 1979, Zha Lung was set aside as a sanctuary, and George Archibald and others were invited to China to discuss how to save endangered birds.

Preserving Cultures

What happens when a traditional people who have lived in isolation for generations encounter rich tourists and advanced technology? Often, such people adopt new ways and their own culture is swallowed up.

The Ladakhis of northwestern India could meet that fate unless they take care to preserve their culture. Helena Norberg-Hodge, an American language expert, has been helping the Ladakhis to do just that.

Until 1975, the land of the Ladakhis, on the eastern side of the Himalayas, had been closed to outsiders. Helena Norberg-Hodge and a team of anthropologists were among the first to visit the high, dry area. They found the Ladakhis leading a self-sufficient, healthy life. They were raising barley and wheat on small plots of irrigated land and living in small houses made of adobe and wood.

As the Ladakhis met the outsiders, they became fascinated with the wealth and the ways of the modern world. Their own ways began to seem primitive to them. Helena Norberg-Hodge was aware of their self-doubts and wanted them to achieve some benefits of the modern world without discarding their own. She helped to bring solar technology to the Ladakhis to heat their homes efficiently.

So far, the Ladakhis have adopted new ways without discarding important old ones.

The modern world can learn from the Ladakhis, who have kept their culture for thousands of years without spoiling their environment. No modern people have done this.

The work of people such as Helena Norberg-Hodge, Rafael Guzman, and George Archibald shows that people care deeply about the fate of our shared planet and that people can make a difference.

Lesson 3 Review

Recalling Information

1. How does the wild corn that was found recently in Mexico differ from modern corn? What is its benefit?
2. Name three international organizations and three private organizations that are working to solve global problems, and state what they are doing.

Interpreting Information

3. If a friend were to say that there is nothing that one person can do about world problems, what would you reply?
4. Why is it desirable to preserve people's cultures and values? Name some important aspects of American culture and state why they should be preserved.

Applying Information

5. What things have been done in your community or in your state to protect plants, animals, and their habitats?
6. What global issue is most adversely affecting your life right now? What can be done about the problem?

Skills for Thinking

FILLING OUT A FORM

Someday soon, you may travel to another country. Before you leave, you will need a special government document that is called a **passport**.

You will be asked to present your passport when you enter other nations. You will also be asked to present your passport when you return to the United States. Among other things, your passport will

- identify your citizenship.
- state your date of birth and your place of birth.
- describe your physical appearance.

What Facts Are Needed and Why?

Study the sections of a passport application form that are shown here. Which sections ask for facts about your citizenship? About your physical appearance? How can you prove that you are a citizen?

Most of the facts about your physical appearance will be recorded on your passport. Find that part of the application form that requires you to attach your photograph. Why do you suppose that the Passport Office requires both a photograph and a written description of the physical appearance of each applicant?

As with all applications, your application for a passport will be processed most promptly if you complete the form legibly and correctly. Copy the passport-application sections that are shown here. Fill in the blanks with the facts. Follow the directions carefully. Which sections are to be filled in only by the Passport Office?

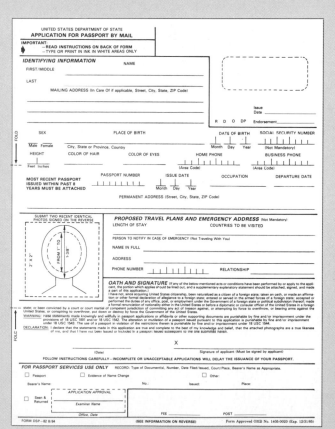

Chapter 23 Review

Summary of Key Facts

In this chapter, you learned that

- many human actions disturb the balance of nature.
- reshaping the environment produces trade-offs that might not have been anticipated.
- as more nations industrialize, the use of nonrenewable resources will increase.
- rapid population growth strains Earth's resources and creates problems for developing nations.
- the first step toward solving global problems is to understand them.
- individuals, working alone and in groups, can help to solve global problems.
- all nations are interdependent. Groups from many nations work together to help to solve environmental problems.

Using Vocabulary

On a separate sheet of paper, rewrite the following sentences, correcting the errors in the definitions.

1. A *trade-off* is a choice that is based on an attempt to balance renewable and nonrenewable resources.
2. *Ecology* is the study of animal life in an environment.
3. The source of *acid rain* is runoff from polluted watersheds.

4. A *perennial plant* grows from seeds that are planted each year.

Discussing the Chapter

1. Why is it necessary to understand the causes of a problem?
2. Explain how technology has improved the lives of people in developing nations. What more can it do?
3. How are rapid population growth and limited resources related?
4. Describe some forms of world cooperation around global problems.
5. Why is it important to preserve unspoiled environments?
6. What evidence demonstrates that some global problems can be solved through technology and cooperative decision making?

Reviewing Skills

1. What documents can you submit to prove that you are a United States citizen when you apply for a passport?
2. To what agency does a citizen apply for a United States passport?

Unit 7 Review

Summary of Key Facts

In this unit, you learned that

- in many developing nations, agriculture is the major economic activity.
- the gross national product measures the value of a nation's goods and services.
- about three-fourths of the world's people live in developing nations.
- a harsh climate, a lack of resources, and political instability may keep a country from developing.
- technology has solved some problems and created others.
- technology can help to solve some of the problems that it has created.
- individuals, working alone and in groups, can help to solve global problems and resolve global conflicts.

Discussing the Unit

1. Why is poverty a characteristic feature of a developing nation?
2. In what ways has the new post-industrial age brought countries closer together?
3. How have political conditions, size, and geography slowed development?
4. Describe two world problems and proposals that have been made to solve them.
5. How does an organization such as OPEC function?
6. Explain some of the trade-offs involved in the use of technology.

Activities

1. Make a list of services or conditions in your community that you think should be improved. Discuss your list in class, and decide how you would improve each service or condition.
2. Use your school library to do a case study on a developing nation. Research the population, the climate, the resources, and the industries of the nation. Share your findings with the class.

Test

Using Vocabulary

On a separate sheet of paper, write the term that will correctly complete each sentence.

developing nations   trade-off
gross national product   ecologist
colonies   acid rain
multinational corporations   famine

1. The ____ is the value of all of the goods and services that are produced by a nation.

2. An ____ is a scientist who studies the relationship between living things and their environments.

3. ____ is precipitation that is mixed with sulphur dioxide and nitrogen oxides.

4. Countries that have begun to build their own industries are called ____ .

5. Almost all of the developing nations were ____ .

6. Worldwide companies are called ____ .

7. A ____ is a choice that is based on an attempt to balance such factors as benefits and costs.

8. A ____ is a drastic and a widespread shortage of food.

The Big Question

What are the main global issues that face our world today?

Write your answer in complete sentences. Draw upon the information in this unit to write a good answer.

Using Map Skills

Use the map on page 453 to complete this exercise.

1. Name the five main islands that form the nation of Indonesia. What sea joins these islands?

2. Which of the islands are occupied by more than one nation?

3. What island nation is north of Celebes?

4. What is the national capital of Indonesia? On which island is it located?

Identifying a Geographic Theme

Think about the geographic theme of **human-environment interactions** as you complete this exercise.

Compare how the people of developing nations relate to their environment with the way people in developed nations relate to theirs.

481

Asia

Europe

ARCTIC OCEAN

GREENLAND
[KALAALLIT·NUNAAT]
(DEN.)

ICELAND

ALASKA (U.S.)

Fairbanks
Anchorage

Dawson

Juneau

Thule

Baffin
Bay

ARCTIC CIRCLE

ATLANTIC OCEAN

Godthaab
(Nuuk)

CANADA

Great
Bear Lake

Yellowknife

Great
Slave Lake

Hudson
Bay

Labrador
Sea

Churchill

Schefferville
Goose Bay

PACIFIC OCEAN

Edmonton

Gander
St. John's

ST. PIERRE AND
MIQUELON (FR.)

Victoria
Vancouver
Seattle
Portland
Spokane

Calgary

Regina

Lake
Winnipeg

Winnipeg

Thunder Bay

Quebec
Montreal
Ottawa

Great
Lakes

Halifax

Minneapolis
St. Paul
Milwaukee
Detroit
Chicago

Toronto
Buffalo
Cleveland

Boston

New York
Philadelphia
Baltimore

San Francisco

Great
Salt Lake

Salt Lake
City

Denver

Kansas
City

Cincinnati
St. Louis

Washington, D.C.
Norfolk

UNITED STATES OF AMERICA

Los Angeles
San Diego

Phoenix

El Paso

Dallas

Memphis

Atlanta

BERMUDA (U.K.)

ATLANTIC OCEAN

Houston
New
Orleans

San
Antonio

Gulf
of Mexico

TROPIC OF CANCER

BAHAMAS

TURKS AND CAICOS ISLANDS (U.K.)

PUERTO RICO (U.S.)
VIRGIN ISLANDS (U.S.) (U.K.)
ANTIGUA AND
BARBUDA

Monterrey

MEXICO

Havana

CUBA

DOMINICAN
REPUBLIC
HAITI
Port-au-
Prince
Santo
Domingo

DOMINICA

ST. KITTS AND NEVIS
MONTSERRAT (U.K.)
GUADELOUPE (FR.)
MARTINIQUE (FR.)
ST. LUCIA
BARBADOS

Guadalajara

CAYMAN ISLANDS
(U.K.)

JAMAICA
Kingston

Caribbean Sea

Mexico City
Veracruz

Acapulco

BELIZE
Belmopan

ST. VINCENT AND THE GRENADINES
GRENADA
TRINIDAD AND
TOBAGO

NORTH AMERICA: POLITICAL

⊛ National capital

GUATEMALA
Guatemala
San Salvador
EL SALVADOR

HONDURAS
Tegucigalpa

NICARAGUA

Managua

NETHERLANDS ANTILLES (NETH.)

Panama
Canal

0   250   500   750   1000 Miles

0 250 500 750 1000 Kilometers

San José

COSTA RICA

San
Panama
City

PANAMA

PACIFIC OCEAN

N
W   E
S

South America

EQUATOR

NORTH AMERICA: PHYSICAL

Elevations

Feet	Meters
13,100	4,000
6,600	2,000
1,600	500
700	200
0	0
Below sea level	Below sea level

▲ Mountain peak

483

WEST INDIES

Caribbean Sea

Central America

PACIFIC OCEAN

Barranquilla
Cartagena
Maracaibo
Barquisimeto
Valencia
Caracas
San Cristóbal
Ciudad Bolívar
VENEZUELA
Orinoco R.
Georgetown
Paramaribo
GUYANA
SURINAM
Cayenne
FRENCH GUIANA (FR.)
Medellín
Bucaramanga
Bogotá
Cali
COLOMBIA

EQUATOR

GALAPAGOS
ISLANDS (EC.)

Quito
ECUADOR
Guayaquil

Iquitos

Manaus
Amazon R.
Belém

Trujillo
Chimbote
PERU

BRAZIL
Recife

Callao
Lima
Cuzco
Lake Titicaca

Arequipa
La Paz
Lake Poopó
BOLIVIA
Santa Cruz
Sucre
Potosí

Salvador

Brasília

Belo
Horizonte

TROPIC OF CAPRICORN

Antofagasta

PARAGUAY
Asunción
Paraná R.
São Paulo
Rio de Janeiro

N
W—E
S

Tucumán

Córdoba
Paraná
Rosario
Mendoza
Valparaíso
Santiago
CHILE

ARGENTINA
Concepción

Bahía Blanca

Pôrto Alegre
URUGUAY
Buenos Aires
La Plata
Montevideo

PACIFIC OCEAN

ATLANTIC OCEAN

Strait of Magellan

FALKLAND ISLANDS (U.K.)

ATLANTIC OCEAN

SOUTH AMERICA: POLITICAL

⊛ National capital

| 0 | 250 | 500 | 750 | 1000 Miles |

| 0 | 250 | 500 | 750 | 1000 Kilometers |

WEST INDIES

Central America

Caribbean Sea

ATLANTIC OCEAN

PACIFIC OCEAN

Maracaibo · · Caracas

· Georgetown
· Paramaribo *DEVIL'S ISLAND*
· Cayenne

Bogotá ·

L L A N O S

G U I A N A H I G H L A N D S

EQUATOR

GALAPAGOS
ISLANDS

Quito ·
Mt. Chimborazo
20,561 ft. (6,267 m)

*Gulf of
Guayaquil*

A
N
D
E
S

M
O
U
N
T
A
I
N
S

· Belém

S E L V A S

Cape
São Roque

Mt. Huascarán
22,205 ft. (6,768 m)

· Recife

Mt. Yerupaja
21,765 ft. (6,634 m)

Lima ·

A
N
D
E
S

PLATEAU OF
MATO GROSSO B R A Z I L I A N

Arequipa ·   · La Paz

H I G H L A N D S

· Brasília

· Sucre

TROPIC OF CAPRICORN

Antofagasta ·

N
W   E
S

A
T
A
C
A
M
A

D
E
S
E
R
T

C H A C O

· Asunción

· Rio de Janeiro
· São Paulo

Mt. Ojos del Salado
22,539 ft. (6,870 m)

Mt. Aconcagua
22,834 ft. (6,960 m)

· Córdoba

Valparaíso ·   · Rosario
Santiago · Mt. Tupungato
22,310 ft. (6,800 m)

P
A
M
P
A
S

· Montevideo

Buenos
Aires ·

Rio de la Plata

PACIFIC OCEAN

*Gulf of
San Matías*

Mt. San Valentín
13,314 ft. (4,058 m)

P
A
T
A
G
O
N
I
A

ATLANTIC OCEAN

FALKLAND ISLANDS

*Strait
of Magellan*

TIERRA
DEL FUEGO

Cape Horn

SOUTH AMERICA: PHYSICAL

Elevations

Feet		Meters
13,100		4,000
6,600		2,000
1,600		500
700		200
0		0
Below
sea level		Below
sea level

▲ Mountain peak

| 0 | 250 | 500 | 750 | 1000 Miles |

| 0 | 250 | 500 | 750 | 1000 Kilometers |

485

ATLANTIC OCEAN

ARCTIC OCEAN

30°N 40°N 50°N 60°N 70°N 80°N 10°W 0° 10°E 20°E 30°E 40°E 50°E 60°E 70°E 80°E 90°E

ARCTIC CIRCLE

Lisbon

PORT.
SPAIN
Madrid

AND.
Marseilles
MONACO
CORSICA
(FR.)
Barcelona

Europe
FRANCE
Loire
Paris
Brussels
BEL.
LUX.
Bern
SWITZ.

Dublin
IRE.
Glasgow
London
UNITED
KINGDOM
Amsterdam
NETH.

NORWAY
Oslo
SWEDEN
FINLAND
Helsinki

ITALY
SAN
MARINO
Milan
Rome
Naples

SARDINIA
(IT.)

Po R.
AUST.
Vienna
Munich
W.
GER.
Hamburg
E.
GER.
Berlin
Prague
CZECH.
HUN.
Budapest

DEN.
Copenhagen

Stockholm
Leningrad
Riga

Moscow
Gorki

Novosibirsk

UNION OF SOVIET SOCIALIST REPUBLICS

POLAND
Warsaw

Danube
YUGO.
Belgrade
ROM.
Bucharest

SICILY
(IT.)

MALTA

ALB.
Tirane
GREECE
Athens

BUL.
Sofia

Kiev

Kharkov

Odessa

Volga R.
Volgograd

Ural R.

Irtysh R.

Mediterranean Sea

CRETE
(GR.)

Istanbul

Black Sea

Caspian
Sea

Asia

Ankara
TURKEY

Urumchi

CYPRUS
Nicosia

SYRIA
Beirut
LEB.
Damascus
ISRAEL
Jerusalem
JORDAN
Amman

IRAQ
Baghdad

Euphrates R.
Tigris R.

Tehran

IRAN

AFG.
Herat
Kabul
Islamabad

Neutral Zone
KUWAIT
Al-Kuwait

PAKISTAN

New Delhi

NEPAL
Katmandu
BHUTAN
Thimbu

BAHRAIN
QATAR
Riyadh
Doha
U.A.E.
Abu Dhabi

Persian Gulf

Africa

Red Sea

SAUDI ARABIA
Mecca

YEMEN
San'a
Aden
P.D.R.
OF YEMEN

Masqat
OMAN

INDIA

Dacca
BAN.

Madras

Arabian Sea

Bay of
Bengal

TROPIC OF CANCER

SRI LANKA
Colombo

Male
MALDIVES

EQUATOR

N
W E
S

INDIAN OCEAN

10°E 0° 10°S 20°S

PACIFIC OCEAN

Abbreviations

AFG.	—AFGHANISTAN
ALB.	—ALBANIA
AND.	—ANDORRA
AUST.	—AUSTRIA
BAN.	—BANGLADESH
BEL.	—BELGIUM
BUL.	—BULGARIA
CAM.	—CAMBODIA
CZECH.	—CZECHOSLOVAKIA
DEN.	—DENMARK
E. GER.	—EAST GERMANY
HUN.	—HUNGARY
IRE.	—IRELAND
LEB.	—LEBANON
LIECH.	—LIECHTENSTEIN
LUX.	—LUXEMBOURG
NETH.	—NETHERLANDS
PORT.	—PORTUGAL
ROM.	—ROMANIA
SWITZ.	—SWITZERLAND
U.A.E.	—UNITED ARAB EMIRATES
W. GER.	—WEST GERMANY
P.D.R. OF YEMEN	—PEOPLE'S DEMOCRATIC REPUBLIC OF YEMEN
YUGO.	—YUGOSLAVIA

EURASIA: POLITICAL

✹ National capital

······· Disputed or undefined boundary

0   250   500   750   1000 Miles

0   250   500   750   1000 Kilometers

PACIFIC OCEAN

MONGOLIA

Ulan Bator

Okhotsk

SAKHALIN (U.S.S.R.)

Irkutsk

GREAT WALL

Beijing

Tientsin

N. KOREA

P'yongyang

Seoul

S. KOREA

JAPAN

Tokyo

PEOPLE'S REPUBLIC OF CHINA

Huang He

Grand Canal

Nanking

Shanghai

Wuhan

East China Sea

Chungking

Chang R.

Taipei

TAIWAN

TROPIC OF CANCER

Hsi R.

Canton

HONG KONG (U.K.)

Victoria

BURMA

Mandalay

Hanoi

LAOS

Vientiane

Irrawaddy R.

Rangoon

THAILAND

Bangkok

CAM.

VIETNAM

Pnompenh

Ho Chi Minh City

South China Sea

Quezon City

Manila

PHILIPPINES

Mekong R.

EQUATOR

MALAYSIA

BRUNEI

Bandar Seri Begawan

Kuala Lumpur

SINGAPORE

Singapore

INDONESIA

PAPUA NEW GUINEA

Port Moresby

Djakarta

ATLANTIC OCEAN

ARCTIC OCEAN

IRELAND

GREAT BRITAIN

Madrid

PYRENEES

BALEARIC IS.

CORSICA

SARDINIA

MALTESE IS.

SICILY

CRETE

Mediterranean Sea

Tyrrhenian Sea

Ionian Sea

Adriatic Sea

Aegean Sea

Europe

Alps

Mont Blanc

Paris

London

Berlin

Vienna

Rome

Budapest

Bucharest

Istanbul

BALKAN MTS.

CARPATHIAN MTS.

Warsaw

Black Sea

North Sea

Baltic Sea

Stockholm

Gulf of Bothnia

ORKNEY IS.

Norwegian Sea

Lapland

North Cape

Murmansk

Kola Peninsula

Barents Sea

NOVAYA ZEMLYA

Kara Sea

Leningrad

Moscow

URAL MOUNTAINS

Sverdlovsk

Novosibirsk

KIRGHIZ STEPPE

CASPIAN DEPRESSION

Caspian Sea

Asia

ALTAI MTS.

Volgograd

Aral Sea

Lake Balkhash

TIAN SHAN

Tashkent

TAKLIMAKAN SHAMO

KUNLUN SHAN

QING ZANG GAOYUAN

CAUCASUS MTS.

Mt. Elbrus 18,481 ft (5,633 m)

Mt. Ararat (5,185 m)

PLATEAU OF ANATOLIA

Asia Minor

CYPRUS

Jerusalem

ELBURZ MTS.

Tehran

PLATEAU OF IRAN

ZAGROS MOUNTAINS

Baghdad

Arabian Peninsula

Riyadh

Mecca

Persian Gulf

RUB'AL-KHALI

Gulf of Oman

Muscat

HINDU KUSH

Kabul

KARAKORAM RANGE

HIMALAYAS

Mt. Everest 29,028 ft (8,848 m)

New Delhi

THAR DESERT

Karachi

Aden

Red Sea

Gulf of Aden

Africa

TROPIC OF CANCER

EQUATOR

Arabian Sea

Bombay

Indian Subcontinent

WESTERN GHATS

EASTERN GHATS

Godavari

Ganges R.

Calcutta

Madras

Bay of Bengal

Colombo

SRI LANKA

MALDIVES

INDIAN OCEAN

N
W E
S

488

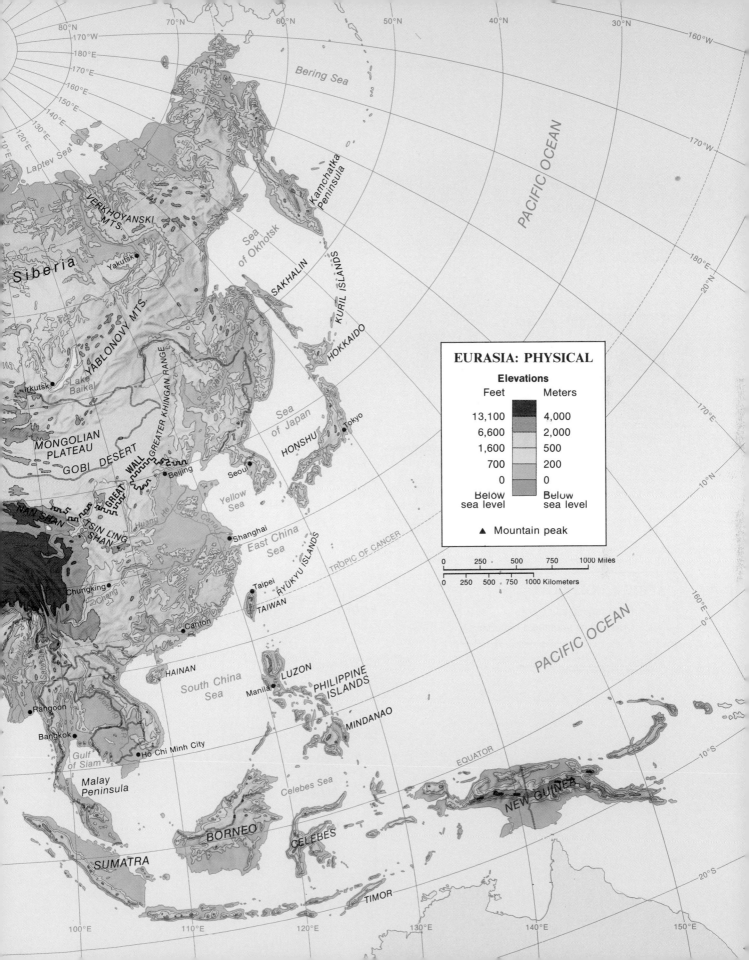

Bering Sea

80°N 70°N 60°N 50°N 40°N 30°N

170°W 180°E 170°E 160°E 150°E 140°E 130°E 120°E

PACIFIC OCEAN

170°W

Laptev Sea

VERKHOYANSKI MTS.

Siberia

Yakutsk •

Sea of Okhotsk

Kamchatka Peninsula

180°E

20°N

SAKHALIN

KURIL ISLANDS

YABLONOVY MTS.

Irkutsk •

Lake Baikal

HOKKAIDO

170°E

GREATER KHINGAN RANGE

MONGOLIAN PLATEAU

Sea of Japan

HONSHU

Tokyo •

10°N

GOBI DESERT

GREAT WALL

Beijing •

Seoul •

NAN SHAN

TSIN LING SHAN

Huang He

Grand Canal

Yellow Sea

Shanghai •

East China Sea

RYUKYU ISLANDS

EURASIA: PHYSICAL

Elevations

Feet	Meters
13,100	4,000
6,600	2,000
1,600	500
700	200
0	0
Below sea level	Below sea level

▲ Mountain peak

170°E

Chungking •

Chang

Canton •

Taipei •

TAIWAN

TROPIC OF CANCER

0   250   500   750   1000 Miles

0   250   500   750   1000 Kilometers

160°E

0°

PACIFIC OCEAN

HAINAN

South China Sea

Manila • LUZON

PHILIPPINE ISLANDS

Rangoon •

Bangkok •

MINDANAO

Ho Chi Minh City •

Gulf of Siam

EQUATOR

10°S

Malay Peninsula

Celebes Sea

NEW GUINEA

SUMATRA

BORNEO

CELEBES

TIMOR

20°S

100°E 110°E 120°E 130°E 140°E 150°E

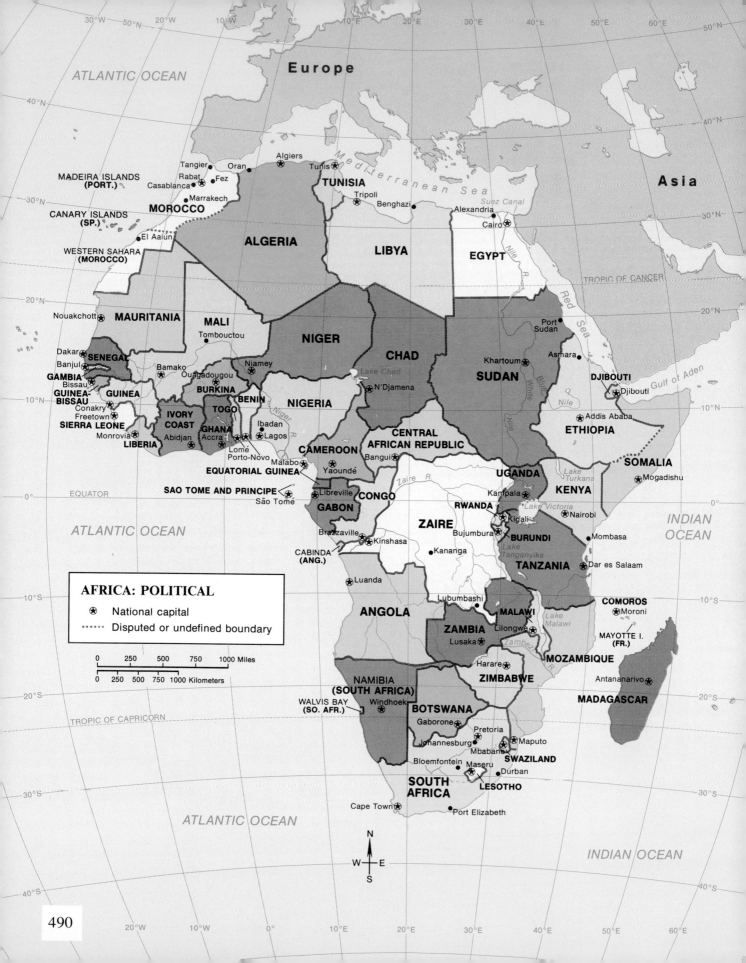

AFRICA: POLITICAL

✷ National capital

····· Disputed or undefined boundary

0	250	500	750	1000 Miles
0	250	500	750	1000 Kilometers

ATLANTIC OCEAN

Europe

Asia

Mediterranean Sea

MADEIRA ISLANDS
(PORT.)

CANARY ISLANDS
(SP.)

WESTERN SAHARA
(MOROCCO)

Tangier
Oran
Algiers
Tunis
Rabat
Fez
Casablanca
Marrakech
El Aaiun

MOROCCO

TUNISIA
Tripoli
Benghazi

ALGERIA

LIBYA

EGYPT
Alexandria
Cairo

Suez Canal

TROPIC OF CANCER

MAURITANIA
Nouakchott

MALI
Tombouctou

NIGER

CHAD

SUDAN
Khartoum
Port
Sudan
Asmara

Red Sea

Dakar
SENEGAL
Banjul
GAMBIA
Bissau
GUINEA-
BISSAU
GUINEA
Conakry
Freetown
SIERRA LEONE
Monrovia
LIBERIA

Bamako
Ouagadougou
BURKINA
Niamey
BENIN
TOGO
IVORY
COAST
GHANA
Abidjan
Accra
Lomé
Porto-Novo

NIGERIA
Ibadan
Lagos

Niger R.

N'Djamena
Lake Chad

CAMEROON

CENTRAL
AFRICAN REPUBLIC
Bangui

DJIBOUTI
Djibouti

Gulf of Aden

Addis Ababa
ETHIOPIA

SOMALIA
Mogadishu

White Nile
Blue Nile
Nile R.

EQUATORIAL GUINEA
Malabo
Yaoundé

SAO TOME AND PRINCIPE
São Tomé

Libreville
CONGO
GABON

Brazzaville
Kinshasa

ZAIRE

Kananga

UGANDA
Kampala
RWANDA
Kigali
BURUNDI
Bujumbura

Lake
Turkana

KENYA
Nairobi
Mombasa

Lake Victoria

Zaire R.

EQUATOR

ATLANTIC OCEAN

INDIAN
OCEAN

CABINDA
(ANG.)

Luanda

ANGOLA

Lubumbashi

TANZANIA
Dar es Salaam

Lake
Tanganyika

COMOROS
Moroni

MAYOTTE I.
(FR.)

ZAMBIA
Lusaka

MALAWI
Lilongwe

Lake
Malawi

Zambezi

MOZAMBIQUE

Harare
ZIMBABWE

Antananarivo

MADAGASCAR

NAMIBIA
(SOUTH AFRICA)

WALVIS BAY
(SO. AFR.)
Windhoek

TROPIC OF CAPRICORN

BOTSWANA
Gaborone

Johannesburg
Pretoria
Maputo
Mbabane
SWAZILAND

Bloemfontein
Maseru
LESOTHO
Durban

SOUTH
AFRICA

Cape Town
Port Elizabeth

ATLANTIC OCEAN

INDIAN OCEAN

N
W E
S

490

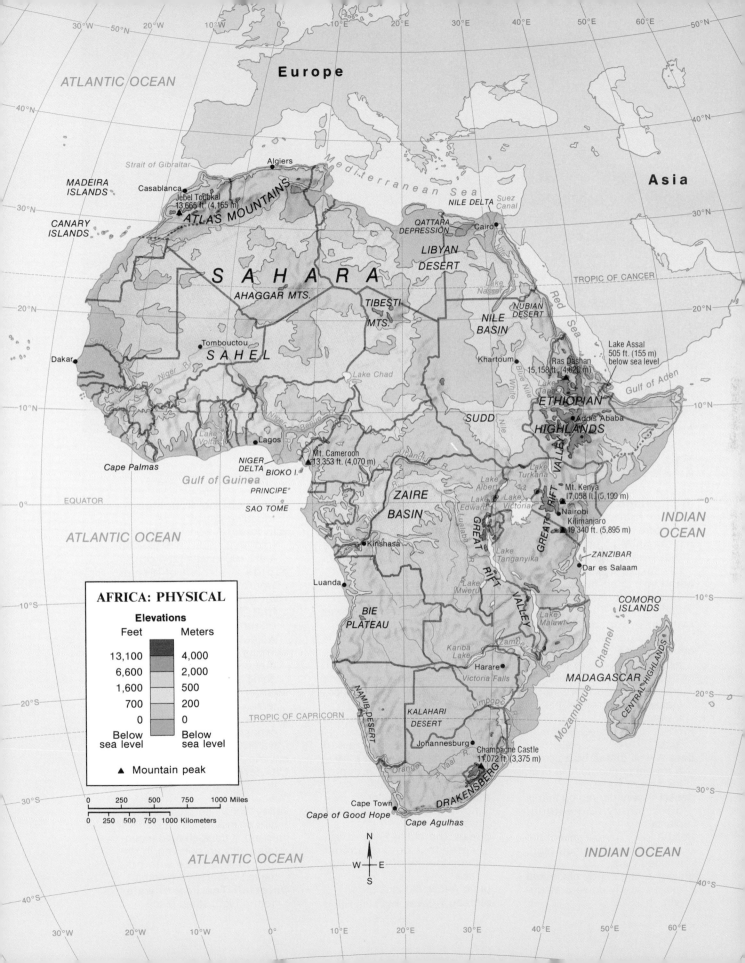

ATLANTIC OCEAN

Europe

30°W 20°W 10°W 0° 10°E 20°E 30°E 40°E 50°E 60°E

Asia

Strait of Gibraltar
Mediterranean Sea

MADEIRA
ISLANDS

Algiers

Casablanca

Jebel Toubkal
13,665 ft. (4,165 m)
▲ ATLAS MOUNTAINS

CANARY
ISLANDS

Suez Canal
NILE DELTA

Cairo

QATTARA
DEPRESSION

LIBYAN
DESERT

S A H A R A

Lake Nasser

TROPIC OF CANCER

AHAGGAR MTS.

TIBESTI
MTS.

NUBIAN
DESERT

Red Sea

NILE
BASIN

Lake Assal
505 ft. (155 m)
below sea level

Tombouctou

S A H E L

Dakar

Senegal R.

Niger R.

Lake Chad

Khartoum

Blue Nile

Ras Dashan
15,158 ft. (4,620 m)

Lake Tana

Gulf of Aden

ETHIOPIAN

White Nile

SUDD

HIGHLANDS

Addis Ababa

Lagos

Niger R. *Benue R.*

Lake
Volta

NIGER
DELTA

BIOKO I.

Cape Palmas

Gulf of Guinea

PRINCIPE

SAO TOME

EQUATOR

ATLANTIC OCEAN

Mt. Cameroon
13,353 ft. (4,070 m) ▲

Ubangi R.

ZAIRE
BASIN

Zaire R.

Kinshasa

Lake
Albert

Lake
Edward

GREAT

Lake
Turkana

Lualaba R.

Lake
Victoria

Mt. Kenya
17,058 ft. (5,190 m)

RIFT

Nairobi

Kilimanjaro
19,340 ft. (5,895 m)

GREAT RIFT VALLEY

ZANZIBAR

Dar es Salaam

INDIAN
OCEAN

Luanda

BIE
PLATEAU

Lake
Mweru

VALLEY

Lake
Tanganyika

Lake
Malawi

COMORO
ISLANDS

Mozambique Channel

MADAGASCAR

CENTRAL HIGHLANDS

Kariba
Lake

Zambezi R.

Harare

Victoria Falls

TROPIC OF CAPRICORN

NAMIB DESERT

KALAHARI
DESERT

Limpopo R.

Johannesburg

Orange R. *Vaal R.*

Champagne Castle
11,072 ft. (3,375 m)
▲

DRAKENSBERG

Cape Town
Cape of Good Hope

Cape Agulhas

ATLANTIC OCEAN

INDIAN OCEAN

AFRICA: PHYSICAL

Elevations

Feet		Meters
13,100		4,000
6,600		2,000
1,600		500
700		200
0		0
Below sea level		Below sea level

▲ Mountain peak

0 250 500 750 1000 Miles

0 250 500 750 1000 Kilometers

N
W — E
S

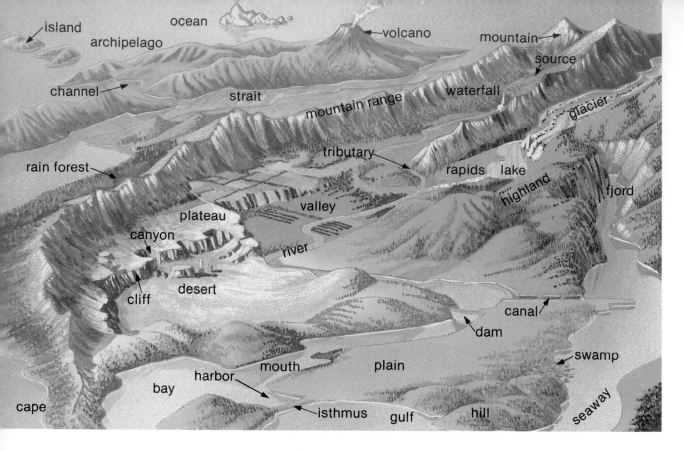

Dictionary of Geography Words

archipelago An expanse of water that contains many scattered islands.

bay A part of an ocean or lake that extends into land; usually smaller than a gulf.

canal A human-made waterway that is used for boats and irrigation.

canyon A deep, narrow valley with steep sides.

cape A piece of land that extends into a body of water.

channel A narrow stretch of water between two landmasses; the deepest part of a waterway.

cliff A high, steep slope of rock.

dam A wall that is built across a stream or river to hold back the flow of water.

desert A very dry region that is often sandy and without plants.

fjord A long, narrow inlet of the sea that lies between high, wooded cliffs.

glacier A large body of ice that moves slowly down a mountain.

gulf A part of an ocean that extends into land; usually larger than a bay.

harbor A sheltered area of water where ships can anchor safely.

highland An area of mountains, hills, or plateaus.

hill A raised landform; lower than a mountain.

island An area of land that is surrounded by water.

isthmus A narrow strip of land that has water on either side and connects two larger bodies of land.

lake A large body of water that is surrounded by land.

mountain A steeply raised landform; higher than a hill.

mountain range A group of connected mountains.

mouth The place where a river flows into a larger body of water.

ocean The entire body of salt water that covers almost three-fourths of Earth's surface.

plain A low, flat land area.

plateau A level, high land that

rises sharply from the surrounding area.

rain forest A wooded area that has an annual rainfall of at least 100 inches (254 cm).

rapids A stretch of a river where water flows quickly.

river A large stream of water that flows into a lake, an ocean, or another body of water.

seaway An inland waterway that can be used by ocean-going ships.

source The place where a waterway begins.

strait A narrow waterway that connects two larger bodies of water.

swamp A low wetland region.

tributary A stream or a river that flows into a larger waterway.

valley A lowland area between hills or mountains.

volcano A cone-shaped mountain, with an opening in the top, that is filled with hot, melted rock called magma.

waterfall The flow of water from a high, steep place.

Countries of the World

COUNTRY	POPULATION	POPULATION DENSITY	AVERAGE ANNUAL POPULATION GROWTH RATE	AVERAGE LIFE EXPECTANCY	GROSS DOMESTIC PRODUCT PER YEAR	AVERAGE ANNUAL PER CAPITA INCOME
Algeria	20,100,000	22 per sq mi (8 per sq km)	3.2%	53	$ 29 billion	$ 1,600
Angola	6,800,000	14 per sq mi (5 per sq km)	1.3%	39	$ 1.82 billion	$ 500
Benin	3,700,000	85 per sq mi (33 per sq km)	2.7%	41	$ 965 million	$ 230
Botswana	900,000	4 per sq mi (1 per sq km)	2.8%	45	$ 401 million	$ 544
Burkina	6,700,000	63 per sq mi (24 per sq km)	2.3%	38	$ 969 million	$ 160
Burundi	4,400,000	409 per sq mi (158 per sq km)	2.5%	41	$ 700 million	$ 171
Cameroon	8,900,000	48 per sq mi (19 per sq km)	2.6%	41	$ 5.2 billion	$ 628
Cape Verde	340,000	193 per sq mi (74 per sq km)	2.1%	45	$ 57 million	$ 200
Central African Republic	2,400,000	9 per sq mi (4 per sq km)	2.7%	40	$ 592 million	$ 257
Chad	4,600,000	10 per sq mi (4 per sq km)	2.4%	43	$ 540 million	$ 73
Comoros	400,000	477 per sq mi (184 per sq km)	2.5%	49	$ 92 million	$ 240
Congo	1,600,000	12 per sq mi (5 per sq km)	2.7%	44	$ 89 million	$ 500
Djibouti	500,000	59 per sq mi (23 per sq km)	9.2%	50	$ 331 million	$ 400
Egypt	44,000,000	116 per sq mi (48 per sq km)	2.7%	54	$ 26 billion	$ 560
Equatorial Guinea	300,000	28 per sq mi (11 per sq km)	2.3%	44	$ 112 million	$ 342
Ethiopia	30,500,000	65 per sq mi (25 per sq km)	2.4%	38	$ 4.07 billion	$ 117
Gabon	700,000	7 per sq mi (3 per sq km)	1.2%	39	$ 2.90 billion	$ 4,487
Gambia	635,000	138 per sq mi (53 per sq km)	2.8%	33	$ 198 million	$ 330
Ghana	12,400,000	135 per sq mi (52 per sq km)	3.3%	52	$ 10.1 billion	$ 380
Guinea	5,300,000	56 per sq mi (22 per sq km)	2.6%	41	$ 1.2 billion	$ 140
Guinea-Bissau	800,000	57 per sq mi (22 per sq km)	1.7%	34	$ 132 million	$ 170
Ivory Coast	8,800,000	71 per sq mi (27 per sq km)	3.4%	43	$ 9.8 billion	$ 1,153
Kenya	17,900,000	80 per sq mi (31 per sq km)	4.0%	51	$ 3.2 billion	$ 196
Lesotho	1,400,000	119 per sq mi (46 per sq km)	2.3%	46	$ 540 million	$ 355
Liberia	2,000,000	47 per sq mi (18 per sq km)	3.1%	46	$ 864.2 million	$ 453

COUNTRIES OF THE WORLD

COUNTRY	POPULATION	POPULATION DENSITY	AVERAGE ANNUAL POPULATION GROWTH RATE	AVERAGE LIFE EXPECTANCY	GROSS DOMESTIC PRODUCT PER YEAR	AVERAGE ANNUAL PER CAPITA INCOME
AFRICA						
Libya	3,200,000	5 per sq mi (2 per sq km)	3.5%	53	$ 19.97 billion	$ 6,335
Madagascar	9,200,000	41 per sq mi (16 per sq km)	2.6%	46	$ 3.3 billion	$ 350
Malawi	6,600,000	144 per sq mi (56 per sq km)	2.8%	42	$ 1.53 billion	$ 220
Mali	7,100,000	15 per sq mi (6 per sq km)	2.9%	38	$ 839 million	$ 140
Mauritania	1,700,000	4 per sq mi (2 per sq km)	1.9%	39	$ 618 million	$ 400
Mauritius	1,000,000	1,266 per sq mi (489 per sq km)	2.0%	67	$ 988 million	$ 1,052
Morocco	22,300,000	129 per sq mi (50 per sq km)	2.9%	54	$ 16 billion	$ 800
Mozambique	12,700,000	42 per sq mi (16 per sq km)	3.1%	44	$ 2.7 billion	$ 220
Niger	5,800,000	12 per sq mi (5 per sq km)	2.9%	39	$ 2.3 billion	$ 475
Nigeria	82,300,000	231 per sq mi (89 per sq km)	3.2%	50	$ 77 billion	$ 750
Rwanda	5,400,000	531 per sq mi (205 per sq km)	3.0%	44	$ 890 billion	$ 178
Sao Tome and Principe	100,000	269 per sq mi (105 per sq km)	3.4%	na	$ 40 million	$ 270
Senegal	5,900,000	78 per sq mi (30 per sq km)	2.7%	44	$ 2.2 billion	$ 342
Seychelles	67,000	926 per sq mi (357 per sq km)	1.8%	65	$ 86 million	$ 1,030
Sierra Leone	3,700,000	163 per sq mi (52 per sq km)	1.9%	44	$ 926 million	$ 176
Somalia	4,600,000	64 per sq mi (25 per sq km)	2.6%	41	$ 407 million	$ 105
South Africa	30,000,000	19 per sq mi (7 per sq km)	2.1%	52	$ 81.9 billion	$ 1,296
Sudan	19,900,000	21 per sq mi (8 per sq km)	3.7%	50	$ 8.8 billion	$ 370
Swaziland	600,000	89 per sq mi (35 per sq km)	2.7%	44	$ 425 million	$ 840
Tanzania	19,900,000	55 per sq mi (21 per sq km)	2.9%	48	$ 4.56 billion	$ 253
Togo	2,800,000	129 per sq mi (50 per sq km)	2.9%	40	$ 766 million	$ 319
Tunisia	6,700,000	106 per sq mi (41 per sq km)	2.4%	55	$ 8.4 billion	$ 1,200
Uganda	13,700,000	150 per sq mi (58 per sq km)	3.2%	49	$ 8.36 billion	$ 240
Zaire	30,300,000	33 per sq mi (13 per sq km)	3.5%	44	$ 6.16 billion	$ 127
Zambia	6,000,000	21 per sq mi (8 per sq km)	3.2%	47	$ 3.24 billion	$ 414
Zimbabwe	10,500,000	53 per sq mi (20 per sq km)	2.2%	52	$ 5.7 billion	$ 509

COUNTRIES OF THE WORLD

	COUNTRY	POPULATION	POPULATION DENSITY	AVERAGE ANNUAL POPULATION GROWTH RATE	AVERAGE LIFE EXPECTANCY	GROSS DOMESTIC PRODUCT PER YEAR	AVERAGE ANNUAL PER CAPITA INCOME
ASIA	Afghanistan	15,100,000	60 per sq mi (23 per sq km)	2.2%	41	$ 3.76 billion	$ 168
	Bahrain	400,000	1,667 per sq mi (643 per sq km)	2.8%	64	$ 3.4 billion	$ 6,315
	Bangladesh	93,300,000	1,678 per sq mi (648 per sq km)	2.8%	47	$ 10.5 billion	$ 105
	Bhutan	1,400,000	77 per sq mi (30 per sq km)	2.3%	44	$ 90 million	$ 70
	Brunei	213,000	96 per sq mi (37 per sq km)	na	62	$ 460 million	$ 2,970
	Burma	37,100,000	142 per sq mi (55 per sq km)	2.4%	53	$ 5.62 billion	$ 174
	Cambodia	6,100,000	87 per sq mi (34 per sq km)	2.9%	45	$ 660 million	$ 90
	China, People's Republic of	1,008,175,000	270 per sq mi (105 per sq km)	1.6%	68	$ 540 billion	$ 566
	India	713,000,000	562 per sq mi (218 per sq km)	1.9%	51	$ 167 billion	$ 150
	Indonesia	151,000,000	262 per sq mi (101 per sq km)	2.1%	48	$ 66.8 billion	$ 415
	Iran	41,200,000	65 per sq mi (23 per sq km)	2.8%	54	$ 76.37 billion	$ 2,160
	Iraq	14,000,000	83 per sq mi (32 per sq km)	3.4%	62	$ 31 billion	$ 2,410
	Israel	4,100,000	511 per sq mi (197 per sq km)	2.0%	72	$ 19.9 billion	$ 3,332
	Japan	118,600,000	814 per sq mi (314 per sq km)	1.0%	74	$ 990 billion	$ 8,460
	Jordan	3,500,000	93 per sq mi (36 per sq km)	3.9%	52	$ 3.2 billion	$ 552
	Korea, North	18,700,000	402 per sq mi (155 per sq km)	3.2%	61	$ 10.4 billion	$ 570
	Korea, South	41,000,000	1,081 per sq mi (417 per sq km)	1.6%	68	$ 59.2 billion	$ 1,187
	Kuwait	1,500,000	193 per sq mi (75 per sq km)	5.9%	69	$ 23.2 billion	$ 11,431
	Laos	3,700,000	40 per sq mi (16 per sq km)	0.9%	35	$ 220 million	$ 85
	Lebanon	2,700,000	672 per sq mi (260 per sq km)	2.5%	63	$ 2.6 billion	$ 884
	Malaysia	14,700,000	116 per sq mi (45 per sq km)	2.5%	68	$ 21.3 billion	$ 714
	Maldives	155,000	1,739 per sq mi (671 per sq km)	2.9%	na	$ 22 million	$ 150
	Mongolia	1,700,000	3 per sq mi (1 per sq km)	2.6%	64	$ 1.2 billion	$ 750
	Nepal	14,500,000	258 per sq mi (99 per sq km)	2.5%	40	$ 2.0 billion	$ 140
	Oman	948,000	11 per sq mi (4 per sq km)	3.0%	47	$ 3.4 billion	$ 2,400

COUNTRIES OF THE WORLD

	COUNTRY	POPULATION	POPULATION DENSITY	AVERAGE ANNUAL POPULATION GROWTH RATE	AVERAGE LIFE EXPECTANCY	GROSS DOMESTIC PRODUCT PER YEAR	AVERAGE ANNUAL PER CAPITA INCOME
ASIA	Pakistan	93,000,000	300 per sq mi (116 per sq km)	2.9%	51	$ 23.2 billion	$ 280
	Philippines	51,600,000	445 per sq mi (172 per sq km)	2.4%	58	$ 35.7 billion	$ 779
	Qatar	250,000	71 per sq mi (27 per sq km)	4.7%	47	$ 6 billion	$ 29,000
	Saudi Arabia	11,100,000	13 per sq mi (5 per sq km)	5.6%	45	$ 165 billion	$ 11,500
	Singapore	2,500,000	11,161 per sq mi (4,303 per sq km)	1.2%	69	$ 9 billion	$ 4,100
	Sri Lanka	15,200,000	600 per sq mi (232 per sq km)	1.7%	68	$ 3.4 billion	$ 168
	Syria	9,700,000	136 per sq mi (52 per sq km)	3.4%	57	$ 9.1 billion	$ 702
	Taiwan	18,500,000	1,332 per sq mi (514 per sq km)	1.9%	72	$ 40.2 billion	$ 2,570
	Thailand	49,800,000	251 per sq mi (97 per sq km)	2.3%	61	$ 36 billion	$ 758
	Turkey	47,700,000	163 per sq mi (63 per sq km)	2.4%	57	$ 59.7 billion	$ 1,300
	United Arab Emirates	1,200,000	37 per sq mi (14 per sq km)	6.2%	60	$ 27 billion	$ 24,000
	Vietnam	56,600,000	441 per sq mi (170 per sq km)	2.2%	44	$ 7.6 billion	$ 150
	Yemen	5,500,000	16 per sq mi (6 per sq km)	2.3%	38	$ 2.7 billion	$ 475
	Yemen, P.D.R. of	2,200,000	73 per sq mi (28 per sq km)	1.8%	45	$ 550 million	$ 310
AUSTRALIA AND OCEANIA	Australia	15,000,000	5 per sq mi (2 per sq km)	1.2%	71	$ 145 billion	$ 9,914
	Fiji	700,000	85 per sq mi (33 per sq km)	1.8%	70	$ 937 million	$ 1,440
	Kiribati	60,000	226 per sq mi (87 per sq km)	1.6%	58	$ 15 million	$ 670
	Nauru	8,000	1,125 per sq mi (429 per sq km)	1.5%	53	$ 155 million	$ 21,400
	New Zealand	3,100,000	30 per sq mi (12 per sq km)	0.9%	72	$ 23.4 billion	$ 7,363
	Papua-New Guinea	3,300,000	19 per sq mi (7 per sq km)	2.7%	49	$ 2.27 billion	$ 480
	Solomon Islands	240,000	18 per sq mi (7 per sq km)	3.5%	51	$ 94 million	$ 440
	Tonga	100,000	334 per sq mi (129 per sq km)	1.1%	56	$ 40 million	$ 430
	Tuvalu	9,000	900 per sq mi (346 per sq km)	1.6%	58	$ 1.2 million	$ 180
	Vanuatu	125,600	20 per sq mi (8 per sq km)	2.8%	51	$ 75 million	$ 590
	Western Samoa	158,000	182 per sq mi (70 per sq km)	1.7%	67	$ 50 million	$ 320

COUNTRIES OF THE WORLD

	COUNTRY	POPULATION	POPULATION DENSITY	AVERAGE ANNUAL POPULATION GROWTH RATE	AVERAGE LIFE EXPECTANCY	GROSS DOMESTIC PRODUCT PER YEAR	AVERAGE ANNUAL PER CAPITA INCOME
EUROPE	Albania	2,800,000	252 per sq mi (97 per sq km)	2.6%	69	$ 1.3 billion	$ 490
	Andorra	38,050	162 per sq mi (63 per sq km)	1.2%	na	na	na
	Austria	7,600,000	235 per sq mi (91 per sq km)	−0.1%	73	$ 76 billion	$ 9,114
	Belgium	9,900,000	840 per sq mi (324 per sq km)	0.7%	71	$ 111 billion	$ 10,800
	Bulgaria	8,900,000	208 per sq mi (80 per sq km)	0.2%	71	$ 144 billion	$ 2,100
	Cyprus	645,000	168 per sq mi (65 per sq km)	0.7%	73	$ 2.2 billion	$ 2,940
	Czechoslovakia	15,400,000	312 per sq mi (120 per sq km)	0.7%	71	$ 77 billion	$ 3,985
	Denmark	5,100,000	307 per sq mi (118 per sq km)	0.2%	73	$ 66 billion	$ 12,956
	Finland	4,800,000	37 per sq mi (14 per sq km)	0.4%	72	$ 50 billion	$ 10,477
	France	54,200,000	257 per sq mi (100 per sq km)	0.4%	72	$ 585 billion	$ 8,980
	Germany, East	16,700,000	400 per sq mi (154 per sq km)	0.0%	72	$ 89 billion	$ 5,340
	Germany, West	61,700,000	643 per sq mi (248 per sq km)	−0.2%	71	$ 679 billion	$ 11,142
	Greece	9,800,000	192 per sq mi (74 per sq km)	0.7%	71	$ 43.8 billion	$ 4,590
	Hungary	10,700,000	298 per sq mi (115 per sq km)	0.3%	70	$ 17 billion	$ 3,000
	Iceland	232,000	5 per sq mi (2 per sq km)	1.2%	75	$ 1.7 billion	$ 9,000
	Ireland	3,500,000	139 per sq mi (50 per sq km)	1.1%	72	$ 17.2 billion	$ 5,000
	Italy	57,400,000	493 per sq mi (191 per sq km)	0.4%	70	$ 394 billion	$ 6,914
	Liechtenstein	26,000	423 per sq mi (164 per sq km)	0.7%	65	$ 340 million	$ 11,330
	Luxembourg	400,000	401 per sq mi (155 per sq km)	−0.04%	73	$ 3.8 billion	$ 10,444
	Malta	400,000	3,279 per sq mi (1,266 per sq km)	0.7%	71	$ 959 million	$ 2,036
	Monaco	26,000	43,153 per sq mi (16,798 per sq km)	0.3%	75	na	na
	Netherlands	14,300,000	900 per sq mi (347 per sq km)	0.4%	72	$ 139 billion	$ 9,749
	Norway	4,100,000	33 per sq mi (13 per sq km)	0.3%	75	$ 57 billion	$ 12,432
	Poland	36,300,000	301 per sq mi (116 per sq km)	1.0%	71	$ 55.2 billion	$ 2,500
	Portugal	9,930,000	278 per sq mi (108 per sq km)	0.9%	69	$ 20.1 billion	$ 2,000

497

COUNTRIES OF THE WORLD

	COUNTRY	POPULATION	POPULATION DENSITY	AVERAGE ANNUAL POPULATION GROWTH RATE	AVERAGE LIFE EXPECTANCY	GROSS DOMESTIC PRODUCT PER YEAR	AVERAGE ANNUAL PER CAPITA INCOME
EUROPE	Romania	22,600,000	246 per sq mi (95 per sq km)	8.7%	70	$ 67.5 billion	$ 3,100
	San Marino	21,537	850 per sq mi (334 per sq km)	0.8%	72	na	na
	Spain	37,900,000	194 per sq mi (75 per sq km)	1.0%	72	$ 201 billion	$ 5,500
	Sweden	8,310,000	48 per sq mi (18 per sq km)	0.4%	74	$ 123 billion	$ 14,821
	Switzerland	6,343,000	395 per sq mi (153 per sq km)	0.2%	75	$ 100.5 billion	$ 15,698
	Union of Soviet Socialist Republics (USSR)	268,800,000	31 per sq mi (12 per sq km)	0.9%	70	$ 1.5 trillion	$ 2,600
	United Kingdom	56,100,000	595 per sq mi (230 per sq km)	0.01%	72	$ 446 billion	$ 7,216
	Vatican City	738	4,300 per sq mi (1,661 per sq km)	na	na	na	na
	Yugoslavia	22,600,000	229 per sq mi (88 per sq km)	0.9%	68	$ 69 billion	$ 3,109
NORTH AMERICA	Antigua and Barbuda	77,000	451 per sq mi (175 per sq km)	na	na	na	na
	Bahamas	260,000	37 per sq mi (14 per sq km)	3.6%	69	$ 1.08 billion	$ 4,650
	Barbados	300,000	1,807 per sq mi (696 per sq km)	2.3%	70	$ 637 million	$ 3,040
	Belize	148,300	23 per sq mi (9 per sq km)	2.9%	60	$ 135 million	$ 1,000
	Bermuda	54,895	2,614 per sq mi (1,017 per sq km)	na	na	na	$ 9,440
	Canada	24,400,000	6 per sq mi (2 per sq km)	0.8%	74	$ 272 billion	$ 10,193
	Costa Rica	2,300,000	117 per sq mi (45 per sq km)	2.6%	68	$ 4.9 billion	$ 2,238
	Cuba	9,800,000	221 per sq mi (86 per sq km)	1.2%	72	$ 13.9 billion	$ 840
	Dominica	82,000	345 per sq mi (133 per sq km)	1.6%	na	$ 33 million	$ 460
	Dominican Republic	5,700,000	304 per sq mi (118 per sq km)	2.5%	61	$ 6.7 billion	$ 1,221
	El Salvador	5,000,000	615 per sq mi (238 per sq km)	3.4%	64	$ 3.77 billion	$ 639
	Grenada	108,000	752 per sq mi (291 per sq km)	2.2%	63	$ 54 million	$ 500
	Guatemala	7,700,000	183 per sq mi (71 per sq km)	3.1%	52	$ 7.8 billion	$ 1,083
	Haiti	6,100,000	569 per sq mi (220 per sq km)	2.4%	50	$ 1.3 billion	$ 260

COUNTRIES OF THE WORLD

	COUNTRY	POPULATION	POPULATION DENSITY	AVERAGE ANNUAL POPULATION GROWTH RATE	AVERAGE LIFE EXPECTANCY	GROSS DOMESTIC PRODUCT PER YEAR	AVERAGE ANNUAL PER CAPITA INCOME
NORTH AMERICA	Honduras	4,000,000	92 per sq mi (36 per sq km)	3.5%	56	$ 5 billion	$ 822
	Jamaica	2,200,000	518 per sq mi (200 per sq km)	1.2%	69	$ 3 billion	$ 1,340
	Mexico	71,300,000	94 per sq mi (36 per sq km)	3.3%	65	$ 128 billion	$ 1,800
	Nicaragua	2,600,000	45 per sq mi (18 per sq km)	0.7%	54	$ 2.3 billion	$ 804
	Panama	1,900,000	65 per sq mi (25 per sq km)	2.8%	59	$ 3.2 billion	$ 1,116
	St. Kitts and Nevis	44,000	423 per sq mi (164 per sq km)	0.8%	na	$ 32 million	$ 580
	St. Lucia	124,000	420 per sq mi (162 per sq km)	2.8%	57	$ 99.2 million	$ 698
	St. Vincent and the Grenadines	120,000	667 per sq mi (257 per sq km)	2.2%	na	$ 43 million	$ 250
	Trinidad and Tobago	1,100,000	556 per sq mi (215 per sq km)	1.9%	66	$ 5.03 billion	$ 4,800
	United States	232,000,000	64 per sq mi (25 per sq km)	0.7%	74	$ 2.42 trillion	$ 8,612
SOUTH AMERICA	Argentina	28,438,000	27 per sq mi (10 per sq km)	1.6%	70	$ 61.5 billion	$ 2,331
	Bolivia	5,600,000	13 per sq mi (5 per sq km)	2.4%	47	$ 6.1 billion	$ 510
	Brazil	127,700,000	39 per sq mi (15 per sq km)	2.3%	61	$ 289 billion	$ 1,523
	Chile	11,500,000	40 per sq mi (16 per sq km)	1.5%	67	$ 19.8 billion	$ 1,950
	Colombia	25,600,000	61 per sq mi (23 per sq km)	2.1%	61	$ 33.9 billion	$ 1,112
	Ecuador	8,500,000	58 per sq mi (22 per sq km)	3.1%	57	$ 11.3 billion	$ 1,050
	Guyana	900,000	11 per sq mi (4 per sq km)	2.1%	67	$ 507 million	$ 603
	Paraguay	3,300,000	21 per sq mi (8 per sq km)	2.5%	62	$ 4.5 billion	$ 1,038
	Peru	18,600,000	37 per sq mi (14 per sq km)	2.6%	58	$ 20.1 billion	$ 655
	Surinam	420,000	6 per sq mi (2 per sq km)	2.8%	66	$ 924 million	$ 2,600
	Uruguay	2,934,942	44 per sq mi (17 per sq km)	0.6%	71	$ 9.4 billion	$ 2,780
	Venezuela	18,700,000	52 per sq mi (20 per sq km)	3.3%	67	$ 59.9 billion	$ 3,639

Glossary

This glossary includes many terms that are used in *Earth's Geography and Environment*, including all the words that are listed in the Vocabulary section at the beginning of each chapter. Each term is printed in **boldface** the first time that it appears in the text. Each glossary entry is followed by a number in parentheses. This number refers to the page on which the term first appears. The glossary is followed by a pronunciation key.

acid rain Precipitation that mixes with harmful chemicals in the atmosphere as it falls; it then kills fish and destroys trees and other living and nonliving things. (464)

age grading The Masai system in which adults progress through stages in the course of their lives. For each stage, there are different responsibilities. (304)

age set In the Masai system of age grading, a group that progresses through each stage together. (304)

agribusiness Large, specialized farming that requires huge investments in land and machinery; also, the combination of all businesses that are related to agriculture. (378)

air mass A huge volume of air that has a uniform temperature and a uniform amount of moisture. (113)

air pressure The weight of the atmosphere. (109)

altitude The height above sea level of an object in the air. (125)

analogy A comparison that shows the similarity or the relationship between two different ideas. (350)

annuals All plants that grow from seeds each year and that die after they are harvested. (475)

anthracite Hard coal that is used to make iron. (393)

aquatic Describes a water region. (191)

arid Describes an area that lacks enough water for agriculture. (141)

atmosphere Air; the mixture of various gases that surrounds Earth; it extends for hundreds of miles above Earth's surface. (102)

average life expectancy The average age or lifespan that is usually reached by members of a group. (255)

axis The imaginary axle which runs through the center of Earth from the North Pole to the South Pole at a 23 1/2° angle. (24)

baby boom Record numbers of children who are born during a specific period of time. (253)

balance of trade The difference in value between a country's sale of goods (exports) and its purchase of goods (imports). (445)

biological resources The plants and the animals of Earth that people use. (207)

biome A natural community or region in which particular kinds of plants and animals exist together, a forest, grassland, or the like. (176)

biosphere The zone of Earth in which living things can exist; it extends only a short distance into the atmosphere and oceans and only a few feet into the Earth. (160)

birthrate The average number of births per thousand people in a population in one year. (254)

bituminous coal Soft coal that is used to make steel. (394)

borough An urban political division, such as one of the five areas that make up New York City. (358)

broadleaf A type of tree that has leaves that are broad. (169)

calories The measurement of energy that food provides. (202)

canopy The top layer of a forest, consisting of the top branches of the tallest trees. (179)

capital Accumulated money or wealth. (392)

cash crop Crops that are raised to be sold for a profit. (267)

chip A single, thin silicon wafer that holds an electronic circuit, which is composed of two or more transistors; an integrated circuit. (419)

civilization A highly developed culture that has achieved a large population, specialization, cities, learning, and advanced technology. (241)

climate The condition of the atmosphere in a place over a period of years. (119)

compound A group of small buildings that are arranged in a cluster. (303)

consumer goods The things, including food and clothing, that people buy to live. (396)

continent Any of the seven major landmasses that exist on Earth. (26)

continental shelf A gently sloping, fairly flat stretch of underwater land that surrounds a continent. (86)

continental slope A cliff area that drops from the edge of a continental shelf to the ocean basin. (87)

coral A limestone formation that is made of the skeletons of tiny sea animals. (344)

culture The total way of life of a group of people. (19)

custom The social behavior that is a part of our culture. (218)

data Factual information; facts and figures. (152)

death rate The average number of deaths per thousand people in a population in one year. (255)

deciduous Describes plants that lose their leaves in certain seasons. (169)

delta Large, often triangular, deposits of sediment that form where a river flows into a shallow sea or a lake. (71)

demographer A person who studies population. (254)

desalination The process by which salt is removed from seawater. (470)

developed nation A country with an advanced technology that creates jobs, which produces a stable economy. (438)

developing nation A country in which the level of technology is simple, affecting the kinds of jobs that are available and limiting the amount of money that can be earned. (438)

division of labor In a social group, the assignment of certain tasks to specific members of the group. (235)

domesticated animals Animals that are raised by humans. (238)

domesticated plants Plants that are raised by humans. (238)

dune A large hill of sand that is found on beaches and in deserts and is created by wind erosion and deposition. (73)

ecologist A scientist who studies the relationship between living things and their environment. (462)

ecosystem A community of living things and its environment, which exists interdependently as a unit or system. (160)

editorial A statement of opinion in which the writer expresses one side or point of view about a subject and uses facts to support that point of view. (368)

elevation The height of a land area in relation to sea level. (42)

environment Everything that surrounds a person or other living thing; also, everything that surrounds a community of living things. (19)

equinox One of the two days in each year, one in the spring and one in the fall, when there are 12 hours of daylight and 12 hours of darkness on all parts of Earth. (122)

erosion The process by which particles of Earth's crust are worn away and transported to other places. (70)

escarpment A steep slope or sheer cliff that separates two relatively flat landforms. (49)

ethnic group A group of people who are united by race or by national background and who share the same language and customs. (427)

evergreen A tree that stays green all year. (169)

exports Goods that a nation sells to other nations. (365)

extended family The basic family unit in most traditional societies; the unit may consist of grandparents, parents, children, and grandchildren. (225)

famine A drastic, widespread food shortage. (469)

fathom A unit of measurement for water depth; equal to 6 feet (1.8 m). (344)

faults The long breaks, caused by shifting tectonic plates, in Earth's crust. (69)

fertile The conditions of soil that is, because of an abundance of nutrients, capable of supporting an abundance of plants. (163)

folds Bends or buckles in Earth's crust that are formed as tectonic plates collide. (68)

forest floor The lowest layer of plant growth, which consists of dead leaves, twigs, mosses, and fungi. (179)

fossil fuels Fuels, such as coal, oil, and natural gas, that have formed on Earth from plants and from animals that lived millions of years ago. (209)

frigid zones Describes the high-latitude areas that lie north of the Arctic Circle and south of the Antarctic Circle; also called polar zones. (123)

front The boundary between two different air masses. (114)

galaxy A huge system in space that is composed of gases, dust, and billions of stars. (21)

gene An element in a living thing that controls the passing along of characteristics from one generation to another. (474)

geography The study of Earth, including its physical features, its life, and its people. (18)

ger A portable shelter that is used by Mongol herders. (308)

glacier A huge, dense mass of snow and ice. (71)

granary A storehouse for grain. (343)

gross national product (GNP) The value of all the goods and the services that a nation produces, both inside and outside its borders, in a year. (442)

groundwater Water that is found underground. (91)

growing season The part of the year when conditions are favorable for the growing of plants. (139)

habitat The special environment or place where a plant or an animal is usually found. (176)

heavy industry An industry that relies on heavy equipment or on heavy materials. (359)

highland A hilly region that consists of both hills and mountains. (47)

high tech High, or scientific, technology; industries that rely on advanced technology. (379)

hill A landform that is characterized by a sloping relief that is less steep than that of a mountain. (47)

human resources People's ability to provide for themselves by using other resources. (207)

hunter-gatherer A person who depends for food on what can be found and caught in his or her environment. (234)

hurricane Dangerous tropical storms that sometimes move into temperate latitudes. (143)

hydrologic cycle   The system through which water moves over, in, and throughout Earth.   (82)

hydrosphere   Any location on Earth where there is water, including oceans, rivers, lakes, and ponds.   (160)

igloo   A house that is built of ice by the Innuit when no other resources are available.   (320)

imports   Goods that a nation buys from other nations.   (366)

Industrial Revolution   The transformation of industry by new sources of power, which permitted significant increases in production and in trade.   (248)

inexhaustible resources   Resources, such as sunlight and wind, that cannot be used up.   (209)

infant mortality rate   In a population, the number of babies who die in their first year compared to the number of babies born in that year.   (255)

interdependent   Things that interact with each other and are linked together as a system.   (160)

interest   A charge for money that is loaned.   (446)

ionosphere   A layer of the thermosphere in which the sun's rays strike particles of oxygen and of nitrogen, changing them into electrically charged atoms that are called ions.   (104)

island   Land that is smaller than a continent and is completely surrounded by water.   (27)

jet stream   A kind of wind that blows between 5 and 9 miles (8 and 14.5 km) above Earth.   (127)

kayak   A lightweight one-person canoe.   (327)

klong   A canal in Thailand that people use for irrigation, for drinking water, for washing, and for travel.   (341)

labor force   The number of available industrial workers.   (399)

lake   A body of water that is completely surrounded by land.   (91)

landform   A distinctive feature, or form, of the land.   (42)

latitude zone   Any of three major climate areas into which Earth is divided by lines of latitude.   (123)

light industry   An industry that does not rely on heavy equipment or on heavy materials.   (359)

literacy   The ability to read and write.   (440)

lithosphere   Any area of Earth where there is land. (160)

longhouse   A huge, wooden structure that is raised on stilts and is built around an open courtyard; people such as the Iban of Borneo live in longhouses.   (284)

magma   The molten rock that rises from Earth's mantle through cracks in the crust and that forms volcanoes.   (66)

mainframe   The largest and the most powerful kind of computer.   (430)

mass produced   Made in large quantities by the assembly-line method.   (373)

material culture   The physical elements of culture that we can see and touch; tools, furniture, baseballs, foods, and the like.   (220)

megalopolis   A combination of two or more metropolitan areas.   (261)

meteorologist   A scientist who studies the atmosphere.   (102)

metropolitan area   A city and its surrounding suburbs.   (261)

microcomputer   The smallest and the least powerful kind of computer.   (430)

migration   A movement of people from one place to another.   (236)

migratory agriculture   A type of farming, often the result of the slash-and-burn method, in which the farmers move when the soil loses its fertility.   (279)

minicomputer   A small computer that is used in medium-sized and small businesses.   (430)

monsoon   A seasonal wind.   (132)

mountain   A landform that is characterized by high relief and by steep slopes.   (43)

multinational corporation   A large corporation that operates throughout the world.   (446)

native commercial forestry   The industry that is developed by forest dwellers to supply others with forest products and to provide a livelihood.   (279)

natural resources   The raw materials of Earth that people use to live.   (206)

needleleaf   A type of tree that has needle-shaped or scaly leaves.   (169)

new town   A new community that was designed and planned before anything was built.   (384)

nomads   People who move from place to place in search of food.   (235)

nonmaterial culture   Elements of culture that are not material and cannot be seen or touched; beliefs, ideas, feelings, customs, and the like.   (220)

nonrenewable resources   Resources that exist in limited amounts, such as copper, silver, oil, and gold.   (209)

nuclear family   The basic family unit in most modern societies, consisting of parents and their children.   (225)

oasis   An area in the desert where water is available.   (146)

ocean basin   The deepest part of the ocean, stretching from continental slope to continental slope and consisting of plains, mountains, and ridges.   (87)

ocean current   A stream of moving water in an ocean.   (85)

orbit The orderly path in which a planet travels around the sun. (23)

ozone layer A special form of oxygen in the atmosphere that protects life on Earth from ultraviolet rays by absorbing them. (104)

pack animal An animal that carries a load of supplies. (298)

pans Shallow, round depressions in the sand of the desert that fill up with water when it rains. (322)

passport A document that is issued to citizens by their government to identify their citizenship when they are traveling in other countries. (478)

per capita GNP The gross national product divided by the number of people who live in that country. (442)

perennials Plants that grow every year without having to be replanted. (475)

permafrost Soil that remains permanently frozen. (149)

photosynthesis The chemical process in which green plants produce food by using energy from the sun. (161)

plain A broad, flat, gently rolling area that is generally lower than the land around it. (52)

planet A huge object that exists in space and that revolves around a star. (23)

plankton The small plants and animals that live in the ocean. (191)

plantation A large farm that usually specializes in one crop and that employs many people. (405)

plateau A fairly flat area at a fairly high elevation. (49)

prairie A type of grassland. (183)

precipitation Water that falls in the form of rain, snow, sleet, or hail. (83)

prefabricated Built in standardized sections for shipment and for quick assembly. (374)

prevailing winds Winds that blow in the same direction, due to permanent high- and low-pressure air masses. (109)

reforestation The process of forest regrowth. (280)

relative humidity The ratio of the amount of moisture that is in the air to the amount of moisture that the air can hold. (107)

relief The difference in height between two related land surfaces. (43)

renewable resources Resources that can be replenished or sustained by human effort. (209)

reserves The areas where there are known deposits of resources that can be obtained with our present technology at a reasonable cost. (212)

river A moving stream of fresh water, flowing in a channel that it has cut into Earth. (88)

sampan A small boat, similar to a canoe, that is used in such Asian countries as Thailand. (341)

savanna A grassland area that is found especially in the wet-and-dry tropics. (140)

scrub A dwarfed or stunted tree or shrub. (181)

sea level The level of the surface of the ocean, which is used as a base to measure both the height and the depth of landforms. (42)

sedentary agriculture A type of farming that is done when people settle in one place. (279)

seedbed An area where plants are raised from seeds for transplanting. (341)

silicon A crystalline element that is a semiconductor of electricity and is an important ingredient in electronic technology. (417)

slash-and-burn agriculture A method of clearing land for crops that consists of cutting down trees and then burning the dead wood; this produces more fertile soil. (278)

socialization The process of cultural learning; learning how to fit into society. (225)

society A group of people with the same culture. (218)

solar system In space, an organization that consists of the sun, the nine planets that revolve around it, and the moons of the planets. (22)

solstice In each year, one of the two days when the hours of daylight reach a limit. On the summer solstice, there is the longest period of daylight; on the winter solstice, there is the shortest period of daylight. (122)

specialization In a social group, the process in which a job that was formerly done by one individual is divided into specific tasks that are done by two or more people. (240)

standard of living The minimum amount of necessities and comforts that people of a country consider essential to the maintenance of their way of life. (375)

steppe A type of grassland that lies in semiarid climate zones. (183)

stock Shares, or parts of ownership, in a business. (413)

stock exchange The place at which individuals and groups buy or sell the stocks of companies in order to make a profit. (413)

subsistence farmer A farmer who produces only enough food for his or her own family's needs. (267)

Sun Belt The southern and the southwestern areas of the United States, in which there is always a mild climate. (396)

sustainable environment An environment that is stable year after year to the benefit of its inhabitants. (363)

taiga A large conifer forest of the subarctic. (147)

technology The tools of a society, including all the skills and the resources that people apply in using them. (221)

tectonic plate A large segment or piece of Earth's crust, which floats and moves about on the softer rock of the mantle. (67)

503

temperate zones The mid-latitude areas that lie between the Tropic of Cancer and the Arctic Circle and between the Tropic of Capricorn and the Antarctic Circle. (123)

temperature A measure of the amount of heat in the atmosphere. (106)

tides The regular rising and falling of the water level of oceans, of seas, and of large lakes. (75)

trade-off A choice that is based on an attempt to balance such factors as benefits and costs. (463)

trade winds Global wind systems, both north and south of the equator, that help to create climate patterns. (138)

traditional culture A culture that developed a long time ago, which has remained much the same over a long period of time. (219)

transhumance A type of seasonal herding in which only some herders move their animals to the mountains, while others of the group maintain a permanent home in the lowland area for farming. (300)

transistor An electronic device that contains a semiconductor to regulate the flow of electric current. (419)

tribe A group of closely related families or clans. (225)

tributary A stream that carries water from other places and that flows into a main river. (89)

tropical zone The low-latitude area that lies between the Tropic of Cancer and the Tropic of Capricorn. (123)

troposphere The layer of the atmosphere that is closest to Earth. (103)

tundra An area in the Arctic regions where it is too cold for trees to grow. (147)

understory The layer of plant growth, consisting of the top branches of shorter trees, that grows below the canopy. (179)

wafer fab The industry that manufactures silicon chips for computers. (420)

weather The condition of the atmosphere over a brief period of time. (106)

weathering The breaking down of Earth's hard, rocky crust into smaller parts and particles. (69)

Pronunciation Key

VOWELS

Sound as in:	Spelling	Symbol
m*a*tter	a	MAT*er
tr*a*de	ay	TRAYD
*a*rmy	ah	AHR*mee
ab*ou*t	ow	uh*BOWT
*ai*rplane	ai	AIR*playn
d*e*sert	eh	DEH*zert
s*ea*	ee	SEE
w*o*rld	er	WERLD
r*i*ch	ih	RIHCH
*i*sland	eye	EYE*luhnd
*o*cean	oh	OH*shuhn
b*ou*ght	aw	BAWT
av*oi*d	oy	uh*VOYD
st*u*dent	oo	STOO*duhnt
w*oo*d	ooh	WOOHD
h*u*ndred	uh	HUHN*druhd
moun*tai*n		MOWN*tuhn
(unstressed vowels)		

CONSONANTS

Sound as in:	Spelling	Symbol
*b*ook	b	BOOHK
*d*ense	d	DEHNS
a*f*raid	f	uh*FRAYD
*g*ain	g	GAYN
*h*istory	h	HIHS*tuh*ree
*j*oin	j	JOYN
*k*ing	k	KIHNG
*l*and	l	LAND
*m*ost	m	MOHST
*n*ext	n	NEHKST
*p*eople	p	PEE*puhl
*r*each	r	REECH
*s*ense	s	SEHNS
*t*itle	t	TEYE*tuhl
*v*illage	v	VIHL*uhj
*w*ork	w	WERK
*y*ear	y	YEER
*z*ero	z	ZEE*roh

CONSONANT PAIRS

*ch*oose	ch	CHOOZ
si*ng*	ng	SIHNG
*sh*ips	sh	SHIHPS
*th*rough	th	THROO
al*th*ough	th	awl*THOH
trea*s*ure	zh	TREHZH*er

Index

The entries in this index show you where to find information on the people, places, and things in *Earth's Geography and Environment*. Words that are followed by * are listed in the Vocabulary section at the beginning of each chapter.

rubber industry, 394
Ruhr region (West Germany), 399, 422–425
rules (cultural), 225–226
runoff (rivers), 89, 90

S

Saar region, 399
Sahara (desert), 50, 141, 316, 319, 404
salt water, 91, 334–335
Samoa, 224
sampan*, 341
sanctuary (wildlife), 467
sandbars, 75–76
satellites, 77, 462
Saudi Arabia, 334, 441, 470
savanna*, 140, 183–184, 295, 296, 302–305
Scandinavia, 147, 320
Scotland, 48, 91
Scott, Robert, 147
scrub*, 181
scrub forests, 181
sea level*, 42, 91
Sears, Paul, 462
seas, 87, 333. *See also* oceans.
seasons, 112, 122, 123, 132, 140, 143–144, 145, 146, 148–149, 150–151, 180, 184, 203
seawater. *See* oceans; salt water.
sedentary agriculture*, 279–280, 281
sediment, 52, 70, 71, 73, 75–76, 82
seedbed*, 341
Semang people, 278
semiarid climate regions, 141, 143, 146
semiconductor, 417, 419
service industries, 262–263, 378
Shakespeare, William, 361
shelter, buildings, and housing, 202, 203–204, 206, 207, 217, 221–222, 239, 254, 261, 277, 284, 290, 303, 309, 317, 319, 320, 328, 329, 343, 346, 358, 360–361, 364, 372, 373–375, 384, 414–415, 420, 428

Shockley, William, 419
shooting stars, 105
shorelines. *See* coastlines.
shrub layer (forest), 179, 180
Siberia, 52
silicon*, 417
Silicon Valley, California, 417–421
silt, 52
Simcoe, John Graves, 412, 413
Sioux Indians, 299
slash-and-burn agriculture*, 278–279, 285, 346
Slater, Samuel, 389, 392, 419
social class, 440, 457
socialization*, 225, 303, 304. *See also* education.
social organization, 304–305
society*, 218, 225, 226
sod, 53
soil, 18, 46, 53–55, 73, 161, 163–166, 205, 209, 245, 279, 338, 341, 446
formation of, 69, 162, 136–164, 209
structure and types of, 164–166
solar system*, 22–24
solstice*, 122–123, 129
South Africa, 143, 406, 407
South America, 26, 27, 242, 264
industrialization, 404, 405–406, 407
people of, 236, 257
physical geography, 27, 45, 46, 47–48, 50, 51, 53–54, 90, 128, 144, 184
See also Latin America.
South Carolina, 125
Southeast Asia, 139, 140
Southern Hemisphere 34–35, 130
South Pacific, 344–348
South Pole, 12, 147
Soviet Union, 54, 55, 147, 149, 185, 212, 263, 300, 320, 397, 400, 472

space exploration, 17, 21–24, 60, 77, 159, 472
Spain, 405
specialization*, 239–240, 241, 378
species, 167
spring equinox, 123, 150–151
standard of living*, 375, 437
stars, 22, 104
statistics, 330
steam power, 249
steel, 249, 394, 399, 401, 402, 422, 456
Steinbeck, John, 18
steppes*, 184, 185, 296–298, 306–309
Stevenson, Adlai, 201
stock*, 413
stock exchange*, 413
Stone Age, 234–236
stratosphere, 103–104
subarctic climate region, 147
subsistence* farmer, 267, 272
subsoil, 164
subtropical climate region, 143
Sumatra, 28
summarization, 250
summer solstice, 122
sun, 22, 103–105, 106
climate and, 120–123, 125, 126
Earth's rotation and, 23, 24, 148
energy source, 82–83, 161
oceans and, 75, 129, 191, 192
Sun Belt*, 396
sustainable environment*, 363
Sweden, 259, 374
Switzerland, 46

T

tableland, 49
taiga* (forest), 147, 287, 288
Tanzania (Africa), 302, 303
taro, 346

tea plantations, 406
technology*, 77, 238, 241, 246–247, 249, 272, 377–380, 417–421, 461–477
agriculture and, 235, 238, 239, 245–246, 263, 280, 299, 324, 346
ancient Rome, 244
culture, 221, 228
developing nations, 438
industrialization, 248–249, 357, 372
Middle Ages, 246–247
navigation, 246, 335–336
traditional societies, 234–237, 321, 325, 327, 329
See also tools.
tectonic plates*, 67–69, 87
temperature zones*, 123
temperature*, 112, 179, 202
air and, 107, 109, 113, 114
altitude and, 125–126
climate zones, 123, 126–127, 139, 140, 141, 143, 145, 147–149
land/water and, 129
ocean currents and, 130
weather and, 106, 114–115, 120
winds and, 112
terminal moraine, 72
terracing, 49, 204, 295
textile industry, 392, 399, 401, 407
Thailand, 340–343
thermometer, 112
thermosphere, 104
three-field system, 245
Tibet, 90
tides*, 74–76, 84–85
timber industry, 49
time measurement, 63
time zones, 38
Tokyo, Japan, 426–429
Tonga Island, 349
tools, 21, 160, 221, 222, 234–238, 276–278, 299, 324, 327, 346–347. *See also* technology *and* specific tools.

Credits